INTRODUCTION TO QUANTUM FIELD THEORY

Introduction to Quantum Field Theory

F. MANDL, M.A., D. Phil.
Department of Theoretical Physics,
University of Manchester

INTERSCIENCE PUBLISHERS INC., NEW YORK
a division of John Wiley & Sons, New York · London · Sydney

Library of Congress Catalog Card Number 59-15393

SECOND PRINTING, JULY, 1964

PRINTED IN THE UNITED STATES OF AMERICA

Preface

My aim in writing this introduction to the theory of quantized fields has been to produce a readable slender volume, serving two purposes. It should explain the basic ideas of field quantization and it should make the reader expert at handling modern perturbation-theoretic methods in quantum field theory. I have therefore concentrated on the beautiful ideas of Dyson and Feynman: the perturbation expansion of the scattering matrix in the interaction picture and its interpretation in terms of graphs. These graphical representations of perturbation theory strongly aid the visualization of the rather complex mathematics and their extreme usefulness is now recognized in all branches of physics. We shall, of course, restrict ourselves to quantum field theory, more particularly to quantum electrodynamics considering both 'finite' processes and radiative corrections.

The introductory character of this book has at every stage affected the mode of presentation. I have taken as my starting point the Hamiltonian formalism, as the reader should be familiar with this from non-relativistic quantum mechanics, rather than one of the more abstract formulations, such as Schwinger's action principle, although the latter have much in their favour. Again, I have not attempted a complete development of renormalization theory. This is in any case better done in terms of the more modern non-perturbation methods which dominate present attempts to deal with the strong interactions but which have so far met with only very limited success.

Since this is an introductory account, references to original papers have only been given when it was felt that the reader might like to follow up ideas mentioned only briefly. Most of the books on field theory listed in the bibliography contain more comprehensive references.

A set of exercises, together with hints for their solutions, form an important part of this book and the reader is strongly urged to attempt these. While some exercises are of a routine nature, filling in gaps left in the text, others introduce and develop important new ideas and applications which might well have found a place in the main body of the book.

The reader is assumed to possess a good knowledge of classical physics, non-relativistic quantum mechanics, the special theory of relativity and the Dirac theory of the electron. The relevant parts of the latter theory are summarized or derived in an appendix.

This book originated from lectures which I have given over the past five years at the University of Rochester, Rochester, N.Y., U.S.A., at the Atomic Energy Research Establishment, Harwell, England, at the University of Oxford and here at Manchester University, and I would like to acknowledge helpful discussions with colleagues and students of mine at these institutions. At Harwell, I had the pleasure of discussing many aspects of this book with Dr. John S. Bell, whose critical abilities are well known. Both he and Dr. Handel Davies, of Christ Church, Oxford, read the manuscript in its entirety, suggesting numerous improvements, and I would like to thank both of them for their help. I am indebted to Professor Willis Lamb for detailed information concerning the agreement between theory and experiments on the Lamb shift and the electron's magnetic moment. I am most grateful to my wife, Betty, who is responsible for many clarifications and corrections. She also helped me with the proof-reading, a task made as bearable as possible by the excellent work and cooperation of the publishers and printers, and I would like to express my thanks to them, particularly to Dr. Paul Rosbaud.

F. MANDL

Manchester, England
August 1959

Contents

CHAPTER 1

The Many-Particle Representation

The main problem to be studied in this book is the interaction of two fields or systems of particles; for example, of mesons and nucleons or photons and electrons. We shall want to consider such processes as the scattering of photons by electrons (Compton scattering) or of pions by nucleons, the inelastic scattering of charged particles with production of photons (Bremsstrahlung) or the annihilation of electron-positron pairs. Hence we must develop a formalism suitable for describing such processes, including cases where particles are created or absorbed as in Bremsstrahlung, for example.

Let us examine a typical such process: Compton scattering. We should of course describe this process using wave packets but, as in ordinary non-relativistic scattering theory, we shall idealize the mathematics and use plane waves. Nevertheless, we shall at times, somewhat loosely, use the 'wave packet' language to visualize things better. We can then specify the initial state, while photons and electrons are far apart and not yet interacting, by giving the momentum $\mathbf{p}$ of the electron and its spin s and the momentum $\mathbf{k}$ of the photon and its polarization vector $\boldsymbol{\varepsilon}$. After the scattering has occurred, photon and electron are again far apart, the final state being specified by corresponding quantities $\mathbf{p}'$, s', $\mathbf{k}'$, $\boldsymbol{\varepsilon}'$. This description is typical of the perturbation-theoretic approach which will be basic throughout this book. It is assumed that the total Hamiltonian of the system subdivides into three parts: the Hamiltonians of two non-interacting systems and an interaction term. The initial and final states are specified in terms of the eigenstates of the non-interacting parts of the Hamiltonian, the interaction merely causing the scattering or the change from the initial to the final state.

The method of specifying a state is now apparent. For each type of particle, we enumerate a complete set of one-particle states. We then specify the number of particles in each of these (these are called the occupation numbers of the one-particle states) and this gives a complete description of the many-particle system. If there are no interactions, the occupation numbers remain constant. As a result of interactions, they will change with time, corresponding to scattering, particle creation, etc.

Let us consider a system of non-interacting particles of mass m, spin zero and no charge. (We shall call these particles 'mesons'.) In this simple case, the momentum $\mathbf{k}$ of the meson suffices to specify its state completely. Its energy $\omega_{\mathbf{k}}$ is relativistically given by

$$\omega_{\mathbf{k}}^2 = m^2 + \mathbf{k}^2. \tag{1.1}$$

(We shall always use natural units: $\hbar = c = 1$.) The relativistic wave equation follows from eq. (1.1) in the usual way by interpreting $\omega_{\mathbf{k}}$ and $\mathbf{k}$ as operators which operate on a wave function $\phi(x)$. In this way one obtains the Klein-Gordon equation

$$(\Box^2 - m^2)\phi(x) = 0. \tag{1.2}$$

We are using the following notation for vectors. The four-vector x_λ, $\lambda = 1, \ldots 4$, will have spatial components x_1, x_2, x_3, and the imaginary time-like component $x_4 = ix_0 = it$. The components of a spatial three-vector $\mathbf{x}$ will be labelled by Latin subscripts $l, m, \ldots$, whereas the components of four-vectors will be labelled by Greek suffixes $\lambda, \mu, \nu \ldots$. The scalar product

$$\sum_{\lambda=1}^{4} k_\lambda x_\lambda$$

will simply be written $k_\lambda x_\lambda$, i.e. summation over repeated Greek suffixes in a product is implied, unless stated otherwise. When this cannot give rise to confusion, we shall also omit the suffix from a four-vector and write x (as in eq. (1.2)) and kx for a scalar product. Finally, in eq. (1.2)

$$\Box^2 \equiv \frac{\partial^2}{\partial x_\lambda \partial x_\lambda}. \tag{1.3}$$

To obtain a complete set of eigensolutions of the Klein-Gordon equation, we must specify boundary conditions. It will be convenient here to localize the system in a cubic box of volume $V = L^3$ and impose periodic boundary conditions at the surfaces of this box. This gives the complete set of orthonormal eigensolutions

$$\phi_{\mathbf{k}}(x) = \frac{1}{\sqrt{V}} e^{ikx}, \tag{1.4}$$

where, on account of the periodicity condition, the vector $\mathbf{k}$ must assume one of the values

$$\mathbf{k} = \frac{2\pi}{L} (\nu_1, \nu_2, \nu_3), \tag{1.5}$$

with ν_1, ν_2, ν_3 integers. We shall refer to these as the *allowed* momenta. The k_0 occurring in eq. (1.4) will, for each allowed momentum $\mathbf{k}$, be that given by the momentum-energy relation (1.1):

$$k_0 = \omega_{\mathbf{k}} \equiv + \sqrt{(m^2 + \mathbf{k}^2)}. \tag{1.6}$$

For the time being, we shall, whenever we write a four-vector $k \equiv (\mathbf{k}, ik_0)$, consider an allowed momentum $\mathbf{k}$ and the k_0 related to it by the energy relation (1.6).

We can now enumerate the allowed momenta in some definite order $\mathbf{k}_1, \mathbf{k}_2, \ldots \mathbf{k}_i \ldots$ and correspondingly the one-particle states $\phi_i(x)$, $i = 1, 2, \ldots$. A system of many such non-interacting particles is then completely specified by stating that n_1 mesons are in the state ϕ_1, n_2 in the state ϕ_2 and so on for all states: n_i in the state ϕ_i. We embody this information about a many-particle state in a *state vector*

$$|n_1, n_2 \ldots n_i \ldots\rangle \equiv \Phi(n_1, n_2 \ldots n_i \ldots) \tag{1.7}$$

which will be the analogue of the wave function in the one-particle theory. In postulating that the state vector (1.7) furnishes a complete description of the many-particle system we have made the quantum-mechanical assumption that the particles are indistinguishable. This state vector may at this point appear a rather abstract concept. Its significance and how it is to be handled will soon become a lot clearer. But it should be realized now that in writing eq. (1.7) I mean no more than was said above. In particular, $\Phi(n_1, n_2 \ldots n_i \ldots)$ is *not* to be thought of as a function of the position vectors or the momenta of the particles or anything of that sort.

We shall take the set of state vectors (1.7) to form an orthonormal basis of an infinitely-dimensional vector space*), defining the scalar product for a pair of arbitrary state vectors (1.7) as

$$\langle n_1, n_2 \ldots n_i \ldots | n_1', n_2' \ldots n_i' \ldots \rangle$$
$$= (\Phi(n_1, n_2 \ldots n_i \ldots), \Phi(n_1', n_2' \ldots n_i' \ldots)) = \prod_{i=1}^{\infty} \delta(n_i, n_i'), \quad (1.8)$$

where $\delta(a, b)$ is the Kronecker delta symbol δ_{ab}.

A general time-dependent state will now be given by a state vector $\Phi(t)$ which is a linear combination of the basis vectors (1.7), the coefficients being functions of time

$$\Phi(t) = \sum_{n_1, \ldots n_i \ldots} c_{n_1 \ldots n_i \ldots}(t) \Phi(n_1 \ldots n_i \ldots), \quad (1.9)$$

$|c_{n_1 \ldots n_i \ldots}(t)|^2$ being interpreted as the probability of finding n_i particles in the state ϕ_i, $(i = 1, 2, \ldots)$, at time t. In writing eq. (1.9), we have used the Schrödinger picture**) which ascribes the temporal development of a system to the state vector.

In general, the occupation numbers of a system will change; for example, if a meson is scattered from the momentum state $\mathbf{k}_1$ to $\mathbf{k}_2$, then n_1 will decrease by unity and n_2 increase by unity. (For this to happen, we require of course scattering centres, i.e. interactions.) We must now turn to the operators in this vector space, which transform one state vector into another, corresponding to these changes of occupation numbers. The fundamental operators (from which all others are built up) are those which change the occupation number of a single state by unity. For

*) A simple non-rigorous discussion of such vector spaces (also called Hilbert or function spaces) will be found in chapter 1 of the author's *Quantum Mechanics*, 2nd ed., London; Butterworths, and New York; Academic Press, 1957. This book will hereafter be referred to as *QM*.

**) Cf. *QM*, section 23.

each allowed momentum $\mathbf{k}_i$, we define an *absorption* (or destruction or annihilation) *operator* $a(\mathbf{k}_i)$, by stating how it transforms a general basis vector:

$$a(\mathbf{k}_i)\Phi(n_1 \ldots n_i \ldots) = \sqrt{n_i}\, \Phi(n_1 \ldots, n_i - 1, \ldots). \quad (1.10)$$

Thus $a(\mathbf{k}_i)$ reduces the occupation number of the ith state by unity, leaving all other occupation numbers the same. The factor $\sqrt{n_i}$ in this definition is desirable for the physical interpretation.

From eq. (1.10) one obtains at once the matrix representation of $a(\mathbf{k}_i)$ and hence that the adjoint operator $a^\dagger(\mathbf{k}_i)$ satisfies

$$a^\dagger(\mathbf{k}_i)\Phi(n_1 \ldots n_i \ldots) = \sqrt{(n_i + 1)}\Phi(n_1 \ldots, n_i + 1, \ldots). \quad (1.11)$$

Thus $a^\dagger(\mathbf{k}_i)$ is a *creation operator*: it increases the occupation number of the ith state by unity, leaving all other occupation numbers unchanged.

From the definitions (1.10—11) (or from the corresponding matrix representations) one verifies directly two very important results:

(i)

$$a^\dagger(\mathbf{k}_i)a(\mathbf{k}_i)\Phi(n_1 \ldots n_i \ldots) = n_i\Phi(n_1 \ldots n_i \ldots) \quad (1.12)$$

i.e. the operator $a^\dagger(\mathbf{k}_i)a(\mathbf{k}_i)$ has the basis vector $\Phi(n_1 \ldots n_i \ldots)$ as eigenfunction with the eigenvalue n_i, the occupation number of the ith state. For this reason we call $a^\dagger(\mathbf{k}_i)a(\mathbf{k}_i)$ the *occupation number operator* for the ith state. A linear superposition of such eigenstates, such as eq. (1.9), is of course no longer an eigenstate.

(ii) The creation and destruction operators satisfy the commutation relations

$$\left.\begin{aligned} [a(\mathbf{k}_i),\ a(\mathbf{k}_j)] &= [a^\dagger(\mathbf{k}_i),\ a^\dagger(\mathbf{k}_j)] = 0, \\ [a(\mathbf{k}_i),\ a^\dagger(\mathbf{k}_j)] &= \delta(\mathbf{k}_i,\ \mathbf{k}_j). \end{aligned}\right\} \quad (1.13)$$

(Writing the components of the vector $\mathbf{k}_i$ as k_{im}, $(m = 1, 2, 3)$, the Kronecker δ-symbol in the last equation is of course to be interpreted as $\prod_m \delta(k_{im},\ k_{jm})$.)

We next define the vacuum state which will be denoted by Φ_0 and which plays an important role in the theory. It is the state in which all single-particle states are empty (i.e. all $n_i = 0$):

$\Phi_0 \equiv \Phi(00\ldots)$. Hence it is not possible to absorb a particle from this state. Mathematically this is expressed by

$$a(\mathbf{k}_i)\Phi_0 = 0, \tag{1.14}$$

for all allowed $\mathbf{k}_i$. This equation is seen to be consistent with our earlier definition (1.10) and in fact is necessary, since eq. (1.10) does not define $a(\mathbf{k}_i)\Phi_0$, the right-hand side of this equation being meaningless in this case.

By successive application of the appropriate creation operators, we can generate all other basis vectors $\Phi(n_1 \ldots, n_i \ldots)$ from the vacuum state. Thus the state with only one meson present, with momentum $\mathbf{k}_i$, is given by $a^\dagger(\mathbf{k}_i)\Phi_0$; from the commutation rules (1.13), it follows that this state is correctly normalized to unity. Similarly, one can write any two-meson state as $a^\dagger(\mathbf{k}_i)a^\dagger(\mathbf{k}_j)\Phi_0$. From the commutation rules (1.13), it follows that this state is symmetric under the interchange of particles, i.e. $\mathbf{k}_i \leftrightarrow \mathbf{k}_j$. Thus our formalism describes a system of particles satisfying Bose-Einstein statistics. This is also evident from the fact that the occupation numbers n_i can assume all values 0, 1, 2, . . ., which is characteristic of *bosons* (i.e. particles satisfying Bose-Einstein statistics). *Fermions* (i.e. particles satisfying Fermi-Dirac statistics) satisfy the Pauli exclusion principle; at most one particle is allowed in any state: the occupation numbers n_i can only assume the values 0 or 1. Hence the above formalism will have to be radically modified to be applicable to fermions.

Since the energy of a particle in the state $\mathbf{k}_i$ is

$$\omega(\mathbf{k}_i) = +\sqrt{(m^2 + \mathbf{k}_i^2)}, \tag{1.15}$$

the energy of the many-particle system in the state $\Phi(n_1 \ldots n_i \ldots)$ is given by

$$\sum_i n_i \omega(\mathbf{k}_i), \tag{1.16}$$

since the mesons do not interact. From eq. (1.12), we then expect the Hamiltonian operator of the many-particle system to be

$$H = \sum_i a^\dagger(\mathbf{k}_i) a(\mathbf{k}_i) \omega(\mathbf{k}_i), \tag{1.17}$$

which has $\Phi(n_1 \ldots n_i \ldots)$ as eigenfunction with eq. (1.16) as eigenvalue.

For the equation of motion of the system we thus obtain, by analogy with one-particle quantum mechanics,

$$i\frac{\partial\Phi(t)}{\partial t} = H\Phi(t), \tag{1.18}$$

with the Hamiltonian function (1.17). This equation gives the time-development of the system. Its energy-eigenstates are obtained by substituting

$$\Phi(t) = \Phi(n_1 \ldots n_i \ldots)\, e^{-iEt} \tag{1.19}$$

into eq. (1.18), giving

$$(H - E)\Phi(n_1 \ldots n_i \ldots) = 0, \tag{1.20}$$

$$E = \sum_i n_i \omega(\mathbf{k}_i), \tag{1.21}$$

as expected: in the absence of interactions the occupation numbers are constants of the motion. This also follows since the occupation number operators

$$a^\dagger(\mathbf{k}_i)a(\mathbf{k}_i) \tag{1.22}$$

commute with the Hamiltonian (1.17).

The above description of a system in terms of discrete 'units' (particles or photons) with given properties (e.g. given momentum) is only one of the possible modes of description. It is not the language used, for example, in describing the electromagnetic field classically. This we would specify by the vectors **E** and **H** as functions of the space-time point x, or by the four-vector potential $A_\alpha(x)$, $\alpha = 1, \ldots 4$, (i.e. the vector potential $\mathbf{A}(x)$ and $A_4(x) = iV(x)$, where V is the scalar potential). Thus, an electron is surrounded by its own electromagnetic field; in the 'particle' language one would say that the electron is surrounded by a photon cloud. Similarly, the interaction of two electrons which in Maxwell's theory occurs through the intermediary of the fields, now results from an exchange of photons between the two clouds. We are here encountering the wave-particle dualism familiar from ordinary quantum mechanics.

This dualism is of course also present in the case of mesons of spin zero (the case discussed so far in this chapter). The only difference is that this case is rather simpler (no spin, no gauge-invariance, etc.) and one single field $\phi(x)$ suffices for a complete description of a system of mesons, instead of the two vector fields **E** and **H** required for the photon field. This meson field plays a role entirely analogous to the photon field. Thus, nuclear forces which are known not to be of electromagnetic origin are ascribed to this meson field. In the particle language, they stem from an exchange of mesons between the meson clouds surrounding each nucleon. A striking illustration of this hypothesis may be seen in the fact that the forces between nucleons are short-range forces, the range being of the order of the Compton wave-length of the pi-meson; this wave-length is 1.4×10^{-13} cm. It was in fact in order to explain the short range of nuclear forces that Yukawa postulated the existence of a particle of the appropriate mass, to act in the way discussed above.

For a theory to possess this wave-particle dualism it must be a theory of *quantized* fields. Such a theory can be obtained in several ways. The method to be used here has several disadvantages. In particular, it singles out the time compared with the spatial coordinates. This hides the relativistic invariance of the theory and for a long time this prevented the development of the theory. Nevertheless we shall, to begin with, follow this approach; it has the virtue of closely resembling the methods used in ordinary quantum mechanics so that the reader should find it much easier to appreciate. This method consists in first formulating a classical field theory in a Hamiltonian formalism and then quantizing this theory according to the usual postulates for a Hamiltonian system. The derivation of this classical theory and its quantization will form the task of the next two chapters.

CHAPTER 2

Classical Fields

Our object in this chapter is to develop a classical field theory in the Hamiltonian form. Only the minimum amount of this theory, required for the quantization procedure in chapter 3, will be derived; we shall be concerned merely with obtaining a complete set of conjugate variables. The procedure follows closely that of classical mechanics. Postulating the existence of a Lagrangian function, the field equations are derived by means of a variational principle from an action integral. From the Lagrangian, momenta conjugate to the original field variables are obtained, and then the transition to the quantized theory is achieved by postulating certain commutation rules to hold between the field variables and the conjugate momenta. The novel feature requiring care, compared with classical particle mechanics, is that we here deal with a system with a non-countable number of degrees of freedom.

In the last chapter we treated particles related to a single field $\phi(x)$ which satisfies the Klein-Gordon equation. We shall now consider the general case of several fields $\phi^\alpha(x)$, $\alpha = 1, \ldots N$, being required to specify the system. This generalization, which does not complicate the analysis, meets most cases that arise in practice. The index α may label the components of one field (for example, for the photon field, described by the four-vector potential $A_\alpha(x)$, α runs from 1 to 4; for the scalar field $\phi(x)$, treated in chapter 1, there is only one component) or it may refer to different quite independent fields. We shall assume that the fields ϕ^α are *real.* If complex fields occur, they must be decomposed into pairs of real fields.

We now restrict ourselves to classical field theories which can be derived from an action integral by means of a variational principle, i.e. we postulate the existence of a Lagrangian density

$$\mathscr{L} = \mathscr{L}(\phi^\alpha, \phi^\alpha_{,\nu}) \tag{2.1}$$

where we have used the abbreviation

$$\phi^\alpha_{,\nu} \equiv \frac{\partial \phi^\alpha}{\partial x_\nu}. \tag{2.2}$$

The Lagrangian density (2.1), depending on the fields and their first derivatives only, does not represent the most general case for which the theory can be developed, but it deals with all cases of practical interest and simplifies the theory greatly.

We define the action integral $I(\Omega)$ for an arbitrary region Ω of the four-dimensional space-time continuum:

$$I(\Omega) = \int_\Omega d^4x \, \mathscr{L}(\phi^\alpha, \phi^\alpha_{,\nu}) \tag{2.3}$$

where d^4x denotes the four-dimensional element $dx_1 dx_2 dx_3 dx_0 = d^3x \, dt$.

We now postulate that the equations of motion of the system, i.e. the field equations, are obtained from the following variational principle which is closely analogous to Hamilton's principle in classical mechanics. If, for an arbitrary region Ω, the fields $\phi^\alpha(x)$ are varied, $\phi^\alpha(x) \to \phi^\alpha(x) + \delta\phi^\alpha(x)$, such that the variations vanish on the surface Γ bounding the region Ω, then the action integral (2.3) has a stationary value, i.e.

$$\delta I(\Omega) = 0. \tag{2.4}$$

Calculating $\delta I(\Omega)$ from eq. (2.3), we get*)

$$\delta I(\Omega) = \int_\Omega d^4x \left\{ \frac{\partial \mathscr{L}}{\partial \phi^\alpha} \delta\phi^\alpha + \frac{\partial \mathscr{L}}{\partial \phi^\alpha_{,\nu}} \delta\phi^\alpha_{,\nu} \right\}$$

$$= \int_\Omega d^4x \left\{ \frac{\partial \mathscr{L}}{\partial \phi^\alpha} - \frac{\partial}{\partial x_\nu} \left(\frac{\partial \mathscr{L}}{\partial \phi^\alpha_{,\nu}} \right) \right\} \delta\phi^\alpha + \int_\Omega d^4x \frac{\partial}{\partial x_\nu} \left\{ \frac{\partial \mathscr{L}}{\partial \phi^\alpha_{,\nu}} \delta\phi^\alpha \right\}, \tag{2.5}$$

where the last line is obtained by partial integration, remembering

*) In eq. (2.5) and thereafter, summations over repeated indices α and ν, occurring in products, are implied.

that

$$\delta\phi^\alpha_{,\nu} = \frac{\partial}{\partial x_\nu}\,\delta\phi^\alpha. \tag{2.6}$$

The last term in eq. (2.5) is a four-dimensional volume integral of a four-dimensional divergence. Hence, by Gauss's theorem, it can be transformed into a surface integral over the surface Γ, giving

$$\int_\Gamma dS_\nu \left\{\frac{\partial\mathscr{L}}{\partial\phi^\alpha_{,\nu}}\,\delta\phi^\alpha\right\}, \tag{2.7}$$

where dS_ν is a surface element on Γ. Since $\delta\phi^\alpha = 0$ on the surface Γ, the surface integral (2.7) vanishes. If $\delta I(\Omega)$ is to vanish for arbitrary variations $\delta\phi^\alpha(x)$, it follows from eq. (2.5) that the following equations must be satisfied:

$$\frac{\partial\mathscr{L}}{\partial\phi^\alpha} - \frac{\partial}{\partial x_\nu}\left(\frac{\partial\mathscr{L}}{\partial\phi^\alpha_{,\nu}}\right) = 0, \quad (\alpha = 1, 2, \ldots N). \tag{2.8}$$

These are the differential equations which the fields $\phi^\alpha(x)$ are to satisfy. They are called Euler's equations for the variational problem (2.4) and correspond to Lagrange's equations in classical mechanics. The relativistic invariance of the theory then demands that the action integral be invariant under Lorentz transformations; it follows from eq. (2.3) that the Lagrangian density must also be a scalar, i.e. invariant under Lorentz transformations.

In order to quantize this classical field theory by the methods used in ordinary quantum mechanics, we must first go over to a Hamiltonian formalism. The latter is usually developed for systems with a countable number of degrees of freedom. We are dealing with a system with a non-denumerably infinite number of degrees of freedom, corresponding to values of the fields ϕ^α, considered as functions of time, at each point of space $\mathbf{x}$. Hence we must use some limiting process.

Consider the system at a fixed instant of time t. Decompose the three-dimensional space (spanned by x_1, x_2, x_3), i.e. the flat space-like surfaces $t = \text{const.}$, into small cells of volume $\delta\mathbf{x}^{(s)}$, which are enumerated by the index $s = 1, 2, \ldots$. The system is now specified by a *countable* number of variables

$$q_s^\alpha = \phi^\alpha(s,\ t), \qquad (\alpha = 1, \ldots N;\ s = 1, 2, \ldots) \tag{2.9}$$

giving the values of the fields in each cell, suitably defined. (Ultimately we shall of course go to the limiting case of the continuum by letting the volumes of the cells tend to zero.) We replace differential coefficients with respect to spatial coordinates by difference coefficients between neighbouring cells and define the Lagrangian of the system by

$$L(t) = \sum_s \delta \mathbf{x}^{(s)} \mathscr{L}^{(s)}, \tag{2.10}$$

where $\mathscr{L}^{(s)}$ is the value of the Lagrangian density (2.1) in the sth cell. We can then define momenta p_s^α *conjugate* to q_s^α by

$$p_s^\alpha = \frac{\partial L}{\partial \dot{q}_s^\alpha} = \frac{\partial L}{\partial \dot{\phi}^\alpha(s,\ t)} = \frac{\partial \mathscr{L}^{(s)}}{\partial \dot{\phi}^\alpha(s,\ t)}\, \delta \mathbf{x}^{(s)}, \tag{2.11}$$

where the dot denotes differentiation with respect to time*). We can now define the Hamiltonian function $H(t)$ in the usual way

$$H = \sum_s p_s^\alpha \dot{q}_s^\alpha - L. \tag{2.12}$$

With a view to going to the limit $\delta \mathbf{x}^{(s)} \to 0$, we define the *conjugate field of* $\phi^\alpha(x)$ by

$$\pi^\alpha(x) = \frac{\partial \mathscr{L}}{\partial \dot{\phi}^\alpha}; \tag{2.13}$$

then eq. (2.11) becomes

$$p_s^\alpha = \pi^\alpha(s,\ t)\, \delta \mathbf{x}^{(s)}, \tag{2.14}$$

and the Hamiltonian (2.12) becomes

$$H = \sum_s \delta \mathbf{x}^{(s)} \{\pi^\alpha(s,\ t) \dot{\phi}^\alpha(s,\ t) - \mathscr{L}^{(s)}\}. \tag{2.15}$$

If we now go to the limit $\delta \mathbf{x}^{(s)} \to 0$, we can write the Hamiltonian as

$$H(t) = \int d^3x\, \mathscr{H}(\mathbf{x},\ t), \tag{2.16}$$

*) The last step in eq. (2.11) comes about as $\dot{\phi}^\alpha(s,\ t)$ occurs only in $\mathscr{L}^{(s)}$; this follows from the restricted form of Lagrangian density (2.1); it does not, for example, contain such terms as $\nabla \phi$ which would bring in the value of ϕ in neighbouring cells.

with the Hamiltonian density

$$\mathscr{H}(x) = \pi^\alpha(x)\dot{\phi}^\alpha(x) - \mathscr{L}(x). \tag{2.17}$$

As example, consider the Lagrangian density

$$\mathscr{L}(\phi, \phi_{,\nu}) = -\tfrac{1}{2}\{\phi_{,\nu}\phi_{,\nu} + m^2\phi^2\} \tag{2.18}$$

whose Lagrange's equation (2.8) is at once seen to be the Klein-Gordon equation (1.2), that is, the Lagrangian density (2.18) describes spinless mesons of mass m. From this density, the conjugate field (2.13) becomes

$$\pi(x) = \dot{\phi}(x), \tag{2.19}$$

and the Hamiltonian density, eq. (2.17), is given by

$$\mathscr{H}(x) = \frac{1}{2}\left\{\pi^2 + \sum_i \left(\frac{\partial\phi}{\partial x_i}\right)^2 + m^2\phi^2\right\}. \tag{2.20}$$

It is now possible, starting from the Hamiltonian equations for the discrete set of conjugate variables q_s^α, p_s^α, to obtain those for the conjugate fields $\phi^\alpha(\mathbf{x}, t)$ and $\pi^\alpha(\mathbf{x}, t)$. As we shall not require these equations, their derivation will be omitted. Instead, we shall in the next chapter quantize the classical conjugate fields ϕ^α and π^α, starting from the conjugate coordinates q_s^α, p_s^α, and in this way regain the particle description of chapter 1.

CHAPTER 3

Field Operators

The classical Hamiltonian field theory, developed in chapter 2, can easily be quantized, by interpreting the conjugate coordinates q_s^α and p_s^α as operators satisfying the usual canonical commutation relations. On account of eqs. (2.9) and (2.14), we can write these

$$\left.\begin{aligned}
&[\phi^\alpha(s,\ t),\ \phi^\beta(s',\ t)] = 0\\
&[\pi^\alpha(s,\ t),\ \pi^\beta(s',\ t)] = 0\\
&[\phi^\alpha(s,\ t),\ \pi^\beta(s',\ t)] = i\delta_{\alpha\beta}\,\frac{\delta_{ss'}}{\delta\mathbf{x}^{(s)}}
\end{aligned}\right\}\quad \begin{matrix}(\alpha,\ \beta = 1,\ldots N)\\ (s,\ s' = 1,\ 2,\ \ldots).\end{matrix} \tag{3.1}$$

If we now let the volume of the cells tend to zero, $\delta\mathbf{x}^{(s)} \to 0$, the commutation relations for the fields at two points $\mathbf{x}$ and $\mathbf{x}'$ *at the same time* t are obtained. So far we have not had to specify how the time development of the system is described (e.g. whether we use the Schrödinger or the Heisenberg picture — cf. *QM*, § 23) as we are only concerned with one instant of time t. For the present, we shall again use the Schrödinger picture in which operators are time-independent. We can then take $t = 0$ and write $\phi^\alpha(\mathbf{x})$ for $\phi^\alpha(\mathbf{x},\ 0)$, etc. The commutation relations for the fields then become

$$\left.\begin{aligned}
&[\phi^\alpha(\mathbf{x}),\ \phi^\beta(\mathbf{x}')] = [\pi^\alpha(\mathbf{x}),\ \pi^\beta(\mathbf{x}')] = 0,\\
&[\phi^\alpha(\mathbf{x}),\ \pi^\beta(\mathbf{x}')] = i\delta_{\alpha\beta}\delta(\mathbf{x}-\mathbf{x}'),
\end{aligned}\right\}\quad (\alpha,\ \beta = 1,\ \ldots N), \tag{3.2}$$

since, in the limit $\delta\mathbf{x}^{(s)} \to 0$, $\delta_{ss'}/\delta\mathbf{x}^{(s)}$ becomes the three-dimensional Dirac delta function $\delta(\mathbf{x}-\mathbf{x}')$, the points $\mathbf{x}$, $\mathbf{x}'$ lying in the sth and s'th cells respectively.

To establish contact with the particle interpretation of chapter 1, we want to Fourier analyse the field operators $\phi(\mathbf{x})$ and $\pi(\mathbf{x})$, where we now again restrict ourselves to the case of a single real field which satisfies the Klein-Gordon equation, i.e. it is described by eqs. (2.18—20). We start again from the classical fields and decompose these:

$$\phi(x) = \frac{1}{\sqrt{V}} \sum_{\mathbf{k}} \frac{1}{\sqrt{2k_0}} \{a(\mathbf{k})\, e^{ikx} + a^*(\mathbf{k})\, e^{-ikx}\} \tag{3.3a}$$

and, from eq. (2.19),

$$\pi(x) = \frac{i}{\sqrt{V}} \sum_{\mathbf{k}} \sqrt{\frac{k_0}{2}} \{-a(\mathbf{k})\, e^{ikx} + a^*(\mathbf{k})\, e^{-ikx}\}. \tag{3.3b}$$

Here summation is over the allowed momenta $\mathbf{k}$ (we now drop the suffix i which we used to label these) and k_0 is the corresponding energy, eq. (1.6), which also occurs in the exponents in the scalar product $kx = \mathbf{kx} - k_0 t$. The expansion coefficients $a(\mathbf{k})$ and $a^*(\mathbf{k})$ in the Fourier series (3.3) should not, at this stage, be confused with the absorption and creation operators introduced in chapter I. In fact, we shall presently see that, with the factor $(2k_0)^{-\frac{1}{2}}$ in eq. (3.3a), etc., we shall be able to make this identification in the quantized theory.

We now interpret $\phi(\mathbf{x})$ and $\pi(\mathbf{x})$ as operators in the Schrödinger picture (i.e. we take $t = 0$) of a quantized theory. Eqs. (3.3) then give for these operators

$$\phi(\mathbf{x}) = \frac{1}{\sqrt{V}} \sum_{\mathbf{k}} \frac{1}{\sqrt{2\omega_{\mathbf{k}}}} \{a(\mathbf{k})\, e^{i\mathbf{kx}} + a^\dagger(\mathbf{k})\, e^{-i\mathbf{kx}}\}, \tag{3.4a}$$

$$\pi(\mathbf{x}) = \frac{i}{\sqrt{V}} \sum_{\mathbf{k}} \sqrt{\frac{\omega_{\mathbf{k}}}{2}} \{-a(\mathbf{k})\, e^{i\mathbf{kx}} + a^\dagger(\mathbf{k})\, e^{-i\mathbf{kx}}\}, \tag{3.4b}$$

where we have written $\omega_{\mathbf{k}}$ for the energy of a meson of momentum $\mathbf{k}$, eq. (1.6). The operator character of $\phi(\mathbf{x})$ and $\pi(\mathbf{x})$ is reflected in the fact that the classical amplitudes $a(\mathbf{k})$ and $a^*(\mathbf{k})$ are now to be interpreted as operators. Correspondingly we have replaced the complex conjugate a^* by the adjoint $a^\dagger$. This ensures that the field operators $\phi(\mathbf{x})$ and $\pi(\mathbf{x})$ are Hermitian, just as our original definition (3.3a) ensured the reality of the classical fields.

From the commutation relations for the fields (3.2) those of the $a(\mathbf{k})$ and $a^\dagger(\mathbf{k})$ follow by substituting eqs. (3.4). One finds that

$$\left.\begin{aligned} &[a(\mathbf{k}),\ a(\mathbf{k}')] = [a^\dagger(\mathbf{k}),\ a^\dagger(\mathbf{k}')] = 0, \\ &[a(\mathbf{k}),\ a^\dagger(\mathbf{k}')] = \delta(\mathbf{k},\ \mathbf{k}'), \end{aligned}\right\} \tag{3.5}$$

i.e. we have regained the commutation relations of the destruction and creation operators, eqs. (1.13), justifying us in applying this nomenclature and interpretation to the operators $a(\mathbf{k})$ and $a^\dagger(\mathbf{k})$ introduced above. Conversely, one easily shows that eqs. (3.5) imply eqs. (3.2) for operators ϕ and π defined by eqs. (3.4).

Let us briefly recapitulate the above very important results and compare them with the corresponding ideas in ordinary quantum mechanics.

In the quantum field theory, the Fourier amplitudes of the fields (a and $a^\dagger$) are to be interpreted as absorption and creation operators, satisfying the commutation relations (3.5). The fields $\phi(\mathbf{x})$ and $\pi(\mathbf{x})$ are of course also operators. They are given in terms of the creation and destruction operators by eqs. (3.4) and satisfy the commutation laws (3.2). Thus in the field theory, $\phi(\mathbf{x})$ is an operator (i.e. it is a function of the a and $a^\dagger$), whereas $\mathbf{x}$ is merely a parameter (a *c*-number). Compare this with the single-particle quantum theory, where $\phi(\mathbf{x})$ is a wave function specifying the state of the system, but the position coordinate is an operator. In the field theory, on the other hand, the state is specified by a state vector $\Phi(n_1 \ldots n_i \ldots)$ which is a function of the occupation numbers. These distinctions as to which quantities are operators, which wave functions, etc. are very important for an appreciation of the mathematical formalism. For this reason, we shall in the next chapter give some very simple examples of how one operates with these quantities and we shall at the same time see more clearly how the physical interpretation is derived from the mathematical symbols which at first acquaintance may appear rather abstract. But first, I want to deal with two other small points.

In chapter 1, I wrote down the expression for the Hamiltonian operator of a system of non-interacting spinless mesons [eq. (1.17)]. We are now in a position to calculate this Hamiltonian from eqs. (2.16), (2.20) and (3.4), putting $t = 0$ in eq. (2.16) since H is now to be interpreted as an operator in the Schrödinger picture. In this way one obtains

$$H = \sum_{\mathbf{k}} (a^\dagger(\mathbf{k})a(\mathbf{k}) + \tfrac{1}{2})\omega_{\mathbf{k}} \tag{3.6}$$

which differs from eq. (1.17) by the presence of the second term, which occurs even when all occupation numbers are zero i.e. in the vacuum state. Thus it represents a zero-point energy (and it is actually infinite) but we can eliminate it altogether by shifting the zero of the scale on which we measure energies; this cannot lead to any physically observable consequences. By calculating the momentum of the meson field (cf. exercise 3.3), the interpretation of $a(\mathbf{k})$ and $a^\dagger(\mathbf{k})$ as absorption and creation operators of mesons of momentum $\mathbf{k}$ is again verified.

We shall always normalize the system in a finite, but large, volume V. Physically significant quantities, such as cross-sections, are of course independent of this normalization volume. It will often be convenient to replace the summation over allowed values of the momentum by an integral, according to the well-known correspondence

$$\frac{1}{V}\sum_{\mathbf{k}} \rightarrow \frac{1}{(2\pi)^3}\int d^3k \tag{3.7}$$

where d^3k is the volume element in momentum space $dk_1 dk_2 dk_3$. In making the replacement (3.7) a small error is made which, however, goes to zero in the limit as we finally let the volume V tend to infinity.

CHAPTER 4

Simple Examples

We shall now consider some very simple examples to illustrate the concepts which have been introduced. We are of course not yet able to treat realistic problems. Nevertheless many of the ideas to be developed in these examples carry over into the more sophisticated approaches.

We shall consider the interaction of neutral pions with nucleons assuming the interaction Hamiltonian density to be

$$\mathscr{H}_I(\mathbf{x}) = g\rho(\mathbf{x})\,\phi(\mathbf{x}), \tag{4.1}$$

i.e. this term is to be added to the Hamiltonian density of the meson field, eq. (2.20). Here $\phi(\mathbf{x})$ is the quantized meson field, eq. (3.4a), and $\rho(\mathbf{x})$ the nucleon density at the point $\mathbf{x}$. The coupling constant g measures the strength of the interaction. This expression is quite analogous to the interaction Hamiltonian density used in electrodynamics. For a charge-current density $-es_\mu(x)$, interacting with an electromagnetic field $A_\mu(x)$, it is given by

$$\mathscr{H}_I(x) = es_\mu(x)A_\mu(x). \tag{4.2}$$

We shall now treat the nucleons as point-particles of infinite mass so that they can be taken as fixed at certain points $\mathbf{x}_1$, $\mathbf{x}_2$, . . . in space. The density function can then be written

$$\rho(\mathbf{x}) = \sum_n \delta(\mathbf{x} - \mathbf{x}_n). \tag{4.3}$$

In a scattering process such nucleons cannot experience a recoil, indicating the very limited usefulness of this type of interaction.

From eqs. (2.16), (4.1) and (4.3), the interaction Hamiltonian becomes

$$H_I = \frac{g}{\sqrt{V}} \sum_{\mathbf{k}} \sum_n \frac{1}{\sqrt{2\omega_{\mathbf{k}}}} \left(a(\mathbf{k})\,\mathrm{e}^{i\mathbf{k}\mathbf{x}_n} + a^\dagger(\mathbf{k})\,\mathrm{e}^{-i\mathbf{k}\mathbf{x}_n}\right). \tag{4.4}$$

This Hamiltonian is linear in absorption and creation operators. Each term of the first or second type will absorb or create a meson of momentum **k**. Hence the only non-zero matrix elements are

$$\left.\begin{array}{l}(\Phi(\ldots, n_{\mathbf{k}}+1, \ldots), H_I\Phi(\ldots, n_{\mathbf{k}}, \ldots)) \\ (\Phi(\ldots, n_{\mathbf{k}}, \ldots), H_I\Phi(\ldots, n_{\mathbf{k}}+1, \ldots))^*\end{array}\right\} = \frac{g}{\sqrt{V}}\left(\frac{n_{\mathbf{k}}+1}{2\omega_{\mathbf{k}}}\right)^{\frac{1}{2}} \sum_n e^{-i\mathbf{k}\mathbf{x}_n},$$

$$(n_{\mathbf{k}} = 0, 1, \ldots) \qquad (4.5)$$

where the occupation numbers shown refer to the momentum state **k**, all other occupation numbers remaining unchanged in these transitions; that is, the only allowed transitions are those changing the occupation numbers of a single state by unity.

It should be noted that the nucleons and mesons are here treated quite differently. Only the meson field is quantized leading to creation and annihilation of mesons, whereas the nucleons are treated classically; they merely serve as sources and sinks of the meson field. Thus in a particular problem the number of nucleons N and their positions $\mathbf{x}_1, \mathbf{x}_2, \ldots \mathbf{x}_N$ are fixed and do not change so that the state vector describing the system will be a function of the meson occupation numbers only. For example, the vacuum state Φ_0 will now be the state with only the N nucleons present but no mesons.

In the following applications, time-independent perturbation theory will be used. This is only useful for weak interactions H_I, i.e. small coupling constants g. Thus it is applicable to electrodynamics but is quite inadequate for mesons where the coupling constant is known to be large.

As first example, we consider the *nuclear force* problem, i.e. we shall calculate the change in energy ΔE between two nucleons at $\mathbf{x}_1$ and $\mathbf{x}_2$ due to their interaction through the meson field. The unperturbed wave function is now the vacuum state Φ_0 (the two nucleons but no mesons present). In first-order perturbation theory

$$\Delta E = (\Phi_0, H_I\Phi_0), \qquad (4.6)$$

and this vanishes on account of eq. (4.5). However, in second-order perturbation theory ΔE will not vanish, the intermediate states which contribute being the states $\Phi(\mathbf{k})$ with one meson of momentum $\mathbf{k}$ present:

$$\Delta E = \sum_{\mathbf{k}} \frac{(\Phi_0, H_I \Phi(\mathbf{k}))(\Phi(\mathbf{k}), H_I \Phi_0)}{(-\omega_{\mathbf{k}})}. \tag{4.7}$$

(Here the denominator is the usual energy difference of second-order perturbation theory: the energy of the initial state Φ_0 minus that of the intermediate state $\Phi(\mathbf{k})$.) Eqs. (4.5) together with (4.7) give

$$\Delta E = \frac{-g^2}{V} \sum_{\mathbf{k}} \frac{1}{2\omega_{\mathbf{k}}^2} \sum_{n=1}^{2} \sum_{m=1}^{2} e^{i\mathbf{k}(\mathbf{x}_n - \mathbf{x}_m)}. \tag{4.8}$$

The summations over m and n give rise to four terms: $m, n = 1, 2$, corresponding to the various ways in which the meson can be emitted and reabsorbed by the two nucleons. We indicate these schematically in fig. 1. The solid lines, labelled 1

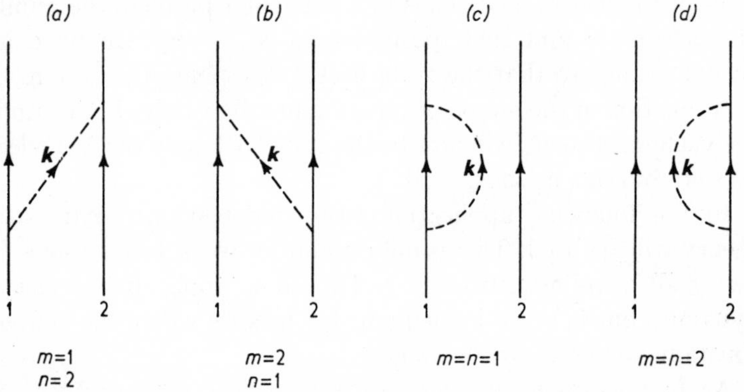

Fig. 1. The nucleon-nucleon interaction.

and 2, represent the nucleons, the dotted lines the mesons. Diagram 1(a) represents the emission of the meson by nucleon 1 at $\mathbf{x}_1$ and its absorption by nucleon 2 at $\mathbf{x}_2$, etc.

Diagrams (c) and (d) are not related to the interactions of nucleons with each other and hence we shall omit them here. They represent nucleon self-energy effects: the interaction of a nucleon with its *own* meson cloud. This modifies the properties of a *free* nucleon. Above we were considering *bare* nucleons i.e.

nucleons without their meson clouds. Diagram (c) represents the simplest of a whole set of virtual processes which convert a bare nucleon into a *physical* nucleon. The self-energy terms ($n = m$) in eq. (4.8) give a linearly divergent contribution, as one sees by going to the limit $V \to \infty$, according to eq. (3.7). This gives for the self-energy terms

$$\frac{-g^2}{(2\pi)^3}\int \frac{d^3k}{(m^2+\mathbf{k}^2)} = -\frac{g^2}{2\pi^2}\int_0^\infty \frac{x^2 dx}{m^2+x^2} \tag{4.9}$$

($x = |\mathbf{k}|$) which diverges linearly at the upper limit $x \to \infty$. We shall see later how to eliminate these divergent self-energy effects by incorporating them in the properties of the physical nucleon. This is the process of mass renormalization.

For the nucleon-nucleon interaction the terms with $m \neq n$ in eq. (4.8) give, again replacing sums over $\mathbf{k}$ by integrals:

$$\Delta E = \frac{-g^2}{2(2\pi)^3}\int \frac{d^3k}{\omega_{\mathbf{k}}^2}\,(\mathrm{e}^{i\mathbf{kx}} + \mathrm{e}^{-i\mathbf{kx}}) \tag{4.10a}$$

$$= \frac{-g^2}{(2\pi)^3}\int d^3k\,\frac{\mathrm{e}^{i\mathbf{kx}}}{m^2+|\mathbf{k}|^2} \tag{4.10b}$$

$$= -g^2\,\frac{\mathrm{e}^{-mr}}{4\pi r}. \tag{4.10c}$$

Here $\mathbf{x} = \mathbf{x}_2 - \mathbf{x}_1$, $r = |\mathbf{x}|$ is the internucleon distance and eq. (4.10b) is obtained by changing the variable of integration in the second integral of eq. (4.10a) from $\mathbf{k}$ to $-\mathbf{k}$.

Eq. (4.10c) is the famous Yukawa potential: it is the potential between two nucleons a distance r apart. It is analogous to the Coulomb potential $1/r$ between two electric charges but unlike the latter it is of short range; its range is of the order of the meson Compton wave length $1/m$, which is 1.4×10^{-13} cm for pions. This potential does not reproduce the observed nuclear forces, nor could this be expected from such a crude theory. We should have used a relativistic theory, allowed for nucleon recoil, described the pions as pseudo-scalar particles and taken charged as well as neutral pions into account. Finally, the interaction being strong, the use of perturbation theory would appear not to be justified*).

As our second example, we consider pion-nucleon scattering on the basis of the same interaction Hamiltonian (4.4). We have only one nucleon now which we take fixed at the point **x**. We consider elastic scattering from the one-meson state $\Phi(\mathbf{k})$ (meson of momentum **k**, energy $\omega_{\mathbf{k}}$) to the one-meson state $\Phi(\mathbf{k}')$ (meson of momentum $\mathbf{k}'$; $|\mathbf{k}'| = |\mathbf{k}|$, $\omega_{\mathbf{k}'} = \omega_{\mathbf{k}}$). Since during this transition *two* occupation numbers change, the lowest order matrix element for this transition vanishes:

$$(\Phi(\mathbf{k}'), H_I \Phi(\mathbf{k})) = 0. \tag{4.12}$$

In second-order theory, two intermediate states contribute:

(a) the no-meson state Φ_0, energy 0.

(b) the two-meson state $\Phi(\mathbf{k}, \mathbf{k}')$, energy $\omega_{\mathbf{k}} + \omega_{\mathbf{k}'} = 2\omega_{\mathbf{k}}$.

These two transitions are again indicated schematically in fig. 2.

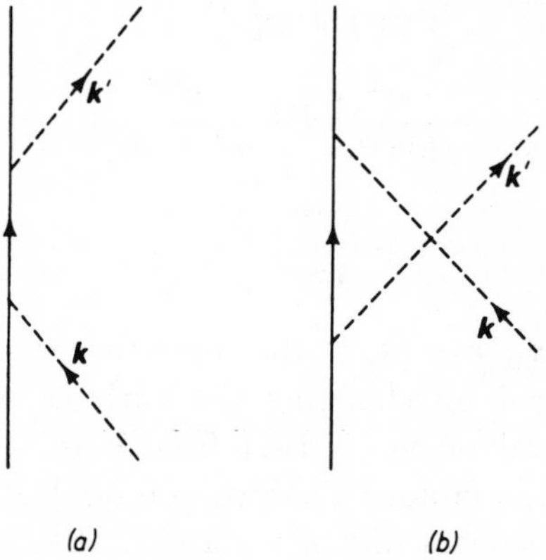

Fig. 2. Meson-nucleon scattering.

*) In fact, one can show that the above second-order result is *exact* (cf. Wentzel, quoted in the bibliography at the end of this book, p. 47). This is a peculiarity of the neutral scalar (i.e. spin zero) theory without recoil. For this theory, Wentzel shows that the total Hamiltonian can be rewritten, by means of a canonical transformation, as

$$\sum_{\mathbf{k}} \omega_{\mathbf{k}} a^{\dagger}(\mathbf{k}) a(\mathbf{k}) - g^2 e^{-mr}/4\pi r. \tag{4.11}$$

They correspond to the meson $\mathbf{k}$ being absorbed 'before' the meson $\mathbf{k}'$ is emitted and vice versa. The matrix element for the transition is then

$$M = \frac{(\Phi(\mathbf{k}'),\, H_I\Phi_0)\,(\Phi_0,\, H_I\Phi(\mathbf{k}))}{\omega_{\mathbf{k}} - 0} + \frac{(\Phi(\mathbf{k}'),\, H_I\Phi(\mathbf{k},\,\mathbf{k}'))\,(\Phi(\mathbf{k},\mathbf{k}'),\, H_I\Phi(\mathbf{k}))}{\omega_{\mathbf{k}} - 2\omega_{\mathbf{k}}}$$

which by eq. (4.5) equals

$$\frac{g^2}{V}\,\frac{1}{2\omega_{\mathbf{k}}}\,\mathrm{e}^{i(\mathbf{k}-\mathbf{k}')\mathbf{x}}\left\{\frac{1}{\omega_{\mathbf{k}}} + \frac{1}{-\omega_{\mathbf{k}}}\right\} = 0. \tag{4.13}$$

Thus there is no scattering, to order g^2, in this theory. This is due to the exact cancellation of the contributions from diagrams 2(a) and (b). This cancellation would not occur if we allowed for recoil effects or considered charged mesons. It is again peculiar to the neutral scalar no-recoil theory and again is not only correct to order g^2 but represents an *exact* result. This is apparent from the transformed Hamiltonian, eq. (4.11), which is the sum of two terms: one containing only meson variables, the other referring to the nucleons only; but there is no interaction term and thus there cannot be any scattering.

CHAPTER 5

The Interaction Picture

Instead of the Schrödinger picture (S.P.) which has so far been used to describe the time-dependence of the system, we shall now introduce the interaction picture (I.P.). This is particularly suited to the perturbation-theoretic treatment of two interacting systems A and B (mesons and nucleons, say). We shall see that it allows us to carry out calculations in a relativistically covariant manner.

In the S.P. the equation of motion of the system is the time-dependent Schrödinger equation

$$i\frac{\partial \Phi^S(t)}{\partial t} = H^S \Phi^S(t) \tag{5.1}$$

where the superscript S labels quantities in the S.P. and H^S is the total Hamiltonian which, we assume, can be decomposed into an interaction-free part

$$H_0^S = H_0^S(A) + H_0^S(B) \tag{5.2}$$

and an interaction

$$H_I^S = H_I^S(A,\ B), \tag{5.3}$$

that is,

$$H^S = H_0^S + H_I^S. \tag{5.4}$$

The state-vectors $\Phi(t)$ and operators $O(t)$ of the I.P. are obtained from the corresponding quantities in the S.P. by the unitary transformation

$$\Phi(t) = \mathrm{e}^{iH_0^S t}\Phi^S(t) \tag{5.5}$$

$$O(t) = \mathrm{e}^{iH_0^S t} O^S \mathrm{e}^{-iH_0^S t}. \tag{5.6}$$

From eqs. (5.5—6) it follows that the two descriptions are

identical at the time $t = 0$ and that (take $O^S = H_0^S$)

$$H_0 = H_0^S, \tag{5.7}$$

where, as throughout, state-vectors and operators without superscript S are in the I.P.

The equation of motion of the state-vectors in the I.P. follows from eq. (5.1). Using eqs. (5.5—7), one easily obtains

$$i\frac{\partial \Phi(t)}{\partial t} = H_I \Phi(t). \tag{5.8}$$

Thus in the I.P. the state-vectors have the time-dependence of the S.P. with the interaction Hamiltonian H_I instead of the total Hamiltonian.

Let us write eq. (5.6) as

$$O(t) = e^{iH_0 t} O(0)\, e^{-iH_0 t}, \tag{5.9}$$

which is thus the equation of motion of the operator $O(t)$ in the I.P. We can, however, also interpret the operator $O(t)$ given by eq. (5.9) as being an operator in the Heisenberg picture (H.P.) with the interaction-*free* Hamiltonian replacing the total Hamiltonian. Thus the operator in the I.P. for the interacting system is *identical* with the operator in the H.P. for the non-interacting systems. Thus in the I.P., both equations of motion and commutators of operators are those of the interaction-free case. These are easily derived. For the meson field they were derived in chapter 3 and can straight away be taken over when dealing with interacting systems. In the H.P., on the other hand, both equations of motion and commutators are modified by interactions. From eq. (5.9), one obtains the differential form of the equation of motion

$$i\frac{\partial O(t)}{\partial t} = [O(t), H_0]. \tag{5.10}$$

We shall presently derive the commutation relations of the meson field in the I.P. and shall see that they are covariant. The Schrödinger equation (5.8) in the I.P. is of course not covariant as the time-derivatives single out surfaces $t = \text{const.}$ in our particular Lorentz frame. However, it is possible to replace these flat space-like surfaces by general curved space-like surfaces and the resulting equation for the state-vectors, replacing eq. (5.8), is covariant*). However, we shall not require this more general formulation of the theory.

We next transform our results for the meson field into the I.P. Writing $a_{\mathbf{k}}$ for the absorption operator $a(\mathbf{k})$, etc., the corresponding I.P. operator is given by

$$a_{\mathbf{k}}(t) = e^{iH_0 t} a_{\mathbf{k}} e^{-iH_0 t} \tag{5.11}$$

with a corresponding definition for $a_{\mathbf{k}}^{\dagger}(t)$. The Fourier expansion (3.4a) of the meson field in the I.P. thus becomes

$$\phi(x) = \frac{1}{\sqrt{V}} \sum_{\mathbf{k}} \frac{1}{\sqrt{2\omega_{\mathbf{k}}}} \{a_{\mathbf{k}}(t) e^{i\mathbf{kx}} + a_{\mathbf{k}}^{\dagger}(t) e^{-i\mathbf{kx}}\}. \tag{5.12}$$

Eq. (5.11) is easily solved. Firstly, we need only consider the term $\omega_{\mathbf{k}} a_{\mathbf{k}}^{\dagger} a_{\mathbf{k}}$ in the meson Hamiltonian (1.17) as all other terms in H_0 commute with $a_{\mathbf{k}}$ and thus drop out from eq. (5.11). Following Schweber *et al.* (loc. cit. § 15b), consider

$$\begin{aligned} \frac{d}{d\lambda} a_{\mathbf{k}}(\lambda t) &= \frac{d}{d\lambda} \{e^{i\omega_{\mathbf{k}}\lambda t a_{\mathbf{k}}^{\dagger} a_{\mathbf{k}}} a_{\mathbf{k}} e^{-i\omega_{\mathbf{k}}\lambda t a_{\mathbf{k}}^{\dagger} a_{\mathbf{k}}}\} \\ &= i\omega_{\mathbf{k}} t\, e^{i\omega_{\mathbf{k}}\lambda t a_{\mathbf{k}}^{\dagger} a_{\mathbf{k}}} [a_{\mathbf{k}}^{\dagger} a_{\mathbf{k}}, a_{\mathbf{k}}] e^{-i\omega_{\mathbf{k}}\lambda t a_{\mathbf{k}}^{\dagger} a_{\mathbf{k}}} \\ &= -i\omega_{\mathbf{k}} t\, e^{i\omega_{\mathbf{k}}\lambda t a_{\mathbf{k}}^{\dagger} a_{\mathbf{k}}} a_{\mathbf{k}} e^{-i\omega_{\mathbf{k}}\lambda t a_{\mathbf{k}}^{\dagger} a_{\mathbf{k}}}, \end{aligned}$$

where the commutation relations (3.5) have been used. Hence

$$\frac{d}{d\lambda} a_{\mathbf{k}}(\lambda t) = -i\omega_{\mathbf{k}} t\, a_{\mathbf{k}}(\lambda t)$$

which gives on integration and putting $\lambda = 1$:

$$a_{\mathbf{k}}(t) = a_{\mathbf{k}} e^{-i\omega_{\mathbf{k}} t} \tag{5.13a}$$

and correspondingly

$$a_{\mathbf{k}}^{\dagger}(t) = a_{\mathbf{k}}^{\dagger} e^{i\omega_{\mathbf{k}} t}. \tag{5.13b}$$

Substituting these equations into eq. (5.12) and writing the exponents as scalar products (kx) of four-vectors, we obtain

*) Cf. Schweber, Bethe and de Hoffmann (see bibliography), vol. 1, § 15a.

finally for the meson field in the I.P.

$$\phi(x) = \frac{1}{\sqrt{V}} \sum_{k_0=\omega_{\mathbf{k}}} \frac{1}{\sqrt{2k_0}} \{a(\mathbf{k})e^{ikx} + a^\dagger(\mathbf{k})e^{-ikx}\} \tag{5.14}$$

where the summation is over all allowed momenta $\mathbf{k}$ and k_0 is given by the corresponding energy $\omega_{\mathbf{k}}$, eq. (1.6), as indicated under the summation sign.

It is often convenient to decompose $\phi(x)$:

$$\phi(x) = \phi^+(x) + \phi^-(x) \tag{5.15}$$

where $\phi^\pm$ are the parts containing only absorption or creation operators respectively. The vacuum definition (1.14) can now be replaced by

$$\phi^+\Phi_0 = 0. \tag{5.16}$$

The operators $\phi^\pm$ are called the positive and negative frequency parts of the field. From eqs. (5.14—15)

$$(\phi^+)^\dagger = \phi^-. \tag{5.17}$$

The commutator $[\phi(x), \phi(x')]$ for two arbitrary space-time points x and x' is easily calculated from the expansion (5.14) and the commutation rules (3.5). Since two creation or two absorption operators commute, only cross-terms will contribute, giving

$$[\phi(x), \phi(x')]$$

$$= \frac{1}{V} \sum_{k_0=\omega_{\mathbf{k}}} \sum_{k'_0=\omega_{\mathbf{k}'}} \frac{1}{2\sqrt{k_0 k'_0}} \{[a_{\mathbf{k}}, a^\dagger_{\mathbf{k}'}]\, e^{i(kx-k'x')} + [a^\dagger_{\mathbf{k}}, a_{\mathbf{k}'}]\, e^{-i(kx-k'x')}\}$$

$$= \frac{1}{(2\pi)^3 2} \int_{k_0=\omega_{\mathbf{k}}} \frac{d^3k}{k_0} \{e^{ik(x-x')} - e^{-ik(x-x')}\},$$

where, anticipating going to the limit $V \to \infty$, we have replaced the summation by a momentum integral according to eq. (3.7). Defining

$$\Delta(x) = \frac{1}{(2\pi)^3} \int_{k_0=\omega_{\mathbf{k}}} \frac{d^3k}{k_0} \sin kx, \tag{5.18}$$

we finally obtain

$$[\phi(x),\ \phi(x')] = i\Delta(x - x'). \tag{5.19}$$

From eq. (5.18), $\Delta(x)$ is a real odd function of x, as is necessary for the consistency of eq. (5.19), since the left-hand side of this equation is the commutator of two Hermitian operators. Furthermore, since the fields ϕ are themselves scalars, the Δ-function must also be an invariant. This will be proved directly in the next chapter. Thus eq. (5.19) is a covariant commutation relation.

From eq. (5.18),

$$\Delta(\mathbf{x},\ t=0) = \frac{1}{(2\pi)^3}\int \frac{d^3k}{\omega_{\mathbf{k}}} \sin \mathbf{kx} = 0 \tag{5.20}$$

since the integrand is an odd function of the vector $\mathbf{k}$. Thus the 'equal-times' commutator

$$[\phi(\mathbf{x},\ t),\ \phi(\mathbf{x}',\ t)] = 0 \tag{5.21}$$

in agreement with eq. (3.2). However, this result admits a much wider interpretation. Since the Δ-function is an invariant, it follows that

$$\Delta(x) = 0, \text{ if } x^2 = \mathbf{x}^2 - t^2 > 0, \tag{5.22}$$

i.e. for *any* space-like vector x, not just for vectors $(\mathbf{x},\ 0)$. For, by a suitable Lorentz transformation, any space-like vector can be transformed into this form. Thus the invariant $\Delta(x)$-function vanishes outside the light-cone $|\mathbf{x}| = t$. Correspondingly the

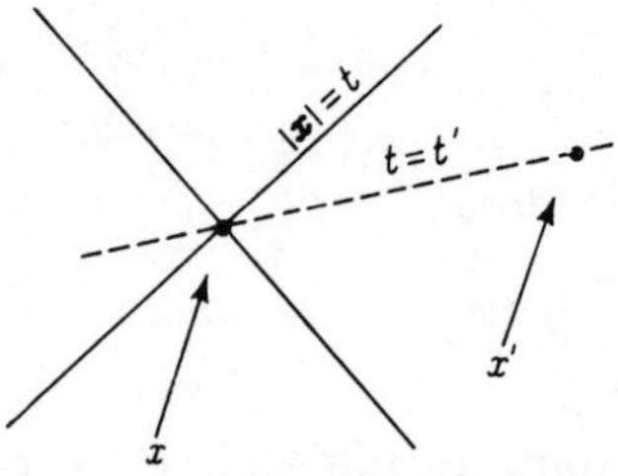

Fig. 3.

commutator (5.19) vanishes for any two points x and x' with a space-like separation: $(x - x')^2 > 0$, i.e. for two points lying outside each other's light-cones, as illustrated in fig. 3. This is exactly what is required by the basic postulates of quantum mechanics and the special theory of relativity. The non-vanishing of the commutator (5.19) of two Hermitian operators means that the measurements of the corresponding observable fields at the space-time points x and x' interfere with each other. But such interference cannot occur if $(x - x')$ is space-like; for this would require a signal to propagate between x and x' with a velocity greater than that of light, contrary to the theory of relativity. Thus the vanishing of the commutator (5.19) for space-like $(x - x')$ represents a most satisfactory link-up of quantum mechanics and the theory of relativity.

CHAPTER 6

Invariant Δ-Functions

In this chapter we shall study further properties of the Δ-function as well as related functions*). At the end of this chapter, these results will be applied to calculate vacuum expectation values of certain combinations of field operators which will be needed later. The reader who is less interested in these purely mathematical developments may omit this chapter, or only glance at it, and read the relevant parts only when required.

The invariant Δ-function (5.18) can be written as

$$\Delta(x) = \frac{1}{(2\pi)^4} \int_C d^4k \, \frac{e^{ikx}}{k^2 + m^2}. \tag{6.1}$$

Here $d^4k = d^3k\,dk_0$, the integration with respect to d^3k being over all momenta $\mathbf{k}$ but k_0 is no longer restricted to the energy $\omega_{\mathbf{k}}$ but is a variable of integration. Since the denominator

$$k^2 + m^2 = -(k_0^2 - \omega_{\mathbf{k}}^2) \tag{6.2}$$

has simple poles at $k_0 = \pm\omega_{\mathbf{k}}$ the k_0-integration must be inter-

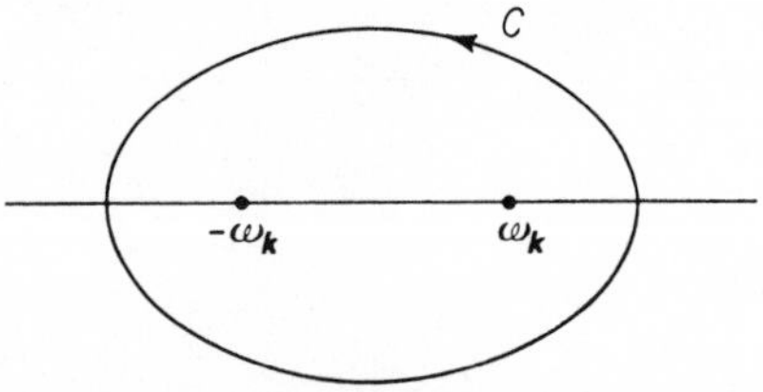

Fig. 4. The contour C for $\Delta(x)$.

*) There is some arbitrariness in the exact definition of these delta-functions (minus signs, etc.) so that care is required when using published results.

preted as a contour integral in the complex k_0-plane along a specified contour C. Eq. (6.1) is equivalent to our earlier definition (5.18) of $\Delta(x)$ if we take for C a closed curve encircling both poles in an anticlockwise direction, as shown in fig. 4. Carying out the contour integral in terms of residues, eq. (6.1) gives

$$\Delta(x) = \frac{-1}{(2\pi)^4}\int d^3k\, e^{i\mathbf{kx}} \int_C \frac{dk_0\, e^{-ik_0x_0}}{k_0^2 - \omega_\mathbf{k}^2}$$

$$= \frac{-1}{(2\pi)^4}\int d^3k\, e^{i\mathbf{kx}}\, 2\pi i \left\{\frac{e^{-i\omega_\mathbf{k}x_0}}{2\omega_\mathbf{k}} + \frac{e^{i\omega_\mathbf{k}x_0}}{-2\omega_\mathbf{k}}\right\}$$

and this agrees with eq. (5.18), if in the second integral we change the variable of integration from $\mathbf{k}$ to $-\mathbf{k}$.

Using the Dirac delta-function, it is also possible to represent $\Delta(x)$ in terms of a fourfold completely real integral (i.e. the k_0-integration is also along the real axis over $-\infty < k_0 < \infty$):

$$\Delta(x) = \frac{-i}{(2\pi)^3}\int d^4k\, e^{ikx}\, \varepsilon(k)\, \delta(k^2 + m^2), \tag{6.3}$$

where

$$\varepsilon(k) = \frac{k_0}{|k_0|} = \begin{cases} +1, & \text{if } k_0 > 0, \\ -1, & \text{if } k_0 < 0. \end{cases} \tag{6.4}$$

One easily sees that eq. (6.3) is correct; for example, writing the δ-function in eq. (6.3) as

$$\delta(k^2 + m^2) = \delta(k_0^2 - \omega_\mathbf{k}^2) = \frac{1}{2\omega_\mathbf{k}}\left[\delta(k_0 + \omega_\mathbf{k}) + \delta(k_0 - \omega_\mathbf{k})\right]$$

and carrying out the k_0-integration, the original definition of $\Delta(x)$, eq. (5.18), is obtained.

The invariance under proper Lorentz transformations of $\Delta(x)$ follows from eq. (6.3), since each factor in this expression is Lorentz-invariant. ($\varepsilon(k)$ is invariant, since proper Lorentz transformations do not interchange past and future.)

It is now clear that several further related delta functions can be obtained from eq. (6.1) by modifying the contour C. These can all be derived from the two special cases

$$\Delta^{\pm}(x) = \frac{1}{(2\pi)^4}\int_{C^{\pm}} d^4k\, \frac{e^{ikx}}{k^2 + m^2} \tag{6.5}$$

where $C^{\pm}$ are the contours shown in fig. 5, encircling the poles at $k_0 = \pm\omega_{\mathbf{k}}$ respectively in an anticlockwise direction.

Thus

$$\Delta(x) = \Delta^{+}(x) + \Delta^{-}(x) \tag{6.6}$$

as follows at once by suitable deformation of the contours, and

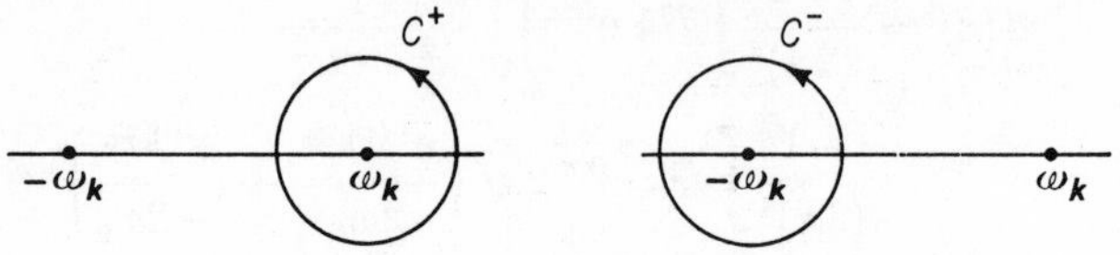

Fig. 5. The contours $C^{\pm}$ for $\Delta^{\pm}(x)$.

the delta function $\{-i\Delta^{(1)}(x)\}$, defined by

$$\{-i\Delta^{(1)}(x)\} = \frac{1}{(2\pi)^4}\int_{C^{(1)}} d^4k \, \frac{e^{ikx}}{k^2 + m^2} \tag{6.7}$$

with the contour $C^{(1)}$ shown in fig. 6, is also given by

$$-i\Delta^{(1)} = \Delta^{+} - \Delta^{-}. \tag{6.8}$$

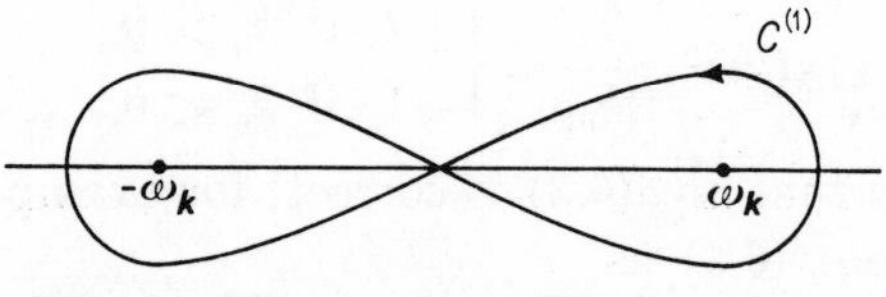

Fig. 6. The countour $C^{(1)}$ for $\Delta^{(1)}(x)$.

From these definitions we easily obtain other representations, e.g.

$$\Delta^{\pm}(x) = \mp \frac{i}{(2\pi)^3 2}\int_{k_0=\omega_{\mathbf{k}}} \frac{d^3k}{k_0}\, e^{\pm ikx}, \tag{6.9}$$

and the properties of these delta functions. From eqs. (6.9), one finds that

$$\Delta^{+}(x) = -\,\Delta^{-}(-x). \tag{6.10}$$

The $\Delta^{\pm}$-functions already occurred in the derivation of eq. (5.19) where we really proved

$$\left.\begin{aligned} [\phi^{+}(x),\ \phi^{+}(x')] &= [\phi^{-}(x),\ \phi^{-}(x')] = 0, \\ [\phi^{\pm}(x),\ \phi^{\mp}(x')] &= i\Delta^{\pm}(x - x'), \end{aligned}\right\} \tag{6.11}$$

using the commutation relations (3.5). Hence eqs. (5.18—19) follow.

We next consider the vacuum expectation values of products of field operators. The typical term is $(\Phi_0, \phi(x)\phi(x')\Phi_0)$. This is easily evaluated from the expansion (5.14) and eq. (5.15). Since this is a transition from the vacuum to the vacuum, only the term $(\Phi_0, \phi^+(x)\phi^-(x')\Phi_0)$ gives a non-vanishing contribution (since ϕ^- can create a particle which ϕ^+ can reabsorb). Hence

$$(\Phi_0, \phi(x)\phi(x')\Phi_0) = \frac{1}{V} \sum_{\substack{k_0=\omega_{\mathbf{k}} \\ k'_0=\omega_{\mathbf{k}'}}} \frac{1}{2\sqrt{k_0 k'_0}} \, e^{i(kx-k'x')} (\Phi_0, a_{\mathbf{k}} a^\dagger_{\mathbf{k}'} \Phi_0).$$

From the commutation relations (3.5), since $a_{\mathbf{k}}\Phi_0 = 0$, this gives, using eq. (3.7),

$$\begin{aligned}(\Phi_0, \phi(x)\phi(x')\Phi_0) &= \frac{1}{(2\pi)^3 2} \int_{k_0=\omega_{\mathbf{k}}} \frac{d^3k}{k_0} \, e^{ik(x-x')} \\ &= i\Delta^+(x-x'). \end{aligned} \tag{6.12}$$

The Dyson *chronological* or *time-ordered* product of the operators $\phi(x)$ and $\phi(x')$ is defined by

$$P\{\phi(x)\phi(x')\} = \begin{cases} \phi(x)\phi(x'), & \text{if } x_0 > x'_0, \\ \phi(x')\phi(x), & \text{if } x'_0 > x_0, \end{cases} \tag{6.13}$$

i.e. the operators are written in chronological order with the time running from right to left. (This has the effect that 'earlier' operators operate 'first'.) Using the ε-symbol, defined in eq. (6.4), this can be written

$$P\{\phi(x)\phi(x')\} = \frac{1+\varepsilon(x-x')}{2}\phi(x)\phi(x') + \frac{1-\varepsilon(x-x')}{2}\phi(x')\phi(x). \tag{6.14}$$

Hence from eqs. (6.12) and (6.10)

$$\begin{aligned}(\Phi_0, P\{\phi(x)\phi(x')\}\Phi_0) &= \frac{1+\varepsilon(x-x')}{2} i\Delta^+(x-x') - \frac{1-\varepsilon(x-x')}{2} i\Delta^-(x-x') \\ &= \tfrac{1}{2}\Delta_F(x-x') \end{aligned} \tag{6.15}$$

which defines the Δ_F-function, i.e.

$$\Delta_F(x) = [1 + \varepsilon(x)]i\Delta^+(x) - [1 - \varepsilon(x)]i\Delta^-(x). \quad (6.16)$$

Thus

$$\frac{1}{2i}\Delta_F(x) = \pm\Delta^\pm(x), \text{ if } x_0 \gtrless 0. \quad (6.17)$$

From the integral representations (6.5) of $\Delta^\pm$ it follows at once that

$$\Delta_F(x) = \frac{-2i}{(2\pi)^4}\int_{C_F} d^4k \frac{e^{ikx}}{k^2 + m^2} \quad (6.18)$$

where the contour C_F goes below the pole at $k_0 = -\omega_{\mathbf{k}}$ and above that at $k_0 = \omega_{\mathbf{k}}$, as shown in fig. 7. That eq. (6.18) is

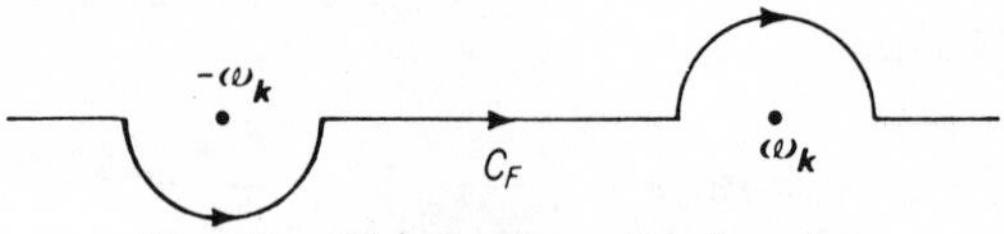

Fig. 7. The contour C_F for Δ_F.

equivalent to eq. (6.17) is easily seen. For $x_0 > 0$, we can close the contour C_F by means of a semi-circle of infinite radius in the lower half-plane Im $k_0 < 0$, for then $e^{-ik_0x_0} \to 0$ as $|k_0| \to \infty$ so that there is no contribution from the integral along this semi-circle. The resulting closed contour encircles the pole at $k_0 = \omega_{\mathbf{k}}$ only, in a *clockwise* sense. Thus from eqs. (6.5) and (6.18), for $x_0 > 0$,

$$\Delta_F(x) = (-2i)\,(-\Delta^+(x))$$

agreeing with eq. (6.17). Similarly the result for $x_0 < 0$ follows by closing the contour C_F by means of an infinite semi-circle in the upper half-plane Im $k_0 > 0$.

Instead of deforming the contour as in fig. 7, we can move the poles an infinitesimal distance η off the real axis (cf. fig. 8) and integrate along the real axis, i.e. we replace eq. (6.18) by

$$\Delta_F(x) = \frac{-2i}{(2\pi)^4}\int d^4k \frac{e^{ikx}}{-\{k_0^2 - (\omega_{\mathbf{k}} - i\eta)^2\}}$$

$$= \frac{-2i}{(2\pi)^4}\int d^4k \frac{e^{ikx}}{k^2 + m^2 - i\varepsilon} \quad (6.19)$$

where $\varepsilon = 2\eta\omega_{\mathbf{k}}$ is a small positive number which we let tend to zero after integration. (This is also the reason why the η^2 term

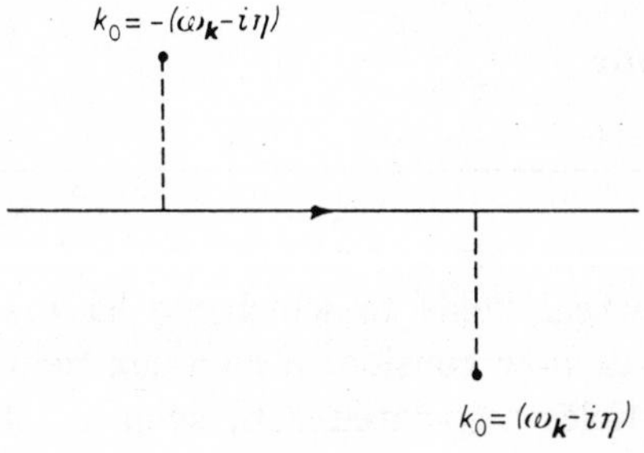

Fig. 8.

has been neglected.) In eq. (6.19) integration with respect to each of the four variables $k_0, \ldots, k_3$ is now along the whole real axis $(-\infty, \infty)$.

CHAPTER 7

Charged Mesons

Instead of the real fields to which we have so far restricted ourselves, we shall now consider a complex field $\phi(x)$. We shall see that the particles associated with such a field can be interpreted as being electrically charged.

Our discussion will, to begin with, be classical. Since a complex field $\phi(x)$ can be decomposed into two *real* fields $\phi_1(x)$ and $\phi_2(x)$,

$$\phi(x) = \frac{1}{\sqrt{2}} (\phi_1(x) - i\phi_2(x)) \tag{7.1}$$

the methods of chapter 2 can at once be applied to this case. However, instead of considering the Lagrangian density $\mathscr{L}$ as a function of ϕ_r and $\partial\phi_r/\partial x_\nu$, $(r = 1, 2)$, the physical significance of the complex fields is brought out more clearly by writing

$$\mathscr{L} = \mathscr{L}(\phi, \phi^*, \phi_{,\nu}, \phi^*_{,\nu}) \tag{7.2}$$

$(\phi_{,\nu} \equiv \partial\phi/\partial x_\nu$ etc.) and treating $\delta\phi$ and $\delta\phi^*$, rather than $\delta\phi_1$ and $\delta\phi_2$, as independent variations. This leads to the field equations

$$\frac{\partial\mathscr{L}}{\partial\phi} - \frac{\partial}{\partial x_\nu}\left(\frac{\partial\mathscr{L}}{\partial\phi_{,\nu}}\right) = 0, \qquad \frac{\partial\mathscr{L}}{\partial\phi^*} - \frac{\partial}{\partial x_\nu}\left(\frac{\partial\mathscr{L}}{\partial\phi^*_{,\nu}}\right) = 0 \tag{7.3}$$

which replace eqs. (2.8).

The Lagrangian density $\mathscr{L}$ must be a real function, in order that the fields ϕ_1 and ϕ_2 remain real at all times. Consequently the field equations (7.3) are the complex conjugates of each other. We shall now impose the further restriction that the Lagrangian density $\mathscr{L}$ must be invariant under the following transformation of the fields:

$$\phi \to \phi\, e^{i\alpha}, \qquad \phi^* \to \phi^*\, e^{-i\alpha}, \tag{7.4}$$

where α is an arbitrary real constant. This transformation is known as a *gauge transformation of the first kind*. The invariance of $\mathscr{L}$ under these gauge transformations will enable us to interpret ϕ and ϕ^* as giving rise to charge and current densities satisfying a continuity equation and, in the quantized theory, as representing charged particles.

As a particular example, consider the Lagrangian density

$$\mathscr{L} = -(\phi_{,\nu}\phi^*_{,\nu} + m^2\phi\phi^*) \tag{7.5}$$

which is the natural generalization of eq. (2.18) for the real field. The field equations (7.3) now become

$$(\Box^2 - m^2)\phi = 0, \qquad (\Box^2 - m^2)\phi^* = 0, \tag{7.6}$$

as must be the case since ϕ_1 and ϕ_2 separately obey the Klein-Gordon equation; for we can write the Lagrangian density (7.5) as

$$\mathscr{L} = \sum_{r=1}^{2} \left\{ -\frac{1}{2}\left(\frac{\partial \phi_r}{\partial x_\nu}\frac{\partial \phi_r}{\partial x_\nu} + m^2\phi_r^2 \right) \right\}. \tag{7.7}$$

The Lagrangian density (7.5), involving only products of ϕ with ϕ^*, or their derivatives, is clearly invariant under the transformation (7.4).

Define the four-vector

$$es_\nu(x) = -ie\left\{ \frac{\partial \mathscr{L}}{\partial \phi_{,\nu}}\phi - \frac{\partial \mathscr{L}}{\partial \phi^*_{,\nu}}\phi^* \right\} \tag{7.8}$$

where e is as yet an undetermined constant. From the equations of motion (7.3) and the gauge invariance of $\mathscr{L}$ it follows, as is shown below, that

$$\frac{\partial s_\nu}{\partial x_\nu} = 0. \tag{7.9}$$

This is the usual continuity equation enabling us to interpret $e\mathbf{s}(x)$ as a current-density vector and the fourth component $e\rho(x) = es_4(x)/i$ as a charge density. Compare also exercise 2.5, where it is shown that a continuity equation, like eq. (7.9), implies a conservation law. For a real field ϕ, the current vanishes identically: from eq. (7.8), $s_\nu(x) = 0$.

For the Lagrangian density (7.5)

$$es_\nu(x) = ie\{\phi^*_{,\nu}\phi - \phi_{,\nu}\phi^*\}, \tag{7.10}$$

and the continuity equation (7.9) is verified directly from the field equations (7.6).

To prove eq. (7.9) more generally, consider an infinitesimal gauge transformation (i.e. α is small, so that $e^{i\alpha} \approx 1 + i\alpha$, etc.)

$$\phi \to \phi(1 + i\alpha), \; \phi^* \to \phi^*(1 - i\alpha). \tag{7.11}$$

A brief calculation shows that this induces a change $\delta\mathscr{L}$ in the Lagrangian density (7.2) given by

$$\delta\mathscr{L} = i\alpha\left[\frac{\partial\mathscr{L}}{\partial\phi}\phi + \frac{\partial\mathscr{L}}{\partial\phi_{,\nu}}\phi_{,\nu}\right] - i\alpha\left[\frac{\partial\mathscr{L}}{\partial\phi^*}\phi^* + \frac{\partial\mathscr{L}}{\partial\phi^*_{,\nu}}\phi^*_{,\nu}\right]. \tag{7.12}$$

Calculating the divergence (7.9) from eq. (7.8) and using the field equations (7.3) and eq. (7.12) one finds that

$$\frac{\partial s_\nu}{\partial x_\nu} = -\frac{1}{\alpha}\delta\mathscr{L} = 0 \tag{7.13}$$

where the last step follows from the invariance of $\mathscr{L}$ under gauge transformations of the first kind, thus proving the continuity equation (7.9). (Cf. exercise 7.1, for an alternative derivation.)

The transition to the quantized theory can be effected either directly for the complex fields ϕ and ϕ^* (they now become non-Hermitian operators ϕ and $\phi^\dagger$) using the methods of chapter 3, or by using eq. (7.1) and the properties of the quantized fields ϕ_1 and ϕ_2. We shall adopt the latter approach. As all these considerations are straightforward generalizations of those for real fields, we shall only briefly indicate some points of special interest to us and shall at once use the interaction picture (i.e. the Heisenberg picture, as we are considering free fields — cf. chapter 5).

We now again restrict ourselves to fields satisfying the Klein-Gordon equation, i.e. derived from the Lagrangian density (7.5). We expand each field $\phi_r(x)$ as in eq. (5.14)

$$\phi_r(x) = \frac{1}{\sqrt{V}}\sum_{k_0=\omega_{\mathbf{k}}}\frac{1}{\sqrt{2k_0}}\{a_r(\mathbf{k})\,e^{ikx} + a_r^\dagger(\mathbf{k})\,e^{-ikx}\}, \tag{7.14}$$

the creation and absorption operators $a_r^\dagger(\mathbf{k})$ and $a_r(\mathbf{k})$ for each field $\phi_r(\mathbf{k})$, $(r = 1, 2)$, satisfying commutation relations similar to eqs. (3.5):

$$[a_r(\mathbf{k}), a_s^\dagger(\mathbf{k}')] = \delta_{rs}\delta(\mathbf{k}, \mathbf{k}'), \tag{7.15}$$

all other commutators vanishing.

Defining

$$a(\mathbf{k}) = \frac{1}{\sqrt{2}}[a_1(\mathbf{k}) - ia_2(\mathbf{k})], \quad b^\dagger(\mathbf{k}) = \frac{1}{\sqrt{2}}[a_1^\dagger(\mathbf{k}) - ia_2^\dagger(\mathbf{k})], \tag{7.16}$$

it follows from

$$\phi = \frac{1}{\sqrt{2}}(\phi_1 - i\phi_2) \qquad \phi^\dagger = \frac{1}{\sqrt{2}}(\phi_1 + i\phi_2) \tag{7.17}$$

and eqs. (7.14) that

$$\phi(x) = \frac{1}{\sqrt{V}} \sum_{k_0=\omega_\mathbf{k}} \frac{1}{\sqrt{2k_0}} \{a(\mathbf{k})\, e^{ikx} + b^\dagger(\mathbf{k})\, e^{-ikx}\}, \tag{7.18a}$$

$$\phi^\dagger(x) = \frac{1}{\sqrt{V}} \sum_{k_0=\omega_\mathbf{k}} \frac{1}{\sqrt{2k_0}} \{a^\dagger(\mathbf{k})\, e^{-ikx} + b(\mathbf{k})\, e^{ikx}\}. \tag{7.18b}$$

From eqs. (7.14—18), the commutation relations of the ϕ_r, $(r = 1, 2)$, of ϕ and $\phi^\dagger$, and of the $a(\mathbf{k})$, $b(\mathbf{k})$ and their adjoints are easily derived. For example, from eqs. (7.15—16)

$$[a(\mathbf{k}), a^\dagger(\mathbf{k}')] = [b(\mathbf{k}), b^\dagger(\mathbf{k}')] = \delta(\mathbf{k}, \mathbf{k}'), \tag{7.19}$$

all other commutators of $a(\mathbf{k})$, $b(\mathbf{k})$ and their adjoints vanishing.

We must next consider the interpretation of the operators (7.16) and their adjoints. The operators a_r and $a_r^\dagger$ are the absorption and creation operators of the mesons associated with the real fields ϕ_r. But we shall see that it is the particular linear combinations (7.16—17) which admit a simple physical interpretation.

From the fact that the operators $a(\mathbf{k})$, $a^\dagger(\mathbf{k})$ and $b(\mathbf{k})$, $b^\dagger(\mathbf{k})$ satisfy the same commutation relations (7.19) as the absorption and creation operators of the real fields, eq. (7.15), and commute with each other, it follows that we can interpret $a(\mathbf{k})$, $a^\dagger(\mathbf{k})$ and $b(\mathbf{k})$, $b^\dagger(\mathbf{k})$ as absorption and creation operators of two different kinds of mesons of momentum $\mathbf{k}$. We shall see presently that they differ in charge. In particular, it follows from eq. (7.19) that the operators

$$N^+(\mathbf{k}) = a^\dagger(\mathbf{k})a(\mathbf{k}),\ N^-(\mathbf{k}) = b^\dagger(\mathbf{k})b(\mathbf{k}) \tag{7.20}$$

have the eigenvalues 0, 1, 2, . . . and are the occupation number operators for these mesons.

This interpretation is confirmed if one calculates the total energy of the system. From the Lagrangian density (7.7) the Hamiltonian can be derived, analogously to eq. (3.6). Dropping the zero-point energy, one obtains

$$H = \sum_{\mathbf{k}} \omega_{\mathbf{k}} \sum_{r=1}^{2} a_r^\dagger(\mathbf{k})\, a_r(\mathbf{k}) = \sum_{\mathbf{k}} \omega_{\mathbf{k}} [N^+(\mathbf{k}) + N^-(\mathbf{k})], \tag{7.21}$$

where eqs. (7.16) and (7.20) have been used.

Next consider the operator

$$Q = \int d^3x\, e\rho(x) = \int d^3x\, [es_4(x)/i] \tag{7.22}$$

which gives the total charge of the system at time $x_0 = t$, the 3-dimensional integral being over all **x**-space. Using eqs. (7.10) and (7.18—19), one obtains after a short calculation

$$Q = e \sum_{\mathbf{k}} [N^+(\mathbf{k}) - N^-(\mathbf{k})]. \tag{7.23}$$

Thus the total charge is a constant of the motion as we would expect. From eq. (7.23) it is now clear that the operators $a(\mathbf{k})$, $a^\dagger(\mathbf{k})$ and $N^+(\mathbf{k})$ are absorption, creation and occupation number operators for a meson of momentum **k** and electric charge $+e$. The operators $b(\mathbf{k})$, $b^\dagger(\mathbf{k})$ and $N^-(\mathbf{k})$ have corresponding meanings for mesons of charge $-e$. If we take $e > 0$, then $a(\mathbf{k})$, etc., refer to positive mesons, $b(\mathbf{k})$, etc., to negative ones. From eq. (7.23) we see that the quantum field theory leads naturally to a quantization of charge, which can only occur as a multiple of the fundamental unit of charge e. From eqs. (7.18), the operator ϕ decreases the charge by e, absorbing a positive or creating a negative meson, while $\phi^\dagger$ has the opposite effect.

The theory here developed is completely symmetric between positive and negative mesons. The only effect of the transformation $e \to -e$ is to interchange positive and negative mesons.

This operation is known as *charge conjugation* and we thus see that the above theory is quite symmetric with respect to charge conjugation. We can put this differently. If we call positive mesons particles and negative ones antiparticles (we could equally well call the negative mesons particles, etc.), then charge conjugation is the operation which interchanges particles and antiparticles. In terms of the fields (7.18), charge conjugation interchanges ϕ and its adjoint $\phi^\dagger$. For the Hermitian field ϕ treated in earlier chapters, which we now see corresponds to electrically neutral mesons, $\phi = \phi^\dagger$; hence we can think of neutral mesons as being their own antiparticles. The occurrence of particles in pairs, as particles and antiparticles, seems a fundamental consequence of relativistic field theories. All experimental evidence seems to confirm this conclusion.

Finally, we wish to show quite generally that the positive and negative frequency parts of a field are associated with absorption and creation operators respectively. [This is the result we had in eq. (5.14—15) and (7.18).] This relation follows merely from the equation of motion of an operator in the Heisenberg picture, eq. (5.10). If we apply this equation, for example, to the operator $a(\mathbf{k})\,e^{ikx}$ which occurs in ϕ, eq. (7.18a), and take the matrix element of the resulting operator equation between states Φ_1 and Φ_2 which are eigenstates of the Hamiltonian H of the system with eigenvalues E_1 and E_2, then we obtain

$$(\omega_{\mathbf{k}} + E_2 - E_1)(\Phi_2,\ a(\mathbf{k})\,e^{ikx}\Phi_1) = 0. \tag{7.24}$$

From this equation it follows that the operator $a(\mathbf{k})\,e^{ikx}$ effects transitions from the state Φ_1 to Φ_2 (i.e. the matrix element in eq. (7.24) is non-zero) only if

$$\omega_{\mathbf{k}} + E_2 - E_1 = 0. \tag{7.25}$$

Since $\omega_{\mathbf{k}} > 0$, this implies $E_1 > E_2$: in the transition $\Phi_1 \to \Phi_2$, the energy of the system has been reduced by $\omega_{\mathbf{k}}$, i.e. $a(\mathbf{k})\,e^{ikx}$ is an absorption operator. Correspondingly, operators with negative frequency parts are creation operators, i.e. they increase the energy of the system and in a sensible interpretation of the formalism must correspond to the emission of particles.

CHAPTER 8

Fermions

So far we have considered spinless particles which satisfy the Klein-Gordon equation and on quantization lead to Bose-Einstein statistics. We now wish to study electrons. These have spin $\frac{1}{2}$ and are described well by the Dirac equation. Furthermore for a system of electrons the Pauli exclusion principle holds, i.e. they obey Fermi-Dirac statistics.

These differences indicate that the formalism developed for bosons must be modified if it is to be applied to fermions. Nevertheless there are strong similarities between the two cases so that we shall at once work in the Heisenberg picture, leaning heavily on the corresponding results for bosons. We shall straightaway consider non-Hermitian operators, since Hermitian fermion fields do not seem to play any role in nature. Consequently our development will most closely resemble the formalism of the last chapter dealing with charged mesons. The theory to be developed has been outstandingly successful in describing electrons and positrons in quantum electrodynamics. It probably also affords quite a good description of nucleons*).

According to Dirac's theory, the electron is described by the equation

$$\left(\gamma_\lambda \frac{\partial}{\partial x_\lambda} + M\right) \psi(x) = 0. \tag{8.1}$$

*) As for spin zero mesons, we shall see that charged spin $\frac{1}{2}$ particles, e.g. electrons and positrons, must be represented by non-Hermitian fields. However, an electrically neutral particle is not necessarily represented by a Hermitian field. The neutron, for example, possesses an intrinsic magnetic moment. Consequently we again have two types of particle according to the sign of the magnetic moment: particle (neutron) and antiparticle (antineutron) and these are again described by non-Hermitian operators.

Here $\psi(x)$ is a 4-component spinor wave function and the γ_λ ($\lambda = 1, \dots 4,$) are 4×4 matrices which satisfy the anticommutation relations

$$\gamma_\lambda \gamma_\mu + \gamma_\mu \gamma_\lambda = 2\delta_{\lambda\mu}, \qquad (\lambda, \mu = 1, \dots 4). \tag{8.2}$$

M is the mass of the electron. There are of course many ways of choosing four anticommuting matrices satisfying eqs. (8.2). For most purposes one does not require an explicit representation as the relevant properties can be obtained directly from the anticommutation rules (8.2). Nevertheless it is sometimes advantageous in practice to work in a specific representation. The representation most frequently found in the literature has the feature that the non-relativistic limit can be obtained in a particularly simple manner*). It does not seem to have any other virtues. However, for understanding the general principles and studying the symmetry properties of the theory one obtains a far more lucid picture by using a different representation**).

The distinguishing property of this representation is that the matrices γ_1, γ_2 and γ_3 are purely real, γ_4 purely imaginary. Representations with these properties are known as Majorana representations. One particular Majorana representation is given by

$$\left.\begin{aligned} \gamma_1 = \begin{pmatrix} 1 & 0 \\ 0 & -1 \end{pmatrix}, \quad \gamma_2 = \begin{pmatrix} 0 & -i\sigma_2 \\ i\sigma_2 & 0 \end{pmatrix}, \quad \gamma_3 = \begin{pmatrix} 0 & -1 \\ -1 & 0 \end{pmatrix} \\ \gamma_4 = \begin{pmatrix} 0 & -i\sigma_1 \\ i\sigma_1 & 0 \end{pmatrix}, \quad \gamma_5 = \begin{pmatrix} 0 & -i\sigma_3 \\ i\sigma_3 & 0 \end{pmatrix}. \end{aligned}\right\} \tag{8.3}$$

These γ-matrices are merely a permutation of the usual representation, eqs. (A 7), and hence also satisfy eqs. (8.2). The four-dimensional spin matrices $\boldsymbol{\sigma} \equiv (\sigma_1, \sigma_2, \sigma_3)$, eqs. (A 6a), are now purely imaginary

$$\sigma_k^* = -\sigma_k, \qquad (k = 1, 2, 3), \tag{8.4}$$

*) The relevant results of the Dirac theory are quoted or derived in the appendix. Equations in this appendix are labelled **A**. The representation referred to above is given in eqs. (A 7).

**) The main results of this chapter will later be stated generally, enabling the reader to use any desired representation.

where an asterisk denotes *complex* conjugation (i.e. changing i into $-i$ but *not* transposing). From the Hermitian character of the γ_λ that of the σ_k follows:

$$\sigma_k^\dagger = \sigma_k, \qquad (k = 1,\ 2,\ 3), \tag{8.5}$$

where a dagger denotes *Hermitian* conjugation.

Let

$$\psi^{(r)}(\mathbf{p}) = u^{(r)}(\mathbf{p})\, e^{ipx}, \quad (r = 1,\ 2), \tag{8.6}$$

be solutions of the Dirac equation (8.1), normalized to $E_\mathbf{p}/M$ particles per unit volume, with momentum and energy eigenvalues $\mathbf{p}$ and

$$E_\mathbf{p} = +\,(M^2 + \mathbf{p}^2)^{\frac{1}{2}}, \tag{8.7}$$

and spin orientation parallel to the vectors $\pm\,\mathbf{p}$ for $r = 1$ and $r = 2$ respectively*):

$$\frac{\boldsymbol{\sigma}\mathbf{p}}{|\mathbf{p}|}\, u^{(r)}(\mathbf{p}) = \pm\, u^{(r)}(\mathbf{p}), \quad \begin{cases} r = 1 \\ r = 2 \end{cases}. \tag{8.8}$$

Since $(\gamma_\lambda \partial/\partial x_\lambda + M)$ is real in the Majorana representation, it follows that the expressions complex conjugate to eq. (8.6),

$$\psi^{(r+2)}(\mathbf{p}) \equiv \psi^{(r)*}(\mathbf{p}) = u^{(r)*}(\mathbf{p})\, e^{-ipx}, \quad (r = 1,\ 2), \tag{8.9}$$

are also solutions of the Dirac equation (8.1), corresponding to momentum and energy eigenvalues $-\mathbf{p}$ and $-E_\mathbf{p}$. Furthermore, taking the complex conjugate of eq. (8.8) it follows, on account of eq. (8.4), that the states (8.9) are spin eigenstates with spin orientation parallel to $\mp\mathbf{p}$ for $r = 1$ and $r = 2$ respectively.

The solutions (8.6) and (8.9) (known as positive and negative energy solutions respectively) *together* form a complete set of solutions of the Dirac equation for all allowed momenta $\mathbf{p}$ satisfying the periodicity condition (1.5). Analogously to eqs. (7.18), we

*) These solutions are discussed in the appendix, eqs. (A 12—21). In eq. (8.9) the notation $\psi^{(r+2)}$ is introduced to conform with that in the appendix.

expand the spinor operator $\psi(x)$ in terms of this set*)

$$\psi(x) = \frac{1}{\sqrt{V}} \sum_{p_0=E_{\mathbf{p}}} \left(\frac{M}{p_0}\right)^{\frac{1}{2}} \sum_{r=1}^{2} \{c_r(\mathbf{p})\, u^{(r)}(\mathbf{p})\, e^{ipx} + d_r^\dagger(\mathbf{p})\, u^{(r)*}(\mathbf{p})\, e^{-ipx}\} \tag{8.10a}$$

and, taking the adjoint,

$$\psi^\dagger(x) = \frac{1}{\sqrt{V}} \sum_{p_0=E_{\mathbf{p}}} \left(\frac{M}{p_0}\right)^{\frac{1}{2}} \sum_{r=1}^{2} \{c_r^\dagger(\mathbf{p})\, u^{(r)*}(\mathbf{p})\, e^{-ipx} + d_r(\mathbf{p})\, u^{(r)}(\mathbf{p})\, e^{ipx}\}. \tag{8.10b}$$

The interpretation of the operators $c_r(\mathbf{p})$, etc., as absorption and creation operators is now strongly suggested by our treatment of charged mesons in the last chapter. From the general arguments following eq. (7.24), the operators $c_r(\mathbf{p})$ and $d_r(\mathbf{p})$ associated with positive frequency parts e^{ipx} are absorption operators and, correspondingly, their adjoints are creation operators. If we take the operator $c_r(\mathbf{p})$ to refer to negatively charged electrons (i.e. charge $-e$, $e > 0$), then $c_r(\mathbf{p})$ will be the absorption operator, $c_r^\dagger(\mathbf{p})$ the creation operator for an electron ('particle') of energy $E_{\mathbf{p}}$, momentum $\mathbf{p}$ and, for $r = 1, 2$, spin orientation parallel and antiparallel to the momentum $\mathbf{p}$ respectively; thinking of the spin as a rotation we call the electron in these two states right-handed and left-handed.

Eqs. (8.10) are *completely* symmetrical in the operators $c_r(\mathbf{p})$ and $d_r(\mathbf{p})$ and in their adjoints. Guided by the results for charged

*) As usual, we use matrix notation, suppressing the indices α, β, . . . (running from 1 to 4) which label spinor components and elements of γ-matrices, etc. For example, eq. (8.10b) stands for

$$\psi_\alpha^\dagger(x) = \frac{1}{\sqrt{V}} \sum_{p_0=E_{\mathbf{p}}} \left(\frac{M}{p_0}\right)^{\frac{1}{2}} \sum_{r=1}^{2} \{c_r^\dagger(\mathbf{p})\, u_\alpha^{(r)*}(\mathbf{p})\, e^{-ipx} + d_r(\mathbf{p}) u_\alpha^{(r)}(\mathbf{p})\, e^{ipx}\}, \quad \alpha = 1, \ldots 4.$$

In elementary treatments of matrices, it is usual to distinguish column and row vectors. We shall nowhere make such a distinction since it is pointless: $\psi^T = \psi$, i.e. $\psi_\alpha^T = \psi_\alpha$ for any vector, T denoting transposition, i.e. interchanging rows and columns. For matrices, on the other hand, we have two distinct entities M and M^T which are only equal for a symmetric matrix. In this case $M = M^T$, i.e.

$$M_{\alpha\beta} = M_{\alpha\beta}^T = M_{\beta\alpha}.$$

bosons, we expect to interpret $d_r(\mathbf{p})$ and $d_r^\dagger(\mathbf{p})$ as absorption and creation operators of the antiparticle of the electron, i.e. the positron (which has the same mass M but positive charge $+e>0$), in states of energy $E_{\mathbf{p}}$, momentum $\mathbf{p}$ and right- and left-handed polarizations respectively. One of the virtues of the Majorana representation is this complete symmetry between particles and antiparticles which makes eqs. (8.10) resemble strongly the charged boson case and greatly facilitates interpretation. It also greatly facilitates the study of symmetry properties of systems under charge conjugation (which interchanges electrons and positrons) and under related symmetry transformations such as time-reversal*). If one does not use a Majorana representation, the components of the spinors in eq. (8.10) get 'mixed up', the spinors occurring in each equation are no longer the complex conjugates of each other and the particle-antiparticle symmetry is hidden.

To justify the above interpretations of the operators $c_r(\mathbf{p}), \ldots$, we must calculate the energy, charge, etc., of the system starting from the Lagrangian density $\mathscr{L}$. The Dirac equation (8.1) and the 'adjoint' equation for

$$\bar{\psi}(x) \equiv \psi^\dagger(x)\gamma_4 \tag{8.11}$$

can be derived as Lagrange's equations [cf. eqs. (7.3)] from

$$\mathscr{L} = -\psi^\dagger(x)\left[\gamma_4\left(\gamma_\mu \frac{\partial}{\partial x_\mu} + M\right)\right]\psi(x), \tag{8.12}$$

treating the fields $\psi_\alpha(x)$ and $\psi_\alpha^\dagger(x)$ ($\alpha = 1, \ldots 4$, corresponding to the four components of the spinors $u^{(r)}(\mathbf{p})$, etc., in eq. (8.10)) as independent variables**). In the same way one obtains for the

*) Wick (see bibliography) gives an excellent account of these symmetry properties.

**) Expressions such as $\psi^\dagger\gamma_4\psi$ in eq. (8.12) or $\psi\gamma_4\psi^\dagger$ in eq. (8.18) below stand for

$$\sum_{\alpha,\beta=1}^{4} \psi_\alpha^\dagger(\gamma_4)_{\alpha\beta}\psi_\beta \quad \text{and} \quad \sum_{\alpha,\beta=1}^{4} \psi_\alpha(\gamma_4)_{\alpha\beta}\psi_\beta^\dagger$$

respectively. The resulting expressions are non-commuting operators only by virtue of their dependence on the absorption and creation operators $c_r(\mathbf{p})$, etc. If the reader experiences any difficulties over these matters, he is advised to write out the spinor indices explicitly.

Hamiltonian density [cf. eqs. (2.13) and (2.17)], since $\partial\mathscr{L}/\partial\dot{\psi}^\dagger_\alpha = 0$,

$$\mathscr{H}(x) = \frac{\partial\mathscr{L}}{\partial\psi_{\alpha,4}}\psi_{\alpha,4} - \mathscr{L} = \psi^\dagger(x)\gamma_4\left(\sum_{k=1}^{3}\gamma_k\frac{\partial}{\partial x_k} + M\right)\psi(x), \quad (8.13)$$

where $\psi_{\alpha,4} = \partial\psi_\alpha/\partial x_4$. From eq. (8.13) one can calculate the Hamiltonian (2.16),

$$H(t) = \int d^3x\,\mathscr{H}(\mathbf{x}, t), \quad (8.14)$$

by substituting the expansions (8.10) and carrying out the **x**-integration using the orthonormality relations (A 21) for the spinors $u^{(r)}(\mathbf{p})$. A straightforward, if slightly tedious, calculation gives

$$H = \sum_{\mathbf{p}} E_{\mathbf{p}} \sum_{r=1}^{2} \{c_r^\dagger(\mathbf{p})c_r(\mathbf{p}) - d_r(\mathbf{p})d_r^\dagger(\mathbf{p})\}. \quad (8.15)$$

In deriving eq. (8.15) care was taken not to permute any of the operators $c_r(\mathbf{p})$, etc., for we do not yet know their commutation relations. We must now determine these. It would be consistent with the above interpretation of c_r, d_r, $c_r^\dagger$ and $d_r^\dagger$ as absorption and creation operators of particles and antiparticles to make them satisfy the *same* commutation relations as were postulated for a, b, $a^\dagger$ and $b^\dagger$ for charged mesons; cf. eq. (7.19). In terms of occupation number operators

$$N_r^-(\mathbf{p}) = c_r^\dagger(\mathbf{p})c_r(\mathbf{p}),\ N_r^+(\mathbf{p}) = d_r^\dagger(\mathbf{p})d_r(\mathbf{p}), \quad (8.16)$$

eq. (8.15) becomes, since we would have $[d_r(\mathbf{p}), d_r^\dagger(\mathbf{p})] = 1$,

$$H = \sum_{\mathbf{p}} E_{\mathbf{p}} \sum_{r=1}^{2} \{N_r^-(\mathbf{p}) - N_r^+(\mathbf{p}) - 1\}. \quad (8.17)$$

Since the operators $N_r^\pm(\mathbf{p})$ have the eigenvalues 0, 1, 2, . . ., the Hamiltonian (8.17) is *not* positive definite*), each positron of momentum $\mathbf{p}$ contributing an energy $(-E_{\mathbf{p}})$.

Before showing how this serious difficulty is resolved, one other point must be discussed. In going from the 'classical' to the quantized theory in which ψ and $\psi^\dagger$ are operators there is, as usual, some ambiguity as regards the order of factors. Instead

*) As in the boson case, eq. (3.6), we shall simply omit the infinite zero-point energy $-2\Sigma E_{\mathbf{p}}$.

of eq. (8.12) we could equally well start from

$$\mathscr{L} = -\psi(x)\left[\gamma_4\left(\gamma_\mu\frac{\partial}{\partial x_\mu} + M\right)\right]\psi^\dagger(x) \tag{8.18}$$

or some linear combination of these two Lagrangians. Since eq. (8.18) differs from eq. (8.12) only in having particles and antiparticles interchanged ($\psi \leftrightarrow \psi^\dagger$), the Lagrangian density (8.18) would lead to eq. (8.17) for the Hamiltonian with $N^+(\mathbf{p})$ and $N^-(\mathbf{p})$ interchanged. Thus the only linear combination of the Lagrangians (8.12) and (8.18) which will ensure a positive definite Hamiltonian is the completely symmetric

$$\mathscr{L} = -\frac{1}{2}\left\{\psi^\dagger(x)\left[\gamma_4\left(\gamma_\mu\frac{\partial}{\partial x_\mu}+M\right)\right]\psi(x)+\psi(x)\left[\gamma_4\left(\gamma_\mu\frac{\partial}{\partial x_\mu}+M\right)\right]\psi^\dagger(x)\right\}. \tag{8.19}$$

But in this case the Hamiltonian merely reduces to a constant. Hence we cannot overcome the above negative-energy difficulty by modifying the Lagrangian.

To resolve this difficulty, we shall postulate the following anticommutation relations, first introduced by Jordan and Wigner:

$$[c_r(\mathbf{p}),\ c_s^\dagger(\mathbf{p}')]_+ = [d_r(\mathbf{p}),\ d_s^\dagger(\mathbf{p}')]_+ = \delta_{rs}\delta(\mathbf{p},\ \mathbf{p}'), \tag{8.20a}$$

where the anticommutator

$$[A,\ B]_+ \equiv AB + BA, \tag{8.21}$$

all other pairs of absorption and creation operators having zero anticommutators; if $c_r \equiv c_r(\mathbf{p})$, $c_s \equiv c_s(\mathbf{p}')$, etc.:

$$\left.\begin{array}{l}[c_r,\ c_s]_+ = [c_r^\dagger,\ c_s^\dagger]_+ = [d_r,\ d_s]_+ = [d_r^\dagger,\ d_s^\dagger]_+ = 0\\ [c_r,\ d_s]_+ = [c_r,\ d_s^\dagger]_+ = [c_r^\dagger,\ d_s]_+ = [c_r^\dagger,\ d_s^\dagger]_+ = 0.\end{array}\right\} \tag{8.20b}$$

From the anticommutation rules (8.20) and the definitions (8.16) of $N_r^\pm(\mathbf{p})$, one shows at once that

$$\{N_r^\pm(\mathbf{p})\}^2 = N_r^\pm(\mathbf{p}), \tag{8.22}$$

i.e. $N_r^\pm(\mathbf{p})$ has the eigenvalues 0 and 1 only: each single-particle state is either empty or has at most one particle in it. Thus the anticommutation relations (8.20) lead to a description of a system of particles which obeys the Pauli exclusion principle: we are dealing with Fermi-Dirac statistics.

One can easily give explicit constructions, in terms of products of 2×2 matrices, for the creation and destruction operators satisfying eqs. (8.20) and for the corresponding state vectors whose arguments are again the occupation numbers of the single-particle states, now restricted to 0 or 1. However, since this matrix representation will not be required we shall omit it*). In practice it suffices to know that these operators satisfy the anticommutation rules (8.20).

The vacuum state Φ_0 is again the state with zero energy and momentum, i.e. there are no electrons or positrons present:

$$c_r(\mathbf{p})\Phi_0 = d_r(\mathbf{p})\Phi_0 = 0 \tag{8.23}$$

for $r = 1, 2$ and all momenta $\mathbf{p}$. States containing one electron or one positron are of the form $c_r^\dagger(\mathbf{p})\Phi_0$ and $d_r^\dagger(\mathbf{p})\Phi_0$ respectively, a two-electron state is of the form $c_r^\dagger(\mathbf{p})c_s^\dagger(\mathbf{p}')\Phi_0$, and so on. From the anticommutation rules (8.20), it follows that

$$\{c_r^\dagger(\mathbf{p})\}^2 = 0, \tag{8.24}$$

and

$$c_r^\dagger(\mathbf{p})c_s^\dagger(\mathbf{p}')\Phi_0 = -c_s^\dagger(\mathbf{p}')c_r^\dagger(\mathbf{p})\Phi_0. \tag{8.25}$$

Eq. (8.24) again shows that we cannot have two electrons in the *same* state, eq. (8.25) that we are dealing with states which are antisymmetric under interchange of particles. These arguments apply equally to positron states.

In analogy to eq. (5.15) we decompose the operators (8.10) into positive (e^{ipx}) and negative (e^{-ipx}) frequency parts

$$\psi(x) = \psi^+(x) + \psi^-(x), \quad \bar{\psi}(x) = \bar{\psi}^+(x) + \bar{\psi}^-(x). \tag{8.26}$$

We have replaced the adjoint $\psi^\dagger$ by $\bar{\psi}$, eq. (8.11), as this is often the more useful quantity in practice. The operators $\psi^\pm$ absorb electrons and create positrons respectively, whereas $\bar{\psi}^\pm$ create electrons and absorb positrons respectively. Instead of eqs.

*) Cf. Wentzel (see bibliography), pp. 172—175.

(8.23), the vacuum can then be defined by

$$\psi^{+}(x)\Phi_0 = \bar{\psi}^{+}(x)\Phi_0 = 0. \tag{8.27}$$

Next consider the current-density four-vector. In analogy to eq. (7.8) we define it by

$$-\,es_\nu(x) = ie\left\{\frac{\partial\mathscr{L}}{\partial\psi_{\alpha,\nu}}\psi_\alpha - \frac{\partial\mathscr{L}}{\partial\psi^\dagger_{\alpha,\nu}}\psi^\dagger_\alpha\right\}. \tag{8.28}$$

The continuity equation (7.9) is again satisfied by the four-current (8.28), in virtue of the gauge invariance (cf. eqs. (7.4), with ψ and $\psi^\dagger$ replacing ϕ and $\phi^\dagger$) of the Lagrangian densities (8.12), (8.18—19).

We must now choose between these three Lagrangian densities, eqs. (8.12), (8.18) and (8.19). We shall use eq. (8.19) which is invariant under the interchange $\psi \leftrightarrow \psi^\dagger$ (which is known as *charge conjugation*) and thus leads to a theory symmetric in electrons and positrons*). From eq. (8.28) the current is then given by**)

$$-\,es_\nu(x) = -\frac{ie}{2}\{\psi^\dagger\gamma_4\gamma_\nu\psi - \psi\gamma_4\gamma_\nu\psi^\dagger\}. \tag{8.29}$$

*) Until recently, invariance under charge conjugation was considered a fundamental requirement of any theory. Recent experiments in β-decay and $\pi - \mu - e$ decay have shown that the interactions responsible for these processes are not invariant under charge conjugation. All the same, it seems desirable to retain the symmetrized Lagrangian for the free fields. In particular, this eliminates infinite 'vacuum charges' similar to the infinite vacuum energies which we found above.

Difficulties and ambiguities similar to the ones found here for fermions also occur for bosons. The general ideas are quite analogous. In the quantized theory we should, in principle, in the last chapter have replaced the Lagrangian density (7.5) by the symmetrized

$$\mathscr{L} = -\frac{1}{2}\left\{\left(\frac{\partial\phi}{\partial x_\nu}\frac{\partial\phi^\dagger}{\partial x_\nu} + m^2\phi\phi^\dagger\right) + \left(\frac{\partial\phi^\dagger}{\partial x_\nu}\frac{\partial\phi}{\partial x_\nu} + m^2\phi^\dagger\phi\right)\right\}.$$

This does not affect the Hamiltonian (7.21). The expression for the current, eq. (7.10), is already the correctly symmetrized current derivable from the above Lagrangian density.

**) Since ψ and $\psi^\dagger$ are now operators, care must be taken with the order of factors in the current. It can be shown that with the Lagrangian density (8.19) the current is correctly expressed by eq. (8.28) as written. This equation leads to eq. (8.29).

This expression can be conveniently rewritten, since in a Majorana representation $\gamma_4^T = -\gamma_4$ and $\gamma_k^T = \gamma_k$, $(k = 1, 2, 3)$, the affix T denoting the transposed matrix. Hence

$$\gamma_4\gamma_\nu = \gamma_\nu^T\gamma_4^T. \tag{8.30}$$

Since

$$\gamma_4^T\psi^\dagger = \psi^\dagger\gamma_4 = \bar{\psi}, \tag{8.31}$$

eq. (8.29) becomes

$$-es_\nu(x) = -\frac{ie}{2}\{\bar{\psi}\gamma_\nu\psi - \psi\gamma_\nu^T\bar{\psi}\} = -\frac{ie}{2}[\bar{\psi}, \gamma_\nu\psi]. \tag{8.32}$$

From eq. (8.32) one obtains for the charge operator Q

$$Q = \int d^3x[-es_4(x)/i] = -\frac{e}{2}\int d^3x(\psi^\dagger\psi - \psi\psi^\dagger). \tag{8.33}$$

Carrying out the integration, using eqs. (8.10), (A 21), (8.20) and (8.16),

$$Q = e\sum_{\mathbf{p}}\sum_{r=1}^{2}[N_r^+(\mathbf{p}) - N_r^-(\mathbf{p})], \tag{8.34}$$

justifying our interpretation in terms of electrons and positrons.

We must now discuss briefly how the above analysis is modified if we do not use a Majorana representation. As discussed in the appendix, we shall still have a complete set of eigensolutions

$$\psi^{(r)}(\mathbf{p}) = u^{(r)}(\mathbf{p})\, e^{i\varepsilon_r px} \quad (r = 1, \ldots, 4), \tag{8.35}$$

of the Dirac equation with the same physical properties (i.e. the same eigenvalues of energy, momentum and spin) as solutions (8.6) and (8.9). But the solutions (8.35) will *not* satisfy

$$\psi^{(r+2)}(\mathbf{p}) = \psi^{(r)*}(\mathbf{p}). \tag{8.36}$$

Denoting quantities in the Majorana representation by the suffix M, the Majorana spinors

$$u_M^{(r)},\ u_M^{(r+2)} = u_M^{(r)*}, \quad (r = 1, 2)$$

are replaced by

$$u^{(r)} = Su_M^{(r)},$$

where S is a non-singular 4×4 matrix. Correspondingly, the fermion field $\psi_M(x)$ is replaced by

$$\psi(x) = S\psi_M(x).$$

The general expansion of the fields, eqs. (8.10), now becomes, in terms of the positive and negative frequency parts (8.26):

$$\left.\begin{aligned}
\psi^+(x) &= \frac{1}{\sqrt{V}} \sum_{p_0=E_\mathbf{p}} \left(\frac{M}{p_0}\right)^{\frac{1}{2}} \sum_{r=1}^{2} c_r(\mathbf{p})\, u^{(r)}(\mathbf{p})\, e^{ipx} \\
\psi^-(x) &= \frac{1}{\sqrt{V}} \sum_{p_0=E_\mathbf{p}} \left(\frac{M}{p_0}\right)^{\frac{1}{2}} \sum_{r=1}^{2} d_r^\dagger(\mathbf{p})\, u^{(r+2)}(\mathbf{p})\, e^{-ipx} \\
\bar{\psi}^+(x) &= \frac{1}{\sqrt{V}} \sum_{p_0=E_\mathbf{p}} \left(\frac{M}{p_0}\right)^{\frac{1}{2}} \sum_{r=1}^{2} d_r(\mathbf{p})\, \bar{u}^{(r+2)}(\mathbf{p})\, e^{ipx} \\
\bar{\psi}^-(x) &= \frac{1}{\sqrt{V}} \sum_{p_0=E_\mathbf{p}} \left(\frac{M}{p_0}\right)^{\frac{1}{2}} \sum_{r=1}^{2} c_r^\dagger(\mathbf{p})\, \bar{u}^{(r)}(\mathbf{p})\, e^{-ipx}.
\end{aligned}\right\} \quad (8.37)$$

The operators $c_r(\mathbf{p})$, etc. here retain the same interpretation and the same anticommutation rules (8.20) as before. Furthermore, the expression for the current (8.32) is generally valid (not only in the Majorana representation) since it consists of inner products in spinor space which are invariant under a change of representation. On the other hand, the Lagrangian density (8.19) will not in general be the correctly symmetrized Lagrangian to be invariant under charge conjugation which is no longer simply given by the transformation $\psi \leftrightarrow \psi^\dagger$. Having used the Majorana representation to set up and interpret the quantized field formalism for fermions, we shall in the following use the general representation (8.37), *restricting ourselves always to representations in which the γ-matrices are Hermitian.*

We saw above that in order to obtain a positive definite Hamiltonian we had to quantize the theory using anticommutation relations, i.e. according to Fermi-Dirac statistics. The lack of positive-definiteness of the energy when quantizing according to Bose-Einstein statistics (commutation rules) is typical of particles of half-odd-integral spin ($\frac{1}{2}$, $\frac{3}{2}$, . . .). It is one of the arguments used by Pauli*) to establish a relation between spin and statistics: systems of particles of half-odd-integral spin only give a positive-definite energy if quantized according to Fermi-Dirac statistics (anticommutation rules, exclusion principle).

Conversely, Pauli has shown that inconsistencies in interpretation arise if one tries to quantize particles with integral spin (0, 1, . . .), such as mesons or photons, according to Fermi-Dirac statistics. For spin 0 particles we saw in chapter 5 that we require [cf. eqs. (5.19), (5.22)]

$$[\phi(x), \phi(x')] = 0 \tag{8.38}$$

if $(x - x')$ is a space-like vector, if we wish to interpret $\phi(x)$ as a measurable observable. It was shown in chapter 5 that this condition is satisfied when quantizing according to Bose-Einstein statistics. We shall now briefly show that this condition is violated if we quantize according to Fermi-Dirac statistics.

For this purpose we calculate the commutator $[\phi(x), \phi(x')]$, assuming the Fourier expansion (5.14) but replacing the commutation rules (3.5) by the anticommutation laws

$$[a(\mathbf{k}), a(\mathbf{k}')]_+ = [a^\dagger(\mathbf{k}), a^\dagger(\mathbf{k}')]_+ = 0, \quad [a(\mathbf{k}), a^\dagger(\mathbf{k}')]_+ = \delta(\mathbf{k}, \mathbf{k}'). \tag{8.39}$$

Analogously to eqs. (5.18—19) we obtain

$$\begin{aligned}[\phi(x), \phi(x')] &= \frac{1}{V}\sum_{\mathbf{k}}\frac{1}{2k_0}\,[\mathrm{e}^{ik(x-x')} - \mathrm{e}^{-ik(x-x')}] \\ &+ \frac{1}{V}\sum_{\mathbf{k}}\sum_{\mathbf{k}'}\frac{1}{\sqrt{k_0k_0'}}\{a(\mathbf{k})a(\mathbf{k}')\,\mathrm{e}^{i(kx+k'x')} + a^\dagger(\mathbf{k})a^\dagger(\mathbf{k}')\,\mathrm{e}^{-i(kx+k'x')} \\ &+ a^\dagger(\mathbf{k})a(\mathbf{k}')\,\mathrm{e}^{-i(kx-k'x')} - a^\dagger(\mathbf{k}')a(\mathbf{k})\,\mathrm{e}^{i(kx-k'x')}\}\end{aligned} \tag{8.40}$$

where $k_0 = \omega_{\mathbf{k}}$ and $k_0' = \omega_{\mathbf{k}'}$ throughout. Hence, since $a(\mathbf{k})\Phi_0 = 0$,

$$(a^\dagger(\mathbf{k})a^\dagger(\mathbf{k}')\Phi_0, [\phi(x), \phi(x')]\Phi_0) = \frac{1}{V}\frac{1}{\sqrt{k_0k_0'}}\,[\mathrm{e}^{-i(kx+k'x')} - \mathrm{e}^{-i(k'x+kx')}]. \tag{8.41}$$

*) Cf. Pauli, W. *Phys. Rev.* **58**, 716, 1940, and Pauli's article in *Niels Bohr and the development of physics*, London; Pergamon Press Ltd., 1955. Pauli only considers the case of non-interacting fields. Very general proofs, for interacting fields, have recently been given by Burgoyne, N. *Nuovo Cim.* **8**, 607, 1958, and by Lüders, G. and Zumino, B. *Phys. Rev.* **110**, 1450, 1958.

This matrix element is, in general, different from zero even if $(x - x')$ is space-like, showing that the commutator (8.38) does not vanish for this case and thus establishing the inconsistency of quantizing spin zero particles according to the exclusion principle*). This relation of spin and statistics for which no exception is known in nature, represents an impressive success for relativistic quantum field theory.

The anticommutation rules for the fields ψ and $\bar{\psi}$ are easily derived from those for the creation and absorption operators, eqs. (8.20), and the Fourier expansions (8.26) and (8.37) of the fields. The calculation, which is straightforward and analogous to that leading to eq. (5.19), is left as an excercise for the reader (cf. exercise 8.6). One finds that

$$\left.\begin{aligned} [\psi_\alpha(x),\ \psi_\beta(x')]_+ &= 0 \\ [\bar{\psi}_\alpha(x),\ \bar{\psi}_\beta(x')]_+ &= 0 \\ [\psi_\alpha(x),\ \bar{\psi}_\beta(x')]_+ &= -\, iS_{\alpha\beta}(x - x') \end{aligned}\right\} \tag{8.42}$$

where α and β label the components of the spinor fields and $S(x)$ is given by

$$S(x) = \frac{1}{(2\pi)^3}\int d^4p\ e^{ipx}(iM + \not{p})\varepsilon(p)\delta(p^2 + M^2). \tag{8.43}$$

Here $S(x)$ and $(iM + \not{p})$ are of course 4×4 matrices in spin space, $\not{p}$ being defined in eq. (A 10).

If we write $\Delta(x, m)$ for the $\Delta(x)$-function defined by eqs. (6.3—4) to indicate its dependence on the parameter m, then eq. (6.3) gives, directly by differentiation under the integral sign,

*) This argument cannot be applied to the Hermitian fermion operators $(\psi + \psi^\dagger)$ and $i(\psi - \psi^\dagger)$, and thus exclude anticommutation rules in this case as well. For these operators are not observables, in the sense that they effect transitions between states with even and odd numbers of fermions. Such transitions are not observed corresponding to the fact that all interaction energies — and all observables generally — are bilinear in ψ and $\bar{\psi}$. The anticommutation rules for the fermion fields then lead to exactly the required commutation properties for observables, such as charge densities (cf. exercise 8.10).

$$\left(\gamma_\mu \frac{\partial}{\partial x_\mu} - M\right) \Delta(x, M) = \frac{-i}{(2\pi)^3} \int d^4p\, e^{ipx} (i\not{p} - M) \varepsilon(p) \delta(p^2 + M^2)$$
$$= S(x). \tag{8.44}$$

Thus the function $S(x)$ occurring in the anticommutation rules of the fermion fields is simply related to the $\Delta(x)$-function occurring in the commutation relations of the boson fields. This at once suggests further S-functions which are obtained by applying the differential operator $(\gamma_\mu \partial/\partial x_\mu - M)$ to the various Δ-functions defined in chapter 6. For example, corresponding to $\Delta_F(x, m)$ defined by eqs. (6.18) or (6.19), we define

$$S_F(x) = \left(\gamma_\mu \frac{\partial}{\partial x_\mu} - M\right) \Delta_F(x, M) \tag{8.45}$$

$$= \frac{2}{(2\pi)^4} \int_{C_F} d^4p\, e^{ipx} \frac{\not{p} + iM}{p^2 + M^2} \tag{8.46}$$

$$= \frac{2}{(2\pi)^4} \int d^4p\, e^{ipx} \frac{\not{p} + iM}{p^2 + M^2 - i\varepsilon}. \tag{8.47}$$

In eq. (8.46) C_F denotes the Feynman contour which occurs in eq. (6.18) [fig. 7] whereas in eq. (8.47), which corresponds to eq. (6.19), the poles have been displaced (as in fig. 8) and the p_0-integration is now along the real axis. It is often convenient to introduce the identity

$$(\not{p} - iM)^{-1} = (\not{p} + iM)(p^2 + M^2)^{-1}$$

and then write eq. (8.46) as

$$S_F(x) = \frac{2}{(2\pi)^4} \int d^4p \frac{e^{ipx}}{\not{p} - iM}. \tag{8.46a}$$

These related S-functions occur in evaluating anticommutators of the positive and negative frequency parts of the fermion fields and in calculating vacuum expectation values of products of fermion operators, in close analogy to the development of chapter 6, and the reader should have no difficulty in dealing with these aspects. We shall only quote certain results which will be of importance later.

From eqs. (8.37) and (8.20) one obtains

$$\left.\begin{aligned}[\psi_\alpha^+(x),\ \bar{\psi}_\beta^-(x')]_+ &= -\ iS_{\alpha\beta}^+(x-x'),\\ [\psi_\alpha^-(x),\ \bar{\psi}_\beta^+(x')]_+ &= -\ iS_{\alpha\beta}^-(x-x').\end{aligned}\right\} \tag{8.48}$$

All other anticommutators (there are eight of them) of the fields $\psi^\pm$, $\bar{\psi}^\pm$ vanish.

Finally, let us define Wick's chronological product (C.P.) (denoted by T) as distinct from Dyson's C.P. (denoted by P) which was defined in eqs. (6.13) or (6.14).

(i) For two boson fields the two definitions agree, i.e.

$$T\{\phi(x)\phi(x')\} = P\{\phi(x)\phi(x')\}. \tag{8.49}$$

(ii) If $A(x)$ is one of the operators $\psi_\alpha(x)$ or $\bar{\psi}_\alpha(x)$, and $B(x')$ is one of the operators $\psi_\beta(x')$ or $\bar{\psi}_\beta(x')$ then we define the Dyson C.P. as before but the Wick C.P. we define by

$$T\{A(x)B(x')\} = \varepsilon(x-x')P\{A(x)B(x')\} = \begin{cases} A(x)B(x'), & \text{if } x_0 > x_0', \\ -B(x')A(x), & \text{if } x_0' > x_0. \end{cases} \tag{8.50}$$

Because of the anticommuting nature of fermion operators, the Wick C. P., which allows for the change of sign when interchanging two fermion fields, is more appropriate in this case. One can then prove, similarly to eq. (6.15), that

$$(\Phi_0,\ T\{\psi_\alpha(x)\bar{\psi}_\beta(x')\}\Phi_0) = -\tfrac{1}{2}S_{F\alpha\beta}(x-x'). \tag{8.51}$$

CHAPTER 9

Photons I

We shall now discuss the quantization of the electromagnetic field. This will subsequently lead us to quantum electrodynamics. It is here that relativistic quantum field theory has had its most striking successes, due to the fact that the coupling constant between the electromagnetic and the electron fields is weak, thus permitting the use of perturbation theory for this interaction.

The theory of photons, however, has difficulties of its own which stem from the fact that we are dealing with particles of zero rest mass, the requirements of gauge invariance, etc. A detailed analysis shows that for many purposes one can just ignore these complications and use a simple approach, similar to that developed for mesons in earlier chapters. In this chapter we shall only discuss these difficulties and their resolutions quite briefly, stating those results which are required in applications. A fuller justification of this treatment will be given in the next chapter.

Classically, the electromagnetic field is described by the electric and magnetic fields **E** and **H** which can be derived from a four-vector-potential $A_\mu(x) = (\mathbf{A},\ iV)$:

$$\mathbf{H} = \text{curl } \mathbf{A} \qquad \mathbf{E} = -\text{ grad } V - \partial\mathbf{A}/\partial t. \tag{9.1}$$

Expressed in terms of the potential, Maxwell's equations for free space become

$$\Box^2 A_\mu - \frac{\partial}{\partial x_\mu}\left(\frac{\partial A_\nu}{\partial x_\nu}\right) = 0. \tag{9.2}$$

The fields **E** and **H** do not determine the potentials uniquely, since for an arbitrary function $\Lambda(x)$ the transformation

$$A_\mu \to A'_\mu = A_\mu + \frac{\partial \Lambda(x)}{\partial x_\mu} \tag{9.3}$$

leaves the fields unaltered. Since only the fields have a direct physical interpretation, but not the potential, the theory must be invariant under the transformation (9.3), which is known as a gauge transformation.

The arbitrariness in the potential can be utilized to simplify eq. (9.2) by demanding that the potential satisfy the *Lorentz condition*

$$\partial A_\nu/\partial x_\nu = 0 \tag{9.4}$$

so that eq. (9.2) reduces to the wave equation

$$\Box^2 A_\mu = 0. \tag{9.5}$$

However, the Lorentz condition (9.4) does not determine the potential uniquely. The gauge transformation (9.3) will lead to a potential A'_μ which also satisfies the Lorentz condition, provided

$$\Box^2 \Lambda(x) = 0. \tag{9.6}$$

A potential satisfying eq. (9.4) is said to belong to the Lorentz gauge.

As a particular case, consider a plane wave described by

$$A_\mu(x) = \varepsilon_\mu(k)\, \mathrm{e}^{\pm ikx}, \tag{9.7}$$

where $k^2 = 0$, corresponding to particles of zero rest mass. Taking

$$\Lambda(x) = \lambda(k)\mathrm{e}^{\pm ikx}, \tag{9.8}$$

which satisfies eq. (9.6), the gauge transformation (9.3) becomes

$$A_\mu(x) \to A'_\mu(x) = [\varepsilon_\mu(k) \pm i\lambda(k)\, k_\mu]\, \mathrm{e}^{\pm ikx}. \tag{9.9}$$

For a free field, i.e. in the absence of electric charges, one can choose a gauge in which $V = 0$ whence the Lorentz condition reduces to div $\mathbf{A} = 0$. This is the condition for a transverse vector field, as we see by Fourier-analysing the vector potential

$$\mathbf{A}(x) = \int \boldsymbol{\varepsilon}(k)\, \mathrm{e}^{ikx} d^4k \tag{9.10}$$

whence we obtain the transversality condition

$$\boldsymbol{\varepsilon}\mathbf{k} = 0. \tag{9.11}$$

In quantizing the electromagnetic field let us, to begin with, completely disregard the Lorentz condition (9.4), so that the components A_μ, $\mu = 1, \ldots, 4$, can be treated as independent variables. Since Maxwell's equations can be obtained from a Lagrangian density (cf. exercise 2.1), it is possible to quantize the electromagnetic field by the methods of chapters 2 and 3. In this way one obtains for the commutation relations of the operators $A_\mu(x)$ in the Heisenberg picture:

$$[A_\mu(x), A_\nu(x')] = i\delta_{\mu\nu} D(x - x'), \tag{9.12}$$

where

$$D(x) = \lim_{m \to 0} \Delta(x, m) = \frac{1}{(2\pi)^4} \int_C d^4k \frac{e^{ikx}}{k^2} \tag{9.13}$$

[cf. eq. (6.1) and exercise 9.1]. Eq. (9.12) is exactly what we would expect by comparison with the meson field, eq. (5.19), since we are now dealing with four independent fields, each satisfying the 'Klein-Gordon equation' (9.5) for particles of zero mass.

The results of chapter 6 can now be applied to the case of photons. In particular, one finds that

$$(\Phi_0, P\{A_\mu(x) A_\nu(x')\}\Phi_0) = \tfrac{1}{2}\delta_{\mu\nu} D_F(x - x') \tag{9.14}$$

where

$$D_F(x) = \lim_{m \to 0} \Delta_F(x, m) = \frac{-2i}{(2\pi)^4} \int d^4k \frac{e^{ikx}}{k^2 - i\varepsilon} \tag{9.15}$$

[cf. eqs. (6.15) and (6.19)].

We again introduce the Fourier decomposition of the operators $A_\mu(x)$:

$$A_\mu(x) = \frac{1}{\sqrt{V}} \sum_{k_0 = |\mathbf{k}|} \frac{1}{\sqrt{2k_0}} \sum_{m=1}^{4} \{a_m(\mathbf{k}) \varepsilon_\mu^{(m)}(\mathbf{k}) e^{ikx} + a_m^\dagger(\mathbf{k}) \varepsilon_\mu^{(m)*}(\mathbf{k}) e^{-ikx}\}. \tag{9.16}$$

Here the $\varepsilon_\mu^{(m)}(\mathbf{k})$ [and similarly the $\varepsilon_\mu^{(m)*}(\mathbf{k})$ in the second term] form a set of four mutually orthogonal unit vectors ($m = 1, \ldots 4$ labels the vectors, $\mu = 1, \ldots 4$ their components) which span the space-time continuum, and any four-vector, for example $A_\mu(x)$, can be written as a superposition of these. The choice of these unit vectors is largely arbitrary. In particular, they can be chosen differently for each wave-vector $\mathbf{k}$, as is indicated by the notation. In practice it is most convenient to choose them as follows.

Let $\mathbf{n}^{(m)}(\mathbf{k})$, $(m = 1, 2, 3)$, be three mutually orthogonal unit vectors forming a right-handed set of axes, with $\mathbf{n}^{(3)}(\mathbf{k}) = \mathbf{k}/|\mathbf{k}|$. Thus $\mathbf{n}^{(1)}$ and $\mathbf{n}^{(2)}$ are transverse to the photon momentum $\mathbf{k}$, whereas $\mathbf{n}^{(3)}$ is parallel to $\mathbf{k}$. To complete the definition of these vectors, one must still, in some convenient way, specify the azimuthal orientation of $\mathbf{n}^{(1)}$ referred to the axis $\mathbf{k}$. We then define the four-vectors

$$\left.\begin{aligned} \varepsilon_\mu^{(m)}(\mathbf{k}) &= (\mathbf{n}^{(m)}(\mathbf{k}),\ 0), \qquad m = 1, 2, 3, \\ \varepsilon_\mu^{(4)}(\mathbf{k}) &= (000i). \end{aligned}\right\} \tag{9.17}$$

With this definition, the vector potentials $\varepsilon^{(1)}$ and $\varepsilon^{(2)}$ describe transverse linear polarization, $\varepsilon^{(3)}$ longitudinal polarization, while a photon with vector potential $\varepsilon^{(4)}$ is referred to as a purely 'time-like' or scalar photon. We shall later have to consider the fact that we are here dealing with four states of polarization, whereas we saw above that classically the free field is usually described by transversely polarized photons only.

The interpretation in terms of photons, which we have here already anticipated, follows from eq. (9.16). Substituted in the commutation relations (9.12), it gives

$$\left.\begin{aligned} [a_m(\mathbf{k}),\ a_n(\mathbf{k}')] = [a_m^\dagger(\mathbf{k}),\ a_n^\dagger(\mathbf{k}')] = 0, \\ [a_m(\mathbf{k}),\ a_n^\dagger(\mathbf{k}')] = \delta_{mn}\delta(\mathbf{k},\ \mathbf{k}'), \end{aligned}\right\} \quad (m, n = 1, \ldots 4). \tag{9.18}$$

These are the commutation relations (3.5) which, as we have repeatedly seen, lead to the interpretation of $a_m(\mathbf{k})$ and $a_m^\dagger(\mathbf{k})$ as absorption and creation operators of photons of momentum $\mathbf{k}$ and polarization specified by m,

$$N_m(\mathbf{k}) = a_m^\dagger(\mathbf{k})a_m(\mathbf{k}) \tag{9.19}$$

being the occupation number operators (eigenvalues 0, 1, 2, . . .) for these photons. This interpretation is of course also consistent with the discussion at the end of chapter 7: the operators associated with the positive (negative) frequency parts are absorption (creation) operators. The vacuum is now defined by

$$a_m(\mathbf{k})\Phi_0 = 0, \quad m = 1, \ldots 4, \text{ all } \mathbf{k}, \tag{9.20}$$

or

$$A_\mu^+(x)\Phi_0 = 0, \quad \mu = 1, \ldots 4. \tag{9.21}$$

There exists a serious difficulty and inconsistency as regards eqs. (9.16) and (9.18) which must now be discussed. Our interpretation of the $a_m(\mathbf{k})$ and $a_m^\dagger(\mathbf{k})$ as absorption and creation operators depended, of course, on $a_m^\dagger$ being the adjoint of a_m, as implied by our notation. But this would mean, from eq. (9.16), that all four components of the vector potential A_μ are Hermitian operators whereas we require $A_4 = iV$ to be anti-Hermitian. Of the several methods which exist for overcoming this difficulty, we shall follow that due to Gupta and Bleuler. In this method the expansion (9.16) and the commutation relations (9.18) are retained, the $a_m^\dagger$ being the adjoints of the a_m for $m = 1, \ldots, 3$, *and* 4. As a result *all four* A_μ are Hermitian operators. To regain the appropriate reality character for A_μ, the definition of the scalar product in Hilbert space is generalized in just such a way that the expectation values of $A_i(x)$, $i = 1, 2, 3$, are always real, that of $A_4(x)$ purely imaginary. The Gupta-Bleuler method also enables one to deal particularly simply with the Lorentz- and transversality-conditions and the gauge-invariance of the theory. We shall return to these questions in the next chapter. Here only a qualitative discussion of some of these aspects will be given.

Above we saw that the transversality of free photons is closely related to the Lorentz condition (9.4). However, this condition is not consistent with the commutation relations (9.12), for the latter imply

$$\left[\frac{\partial A_\mu(x)}{\partial x_\mu}, A_\nu(x')\right] = i\frac{\partial}{\partial x_\nu} D(x - x') \neq 0, \tag{9.22}$$

as is verified from an explicit representation of the D-function.

Instead of retaining eq. (9.4) as an operator equation, one may try and interpret it as a subsidiary condition which restricts the permissible states Φ to those which satisfy

$$\frac{\partial A_\mu}{\partial x_\mu}\Phi = 0. \tag{9.23}$$

Some objections may be raised against this approach, due to Fermi, but it leads to a perfectly workable theory. A much simpler formalism, which, in particular, brings out the relativistic properties clearly, is due to Gupta and Bleuler. They suggested replacing eq. (9.23) by the weaker restriction

$$\frac{\partial A_\mu^+}{\partial x_\mu}\Phi = 0, \tag{9.24}$$

involving absorption operators only. Eq. (9.24) states that only those states Φ are admissible in which certain types of photons are not present to be absorbed. As will be shown in chapter 10, eq. (9.24) suffices to establish Maxwell's equations for the expectation values of the fields which is all that is required to obtain the classical theory as a limiting case, in the usual manner.

Expressed in momentum space, the subsidiary condition (9.24) becomes

$$[a_3(\mathbf{k}) - a_4(\mathbf{k})]\Phi = 0, \tag{9.25}$$

where we used eqs. (9.16—17). Eq. (9.25) states the restriction which the physically allowed states Φ must satisfy. It is a restriction on the combination of longitudinal and time-like photons; it does not affect the transverse photons. Since the free-field Hamiltonian is diagonal in the occupation number operators, the subsidiary condition is obviously compatible with the equations of motion, i.e. if satisfied initially, it holds at all later times. (This is clearly necessary for a sensible theory.)

Suppose we have a state with a given set of transverse photons present and no others. From this state one can then construct a whole set of states with the *same* transverse photons and, in addition, mixtures of longitudinal and time-like photons which satisfy the subsidiary condition (9.25). One can show that these states are related by gauge transformations, i.e. they represent the *same* physical state but described in terms of *different* potentials A_μ, related by gauge transformations.

So far we have only considered free fields and this will afford an appropriate description for photons present initially or finally in scattering problems, for example in Compton scattering or

Bremsstrahlung. For we shall use an adiabatic cut-off procedure*) in scattering problems. This amounts to saying that initially (long before the scattering takes place) and finally (long after the scattering occurred) the coupling constant responsible for the interaction (the electronic charge in the case of quantum electrodynamics) is 'switched off' so that we are dealing with the free fields. For the initial state we can then, by a suitable choice of gauge, ensure that only transverse photons are present. However, it can be shown that for the final state too we may use a state vector containing only transverse photons, provided we calculate with a gauge-invariant theory.

Although initial and final states can be described in terms of transverse photons only, we cannot dispense with longitudinal and time-like photons altogether. For when charges are present, these photons represent the instantaneous static Coulomb interaction between these charges. In fact, in the older treatments of quantum electrodynamics**), one separated off this Coulomb interaction and only quantized the transverse part of the field. Electron-electron scattering was thus described in terms of this Coulomb scattering plus an exchange of transverse photons. We now describe the same process as an exchange of *four* types of photons. That these two modes of description are equivalent has also been shown by Bleuler.

In practice, the covariant treatment in terms of four types of photons is usually considerably simpler than the older method. Furthermore the separation of the transverse field is not a relativistically invariant procedure and we shall see later that such a procedure is essential if we wish to calculate radiative corrections (i.e. corrections to results obtained by the lowest order of perturbation theory).

*) Cf. chapter 12.
**) Cf. for example, Heitler (see bibliography).

CHAPTER 10

Photons II

In this chapter the Gupta-Bleuler formalism*) will be developed in greater detail**).

As stated in the last chapter, the Fourier expansion (9.16) and the commutation relations (9.18) are retained in the Gupta-Bleuler method. As a result the scalar photons are treated on the same footing as transverse and longitudinal photons; a_m, $m = 1, \ldots 4$, are absorption operators; $a_m^\dagger$, $m = 1, \ldots 4$, creation operators; all four components of the potential $A_\mu(x)$, $\mu = 1, \ldots 4$, are Hermitian operators. However, since $A_4 = iV$, we require the expectation value of A_4 in any state to be purely imaginary. To achieve this, the definition of the scalar product of two state vectors is modified.

We now replace the definition

$$N(\Phi) = (\Phi, \Phi) \tag{10.1}$$

of the *norm* of a state-vector Φ by

$$N(\Phi) = (\Phi, \eta\Phi), \tag{10.2}$$

where η is an operator, to be defined below. We shall want the norm always to be real so that η has to be a Hermitian operator

$$\eta^\dagger = \eta. \tag{10.3}$$

The norm (10.2) will, in general, no longer be positive-definite.

*) The various methods for treating photons, together with references, are discussed in the book by Jauch and Rohrlich (see bibliography). For the Gupta-Bleuler method, cf. the paper by Bleuler, K., *Helv. phys. Acta*, **23**, 567, 1950, which we are following, and also the article by Källén in the Encyclopedia of Physics (see bibliography).

**) The reader may omit this chapter, if he feels so inclined, as a knowledge of its contents will not be required in the remainder of this book.

State vectors now divide into three classes according as to whether their norm is positive, negative or zero. Only for the first of these classes will the usual probability interpretation go through, so that we want physically sensible states to be restricted to this class. This, as we shall see, is exactly ensured by the subsidiary condition (9.24). η is called the metric operator and a theory in which the norm (10.2) is no longer positive definite is said to involve an indefinite metric.

The expectation value of an operator O is now defined by

$$\langle O \rangle = (\Phi,\ \eta O \Phi). \tag{10.4}$$

This is real for a Hermitian operator O if

$$[\eta,\ O] = 0; \tag{10.5a}$$

it is purely imaginary if

$$[\eta,\ O]_+ = 0. \tag{10.5b}$$

Hence to make the expectation values of $A_r(x)$, $r = 1, 2, 3$, real, that of $A_4(x)$ imaginary, we shall define the metric operator η so as to satisfy

$$\left.\begin{aligned} [\eta,\ A_r(x)] &= 0, \qquad (r = 1, 2, 3) \\ [\eta,\ A_4(x)]_+ &= 0, \end{aligned}\right\} \tag{10.6}$$

or, in momentum space,

$$\left.\begin{aligned} [\eta,\ a_m(\mathbf{k})] &= 0, \qquad (m = 1, 2, 3) \\ [\eta,\ a_4(\mathbf{k})]_+ &= 0. \end{aligned}\right\} \tag{10.7}$$

It follows from eqs. (10.6) or (10.7) that η^2 commutes with all operators, i.e. it is a c-number. By a suitable choice of a numerical factor it can be made to satisfy [cf. eq. (10.3)]

$$\eta^2 = \eta\eta^\dagger = 1. \tag{10.8}$$

Let $n_m(\mathbf{k})$ be the occupation number for photons specified by $\mathbf{k}$ and m $(=1, \ldots 4)$. Using the matrix representation of the operators $a_m(\mathbf{k})$ [cf. eqs. (1.10—11)],

$$\left.\begin{aligned} &(\Phi(\ldots n_m(\mathbf{k})\ldots),\ a_m(\mathbf{k})\Phi(\ldots n'_m(\mathbf{k})\ldots)) \\ &= (\Phi(\ldots n'_m(\mathbf{k})\ldots),\ a^\dagger_m(\mathbf{k})\Phi(\ldots n_m(\mathbf{k})\ldots)) \\ &\qquad\qquad = [n_m(\mathbf{k}) + 1]^{\frac{1}{2}}\,\delta[n_m(\mathbf{k}) + 1,\ n'_m(\mathbf{k})], \end{aligned}\right\} \tag{10.9}$$

(the operators $a_m(\mathbf{k})$ and $a_m^\dagger(\mathbf{k})$ being diagonal in all other occupation numbers), it is verified directly that eqs. (10.7) are satisfied if, in this representation, η is the diagonal operator given by

$$(\Phi(\ldots n_m(\mathbf{k})\ldots), \eta\Phi(\ldots n'_m(\mathbf{k})\ldots)) = (-1)^{n_4} \prod_{\mathbf{k}} \prod_{m=1}^{4} \delta[n_m(\mathbf{k}), n'_m(\mathbf{k})], \quad (10.10)$$

where n_4 is the *total* number of *scalar* photons in the state $\Phi(\ldots n_m(\mathbf{k})\ldots)$, i.e.

$$n_4 = \sum_{\mathbf{k}} n_4(\mathbf{k}). \quad (10.11)$$

From the subsidiary condition (9.24), it follows that the Lorentz condition holds for expectation values

$$\left\langle \frac{\partial A_\mu}{\partial x_\mu} \right\rangle = \left(\Phi,\, \eta \frac{\partial A_\mu}{\partial x_\mu} \Phi\right) = 0, \quad (10.12)$$

which suffices to establish the connection of the quantized theory and classical electrodynamics. To prove eq. (10.12), we note that, from eqs. (10.6—7) and the analogue of eq. (5.17),

$$\left(\eta \frac{\partial A_\mu^-(x)}{\partial x_\mu}\right)^\dagger = \frac{\partial A_\mu^+(x)}{\partial x_\mu^*} \eta = \eta \frac{\partial A_\mu^+(x)}{\partial x_\mu}, \quad (10.13)$$

so that, using the subsidiary condition (9.24),

$$\left(\Phi,\, \eta \frac{\partial A_\mu}{\partial x_\mu} \Phi\right) = \left(\Phi,\, \eta \frac{\partial A_\mu^-}{\partial x_\mu} \Phi\right) = \left(\eta \frac{\partial A_\mu^+}{\partial x_\mu} \Phi,\, \Phi\right) = 0. \quad (10.14)$$

We must next see what restrictions and properties the subsidiary condition (9.24) implies for the state vectors. We saw from eq. (9.25),

$$[a_3(\mathbf{k}) - a_4(\mathbf{k})]\Phi = 0, \quad (10.15)$$

that it is a restriction on the permissible admixtures of longitudinal and scalar photons in the state Φ.

Let $\Phi_{\mathbf{k}}(n_3, n_4)$ denote a state with $n_3(n_4)$ longitudinal (scalar) photons of momentum $\mathbf{k}$ present only, normalized to unity. Since

$$[\{a_3(\mathbf{k}) - a_4(\mathbf{k})\},\, \{a_3^\dagger(\mathbf{k}) + a_4^\dagger(\mathbf{k})\}] = 0, \quad (10.16)$$

the subsidiary condition (10.15) will be satisfied by the following state vectors

$$\Phi_{\mathbf{k}}^{(\nu)} = \frac{1}{\sqrt{(\nu!)}} \{a_3^\dagger(\mathbf{k}) + a_4^\dagger(\mathbf{k})\}^\nu \Phi_{\mathbf{k}}(0, 0), \quad \nu = 0, 1, 2, \ldots, \tag{10.17}$$

i.e.

$$\left.\begin{aligned}
\Phi_{\mathbf{k}}^{(0)} &= \Phi_{\mathbf{k}}(0, 0)\\
\Phi_{\mathbf{k}}^{(1)} &= \Phi_{\mathbf{k}}(1, 0) + \Phi_{\mathbf{k}}(0, 1)\\
\Phi_{\mathbf{k}}^{(2)} &= \Phi_{\mathbf{k}}(2, 0) + \sqrt{2}\, \Phi_{\mathbf{k}}(1, 1) + \Phi_{\mathbf{k}}(0, 2)\\
&\ldots\ldots\ldots\ldots\ldots\ldots\ldots\ldots\\
\Phi_{\mathbf{k}}^{(\nu)} &= \Phi_{\mathbf{k}}(\nu, 0) + \sqrt{\nu}\, \Phi_{\mathbf{k}}(\nu - 1, 1)\\
&\quad + \ldots + \sqrt{({}^\nu C_r)}\, \Phi_{\mathbf{k}}(\nu - r, r) + \ldots + \Phi_{\mathbf{k}}(0, \nu)\\
&= \sum_{r=0}^{\nu} \sqrt{({}^\nu C_r)}\, \Phi_{\mathbf{k}}(\nu - r, r).
\end{aligned}\right\} \tag{10.18}$$

From eqs. (10.17—18) one obtains

$$(\Phi_{\mathbf{k}}^{(\nu)}, \eta \Phi_{\mathbf{k}'}^{(\nu')}) = \delta_{\mathbf{k}\mathbf{k}'} \delta_{\nu\nu'} \sum_{r=0}^{\nu} (-1)^r\, {}^\nu C_r = \delta_{\mathbf{k}\mathbf{k}'} \delta_{\nu\nu'} \delta_{\nu 0}. \tag{10.19}$$

It follows that the general state-vector, satisfying the subsidiary condition, is of the form

$$\Phi = \sum_i \sum_\nu c_i(\nu_1, \nu_2, \ldots \nu_r, \ldots) \Phi_T^{(i)} \{\prod_{r=1}^{\infty} \Phi_{\mathbf{k}_r}^{(\nu_r)}\} \tag{10.20}$$

where $\sum_\nu$ denotes summations over $\nu_1, \nu_2, \ldots = 0, 1, 2, \ldots$, and where the vectors $\Phi_T^{(i)}$ form a complete set of states with transversely polarized photons present only. Splitting off the term containing no longitudinal or scalar photons, eq. (10.20) can be written

$$\Phi = \Phi_T \Phi_{LS}^{(0)} + \Phi_{LS} \tag{10.21}$$

where

$$\Phi_{LS}^{(0)} = \prod_r \Phi_{\mathbf{k}_r}^{(0)} \tag{10.22}$$

is the 'vacuum of longitudinal and scalar photons' and Φ_T is a general vector containing transverse photons only (i.e. of the form $\sum_n \alpha_n \Phi_T^{(n)}$); Φ_{LS} is orthogonal to $\Phi_{LS}^{(0)}$ and thus necessarily contains longitudinal and scalar photons. It comprises all terms in eq. (10.20) for which not all ν_r vanish. We see from eq. (10.20) that a general state satisfying the subsidiary condition cannot contain arbitrary numbers of longitudinal and scalar photons; rather these are restricted to occur in certain mixtures, given by eqs. (10.17—18), the coefficients $c_i(\nu_1, \ldots)$ in eq. (10.20) being arbitrary. We shall refer to these admixtures of longitudinal and scalar photons as *allowed* admixtures and to the corresponding states as allowed states. We shall see presently that, for a given Φ_T, but different allowed admixtures, the state (10.21) corresponds to a description of the electromagnetic field in terms of potentials related by a gauge transformation.

From eqs. (10.17—22), it follows that for two allowed states Φ and Φ'

$$(\Phi, \eta\Phi') = (\Phi_T, \Phi'_T), \tag{10.23}$$

independently of the allowed admixtures of longitudinal and scalar photons.

To see that different allowed admixtures correspond to different gauges, let us consider the state in which there are no transverse photons present ($\Phi_T^{(0)}$) but an allowed admixture of longitudinal and scalar photons:

$$\Phi = \Phi_T^{(0)}\{\Phi_{LS}^{(0)} + \sum_{\binom{\nu_1, \nu_2 \ldots = 0, 1, \ldots}{\text{NOT ALL } \nu_r = 0}} c(\nu_1, \nu_2, \ldots) \prod_r \Phi_{\mathbf{k}_r}^{(\nu_r)}\}, \tag{10.24}$$

the coefficients $c(\nu_1, \nu_2, \ldots)$ being arbitrary. A brief calculation (cf. exercise 10.1) of the expectation value of the potential $A_\mu(x)$ in the state (10.24) then gives, using eqs. (10.17—24),

$$\langle A_\mu(x)\rangle = (\Phi, \eta A_\mu(x)\Phi) = \frac{\partial \Lambda}{\partial x_\mu}, \tag{10.25}$$

with

$$\Lambda(x) = \frac{i}{\sqrt{V}} \sum_s \frac{1}{\sqrt{2k_0^3}} \{-c_1(\mathbf{k}_s)\, \mathrm{e}^{ik_s x} + c_1^*(\mathbf{k}_s)\, \mathrm{e}^{-ik_s x}\}, \tag{10.26}$$

where $k_0 = |\mathbf{k}_s|$ and $c_1(\mathbf{k}_s)$ is the coefficient $c(\nu_1, \nu_2, \ldots)$ in eq. (10.24) with

$$\left.\begin{aligned} \nu_s &= 1, \\ \nu_r &= 0, \quad r \neq s. \end{aligned}\right\} \tag{10.27}$$

Eqs. (10.25—26) show that altering the allowed admixture in a state corresponds to a gauge transformation. Here this has been shown for the coefficients $c_1(\mathbf{k})$ only, but the other coefficients in eq. (10.24) occur in a similar manner if one calculates expectation values of products of potentials and their gauge transformations. This suggests that physically significant results (i.e. ones independent of the choice of gauge) are independent of these different allowed admixtures of longitudinal and scalar photons. Considerations quite analogous to the above for the 'transverse vacuum' $\Phi_T^{(0)}$, eq. (10.24), are applicable to any transverse state Φ_T. A particularly simple and useful gauge corresponds to defining the vacuum as the state in which there are no photons of any kind present (i.e., in eq. (10.24), all $c(\nu_1, \nu_2, \ldots) = 0$)

$$\Phi_0 = \Phi_T^{(0)} \prod_r \Phi_{\mathbf{k}_r}^{(0)}. \tag{10.28}$$

This corresponds to the gauge in which

$$(\Phi_0, \eta A_\mu \Phi_0) = (\Phi_0, A_\mu \Phi_0) = 0. \tag{10.29}$$

We shall now discuss very briefly how these considerations are to be modified when we are not dealing with the free electromagnetic field but there are electric charges present, described by a four-current $[-es_\mu(x)]$ and giving rise to an interaction Hamiltonian density (4.2). The state-vector in the I.P. now becomes a time-dependent quantity $\Phi(t)$, satisfying the equation of motion (5.8). The subsidiary condition and the allowed states are modified, the subsidiary condition becoming*)

$$\Omega^+(x', t)\Phi(t) = 0, \tag{10.30}$$

for all values of x'; here

$$\Omega^+(x', t) = \frac{\partial A_\mu^+(x')}{\partial x'_\mu} + e \int_{x_0=t} D^+(x' - x)\rho(x)\, d^3x, \tag{10.31}$$

with $\rho = (s_4/i)$ and $D^+(x)$ the positive frequency part of $D(x)$,

*) For a more complete discussion of the case of interacting fields, cf. Bleuler, loc. cit.

eq. (9.13)*). One can then show that the generalized subsidiary condition (10.30) is compatible with the equations of motion, i.e. if true at one instant of time t_0, it is valid at all times t.

As mentioned in the last chapter, and discussed further in chapter 12, we shall use the adiabatic hypothesis when considering scattering problems. This corresponds to treating the coupling constant e as a function of time, $e = e(t)$, in such a way that $e \to 0$ as $|t| \to \infty$; i.e. a long time before and a long time after the scattering event occurs, the interaction is 'switched off'. We see from eqs. (10.30—31) that this implies that the initial state $\Phi_i = \Phi(-\infty)$ and the final state $\Phi(+\infty)$, into which Φ_i develops by virtue of the equation of motion (5.8), both satisfy the free field subsidiary condition (9.24). Hence the allowed state vectors for these states are of the form of eqs. (10.20—22), together with eq. (10.17).

For the initial state $\Phi_i = \Phi(-\infty)$ we can then take a state in which no longitudinal or scalar photons are present: this corresponds to a particular choice of gauge. The state $\Phi(+\infty)$ will then also be an allowed state. In scattering theory, one is interested in the amplitude $(\Phi_j, \eta\Phi(+\infty))$ for a transition from the state Φ_i to some particular final state Φ_j. It follows from eq. (10.23), that this amplitude is independent of the admixture of longitudinal and scalar photons, so that we can, in particular, always take Φ_j to be a state which contains no longitudinal or scalar photons. Furthermore, one may then omit the metric operator from the amplitude and simply write it as $(\Phi_j, \Phi(+\infty))$. To sum up these important results: using the adiabatic hypothesis in scattering problems, one may describe both the initial state $\Phi_i = \Phi(-\infty)$ and the particular final state Φ_j of interest (i.e. we are considering the probability amplitude for a transition $\Phi_i \to \Phi_j$) in terms of transverse photons only and one may then also omit the metric operator, which is now simply unity, from these amplitudes. We may not, of course, discard longitudinal

*) Our definitions of the various D-functions differ from those used by Bleuler by a minus sign. In addition, we have taken a current density $[-es_\mu(x)]$ where Bleuler has simply taken $s_\mu(x)$. As a result of these *two* changes, the signs in eq. (10.31) and in Bleuler's equation (3.6) agree.

and scalar photons altogether. They are an alternative description of the instantaneous Coulomb interaction between charged particles during the scattering event when these particles are close together*). In our development of the theory they occur through the D_F-function, eqs. (9.14—15), which represents an exchange between charged particles of *four* types of photon. As stated previously, this description emphasizes the relativistic properties of the theory and leads to considerable simplifications compared to the older methods, in which only the transverse field was quantized.

*) Cf. Bleuler, loc. cit.

CHAPTER 11

Interactions

The very idealized interaction (4.1) which we introduced in chapter 4 treated only the boson field as quantized, the fermions being described by a classical source term. We shall now consider the more realistic case of two quantized fields.

We shall begin by analysing the interaction of electrons and photons, i.e. quantum electrodynamics. The interaction Hamiltonian density for this case was already quoted in chapter 4, eq. (4.2),

$$\mathscr{H}_I(x) = es_\mu(x)A_\mu(x), \tag{11.1}$$

A_μ now being the photon field discussed in chapter 9 and $s_\mu(x)$ the electron-positron current, eq. (8.32). However, as we are here only concerned with the qualitative features of the interaction, we shall not now bother to write the current in the correctly symmetrized form (8.32), which corresponds to writing the factors in a certain order, but shall use the expression of the single-particle Dirac theory

$$s_\mu = i\bar{\psi}(x)\gamma_\mu\psi(x), \tag{11.2}$$

whence eq. (11.1) becomes, decomposing the fields into positive and negative frequency parts and suppressing the argument x,

$$\mathscr{H}_I(x) = ie(\bar{\psi}^+ + \bar{\psi}^-)\gamma_\mu(\psi^+ + \psi^-)(A_\mu^+ + A_\mu^-). \tag{11.3}$$

Let us recall that the operators $\psi^\pm$, etc., depend on absorption and creation operators as follows [cf. eqs. (8.37) and (9.16)]:

$$\left.\begin{array}{l}\psi^+ \text{ is linear in electron absorption operators}\\ \bar{\psi}^- \text{ is linear in electron creation operators}\\ \bar{\psi}^+ \text{ is linear in positron absorption operators}\\ \psi^- \text{ is linear in positron creation operators}\\ A_\mu^+ \text{ is linear in photon absorption operators}\\ A_\mu^- \text{ is linear in photon creation operators.}\end{array}\right\} \tag{11.4}$$

It follows that the term

$$ie\bar{\psi}^{-}\gamma_{\mu}A_{\mu}^{+}\psi^{+} \tag{11.5}$$

in the Hamiltonian (11.3) effects transitions in which an electron is absorbed (ψ^{+}), a photon is absorbed (A_{μ}^{+}) and an electron is emitted ($\bar{\psi}^{-}$). We represent this "electron scattering" event graphically in fig. 9. The continuous lines represent electrons,

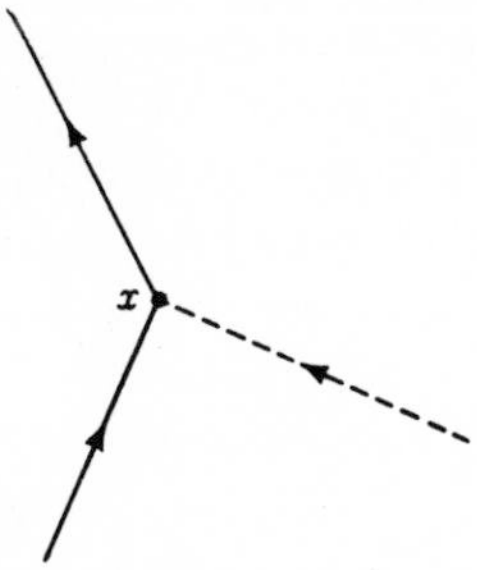

Fig. 9.

the dotted line the photon. At the "vertex" (x) the incident particles, labelled with arrows pointing towards the vertex, are absorbed, the emitted particle, labelled with an arrow pointing away from the vertex, is created.

In the same way all other terms in eq. (11.3) admit interpretations as electron scattering, positron scattering and creation or annihilation of an electron-positron pair. In each case a photon is emitted or absorbed, depending on whether the term contains A_{μ}^{-} or A_{μ}^{+}. To represent these events by Feynman graphs, as diagrams such as fig. 9 are called, we must distinguish between electrons and positrons. For fermions, an arrow pointing towards a vertex will denote absorption of an electron or creation of a positron at that vertex, an arrow pointing away, electron creation or positron absorption. Hence an arrow on a fermion line pointing towards a vertex x is associated with the operators $\psi^{\pm}(x)$, an arrow pointing away with $\bar{\psi}^{\pm}(x)$. With these conventions the different terms of eq. (11.3) are represented by the graphs of fig. 10. In every case one fermion line ends at the vertex and one begins at it: following along a fermion line, the arrows are all in the same sense. To distinguish electrons from positrons in the graphs [e.g. electron scattering, fig. 10(a), from positron scattering, fig. 10(b)] we use the convention that arrows on electron lines point 'upwards', while positron lines point 'downwards'*).

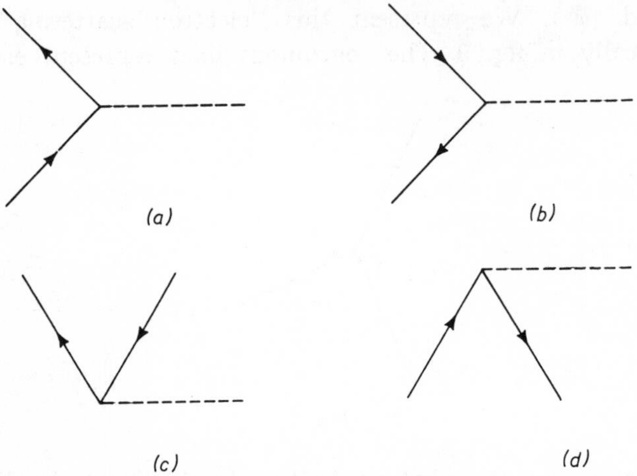

Fig. 10. (a) electron scattering: $ie\bar{\psi}^-\not{A}\psi^+$; (b) positron scattering: $ie\bar{\psi}^+\not{A}\psi^-$; (c) pair creation: $ie\bar{\psi}^-\not{A}\psi^-$; (d) pair annihilation: $ie\bar{\psi}^+\not{A}\psi^+$.

In fig. 10 we have not specified whether the photon is absorbed or emitted and have written the corresponding interactions in terms of A_μ rather than $A_\mu^\pm$. In chapter 13 we shall see that the energy-momentum four-vectors of the three particles connected to a vertex satisfy an energy-momentum conservation theorem. It is, for example, not possible for the three particles at a vertex to be all emitted or all absorbed. We have explained the conventions which we shall use in drawing graphs in some detail; for we shall find such graphs an exceedingly useful aid to the intuitive physical interpretation of the mathematical formalism which will be developed in the next two chapters.

In the case of quantum electrodynamics the interaction is known from classical physics. In general, for example when considering the pion-nucleon force, we do not know how to build up the interaction from the individual fields. However, requiring

*) This last convention will be relaxed in chapter 14.

the theory to display certain invariance and symmetry properties (e.g. invariance under Lorentz transformations) severely restricts the possible forms of the interaction. We now wish to study some of these aspects.

We shall only consider *local* interactions; these depend on the values of the fields and their spatial and time derivatives at one point x only. The electrodynamic interaction (11.1) is of this type. It is possible to consider more general non-local interactions but such theories meet considerable difficulties, particularly as regards Lorentz invariance.

For local interactions which do not involve derivatives of the fields, invariance under Lorentz transformations implies that $\mathscr{H}_I(x)$ is a scalar under Lorentz transformations. To see this, we shall assume that both the theories of the non-interacting and the interacting fields can be derived from Lagrangian densities $\mathscr{L}_0$ and $\mathscr{L}$ by means of the Lagrangian-Hamiltonian formalism developed in chapter 2. We saw in chapter 2 that the relativistic invariance of the theory demands that $\mathscr{L}_0$, $\mathscr{L}$ and hence also the interaction Lagrangian density

$$\mathscr{L}_I = \mathscr{L} - \mathscr{L}_0 \tag{11.6}$$

be scalars. If we derive the Hamiltonian densities $\mathscr{H}_0$ and $\mathscr{H}$ corresponding to the Lagrangians $\mathscr{L}_0$ and $\mathscr{L}$, then it follows from eqs. (2.13) and (2.17) that the interaction Hamiltonian density

$$\mathscr{H}_I \equiv \mathscr{H} - \mathscr{H}_0 = - \mathscr{L}_I, \tag{11.7}$$

provided $\mathscr{L}_I$ depends only on the fields but not on the derivatives of the fields. Hence in this case $\mathscr{H}_I$ too must be a scalar, as is indeed the case for eq. (11.1). This represents a very severe restriction on the form of the interaction.

As an example consider a meson field $\phi(x)$ interacting with nucleons described by the spinor fields $\psi(x)$ and $\bar{\psi}(x)$. Let us suppose that we are dealing with neutral *scalar* mesons, i.e. uncharged particles of spin zero and even intrinsic parity. In other words, under inversion of spatial coordinates: $\mathbf{x} \rightarrow \mathbf{x}' = -\mathbf{x}$, the field ϕ remains unchanged:

$$\phi(\mathbf{x}, t) \rightarrow \phi'(\mathbf{x}, t) = \phi(-\mathbf{x}, t). \tag{11.8}$$

We must then build up a scalar from ϕ and the five basic covariants, eqs. (A 11), which can be formed from ψ and $\bar{\psi}$. Restricting ourselves to interactions linear in ϕ, ψ and $\bar{\psi}$, the only interaction not involving derivatives is

$$\mathscr{H}_I(x) = g\bar{\psi}(x)\phi(x)\psi(x). \tag{11.9}$$

This interaction is of the form of eq. (11.3) and admits interpretation in terms of similar Feynman diagrams. The coupling constant g (corresponding to e in eq. (11.3)) measures the strength of the interaction of the two fields.

If instead of scalar mesons we have pseudoscalar mesons, i.e. under space inversion

$$\phi(\mathbf{x},\ t) \rightarrow \phi'(\mathbf{x},\ t) = -\phi(-\mathbf{x},\ t), \tag{11.10}$$

then, with the same restrictions, the only possible interaction would have been

$$\mathscr{H}_I(x) = ig\bar{\psi}(x)\gamma_5\phi(x)\psi(x). \tag{11.11}$$

The factor i has here been introduced so that for a real coupling constant g the operator $\mathscr{H}_I$ is Hermitian, as required for an energy density.

For later use we note that the interaction (11.11) can, by purely algebraic manipulation of the spinor part using the anticommutation relations, be written in a form analogous to the correctly symmetrized interaction of electrodynamics (cf. exercise 11.1):

$$\mathscr{H}_I(x) = \frac{i}{2}g[\bar{\psi},\ \gamma_5\psi]\phi. \tag{11.12}$$

The above interactions are based on the assumption that the laws of nature are invariant under inversion, i.e. they are the same whether expressed with reference to a right-handed or a left-handed coordinate system. This is known as parity conservation. At present, we believe parity conservation to hold for the so-called strong interactions, e.g. the pion-nucleon interaction (and hence the nucleon-nucleon interaction) and electromagnetic interactions. We know that parity is not conserved in weak interactions, e.g. beta-decay and the decays of hyperons, K-mesons, pions and muons. If one gives up parity conservation for a particular interaction, say that responsible for beta-decay, then the corresponding $\mathscr{H}_I$, need no longer be invariant under spatial inversion.

For interactions involving derivatives, the interaction Lagrangian density $\mathscr{L}_I$ will still be a scalar, but eq. (11.7) will no longer be correct. On account of eqs. (2.13) and (2.17) additional terms will appear in $\mathscr{H}_I$. There are also other complications. However, it can be shown that, in the development of perturbation theory which will be given in the next chapter, these additional terms and complications can be neglected, i.e. the interaction Lagrangian can be used as though it were the interaction Hamiltonian*). Hence derivative coupling can be treated in the same way as non-derivative coupling. For example, for pseudoscalar mesons interacting with nucleons we obtain the so-called $ps(pv)$-interaction [here ps stands for the pseudo-scalar nature of the meson, the pv in brackets for the pseudo-vector covariant of the spinor fields — similarly, interactions (11.9) and (11.11) are called $s(s)$- and $ps(ps)$-theories —]

$$\mathscr{H}_I(x) = i\frac{f}{m}\bar{\psi}\gamma_5\gamma_\mu\frac{\partial\phi}{\partial x_\mu}\psi. \tag{11.13}$$

On account of the factor $1/m$ the coupling constant f, like g in eq. (11.11), is dimensionless. The $ps(ps)$-interaction does not possess a non-relativistic limit (i.e. for nucleons whose velocity v is small compared to that of light). By this we mean that in the representation (A 7) the 'off-diagonal' operator γ_5 connects the large and small components of the four-spinors. The $ps(pv)$-interaction on the other hand does possess such a limit, the non-relativistic $ps(pv)$-interaction, given by (cf. exercise 11.2)

$$\mathscr{H}_I^{NR}(x) = \frac{f}{m}(\psi^\dagger\boldsymbol{\sigma}\psi)\ \mathrm{grad}\ \phi. \tag{11.14}$$

Although $ps(ps)$- and $ps(pv)$-interactions are fundamentally quite different, one can show that to the first order in the coupling

*) Cf. Matthews, P. T. *Phys. Rev.* **76**, 684, 1949 and ibid. p. 1419 (erratum).

constants they are equivalent*), if one takes

$$f/m = g/(2M). \tag{11.15}$$

We mention briefly that for interactions with the electromagnetic field, expressed in terms of the vector potential $A_\mu(x)$, gauge invariance imposes a further severe restriction on the form of the interaction. It is of course only the *total* Hamiltonian, not the interaction term by itself, which need be gauge invariant. We must now extend the definition of a gauge transformation given in eq. (9.3). For it may be possible to compensate for changes induced by this transformation by a gauge transformation of the first kind, applied to the fields of the charged particles with which the photons interact (ϕ and $\phi^\dagger$ for mesons, eqs. (7.4), and ψ and $\psi^\dagger$ for fermions, cf. the remarks following eq. (8.28)). The theory need then only be invariant under such joint transformations, known as *gauge transformations of the second kind*. For quantum electrodynamics, these generalized gauge transformations are

$$A'_\mu = A_\mu - \frac{\partial \Lambda(x)}{\partial x_\mu}, \quad \psi' = \psi\, \mathrm{e}^{ie\Lambda(x)}, \quad \bar{\psi}' = \bar{\psi}\, \mathrm{e}^{-ie\Lambda(x)}, \tag{11.16}$$

(cf. exercise 11.3).

In eq. (11.11) we wrote down the $ps(ps)$-interaction for neutral mesons. It corresponds to such basic processes as $P \rightarrow P + \pi^0$, etc. However, we must also consider charged mesons which are observed experimentally in such processes as $N \rightarrow P + \pi^-$ or $\pi^+ + N \rightarrow P$, etc. The emission of a π^-- or the absorption of a π^+-meson is here accompanied by the neutron transforming into a proton, corresponding to the conservation of charge which seems very well established. We can think of the neutron and proton as two different charge states of the same particle, the nucleon. During the process, the charge of the nucleon changes, in the same way in which its spin might 'flip'.

This analogy between charge states and spin states can be taken very far. If we represent the proton and neutron states of a

*) Cf. Schweber, Bethe and de Hoffmann (see bibliography), vol. I, § 26.

nucleon as

$$P = \begin{pmatrix} 1 \\ 0 \end{pmatrix} \qquad N = \begin{pmatrix} 0 \\ 1 \end{pmatrix} \tag{11.17}$$

then we can think of these two vectors as spanning a 2-dimensional *isobaric spin space* (more briefly called i-spin space, it is also referred to as isotopic spin space), quite analogous to the ordinary spin space for a particle with a Pauli spin of $\frac{1}{2}$. We can then introduce operators analogous to the Pauli matrices, operating in i-spin space:

$$\tau_1 = \begin{pmatrix} 0 & 1 \\ 1 & 0 \end{pmatrix} \qquad \tau_2 = \begin{pmatrix} 0 & -i \\ i & 0 \end{pmatrix} \qquad \tau_3 = \begin{pmatrix} 1 & 0 \\ 0 & -1 \end{pmatrix} \tag{11.18}$$

and

$$\tau_\pm = \frac{1}{\sqrt{2}} (\tau_1 \pm i\tau_2), \tag{11.19}$$

whence

$$\left.\begin{aligned} \tau_3 P &= P \qquad & \tau_+ N &= \sqrt{2}P \\ \tau_3 N &= -N \qquad & \tau_- P &= \sqrt{2}N. \end{aligned}\right\} \tag{11.20}$$

Thus the proton and neutron states of the nucleon are eigenstates of τ_3 with eigenvalues ± 1, respectively, and the nucleon has isobaric spin $\frac{1}{2}$, in the same sense in which it has ordinary spin $\frac{1}{2}$.

We now apply these ideas to the interaction of charged mesons and nucleons. Remembering that the operator

$$\phi_c = \frac{1}{\sqrt{2}} (\phi_1 - i\phi_2), \tag{11.21}$$

eq. (7.17), (we use the index c to distinguish the charged field from the neutral field which will be denoted by ϕ_0), absorbs positive and creates negative pions, we can write the $ps(ps)$-interaction in the following form, which ensures charge conservation

$$\begin{aligned} \mathscr{H}_I(x) = ig_c[\bar{\psi}_P \gamma_5 \psi_N \phi_c + \bar{\psi}_N \gamma_5 \psi_P \phi_c^\dagger] \\ + ig_N \bar{\psi}_N \gamma_5 \psi_N \phi_0 + ig_P \bar{\psi}_P \gamma_5 \psi_P \phi_0. \end{aligned} \tag{11.22}$$

Here ψ_P and $\bar{\psi}_P$ refer to the proton field (ψ_P absorbs protons or creates antiprotons, $\bar{\psi}_P$ performs the inverse functions), ψ_N and $\bar{\psi}_N$ similarly to the neutron field. The first term corresponds to one of the elementary processes

$$\left.\begin{array}{ll} N \to P + \pi^- & \pi^+ + N \to P \\ \bar{P} \to \bar{N} + \pi^- & \pi^+ + \bar{P} \to \bar{N} \end{array}\right\} \tag{11.23}$$

where $\bar{P}$ and $\bar{N}$ denote the antiproton and antineutron. The second term in eq. (11.22) represents the four charge-conjugate reactions, i.e. with particles and antiparticles interchanged. Thus the first process becomes

$$\bar{N} \to \bar{P} + \pi^+ \tag{11.24}$$

and so on. The remaining two terms correspond to the eight possible processes involving absorption or emission of a neutral pion by a nucleon. The three coupling constants g_c, g_N and g_P in eq. (11.22) must be real so that $\mathscr{H}_I$ is Hermitian; otherwise they are arbitrary.

Let us combine the proton and neutron fields into an eight-component spinor operator

$$\psi = \begin{pmatrix} \psi_P \\ \psi_N \end{pmatrix}. \tag{11.25}$$

(But it is more useful to think of this as a two-component quantity, whose components are the four-spinors ψ_P and ψ_N.) From eqs. (11.18—19) it follows at once that

$$\left.\begin{array}{l} \bar{\psi}\tau_+\gamma_5\psi = \sqrt{2}\,\bar{\psi}_P\gamma_5\psi_N \\ \bar{\psi}\tau_-\gamma_5\psi = \sqrt{2}\,\bar{\psi}_N\gamma_5\psi_P \end{array}\right\} \tag{11.26}$$

and

$$\left.\begin{array}{l} \bar{\psi}\dfrac{1-\tau_3}{2}\gamma_5\psi = \bar{\psi}_N\gamma_5\psi_N \\[2ex] \bar{\psi}\dfrac{1+\tau_3}{2}\gamma_5\psi = \bar{\psi}_P\gamma_5\psi_P \end{array}\right\} \tag{11.27}$$

which are of course just the analogous results to eq. (11.20): τ_+ transforms a neutron into a proton, and so on. Substituting eqs. (11.26—27), (11.21) and (11.19) in eq. (11.22), we can rewrite the interaction as

$$\left.\begin{aligned}\mathscr{H}_I(x) &= \frac{i}{\sqrt{2}} g_c \bar{\psi}(\tau_1\phi_1 + \tau_2\phi_2)\gamma_5\psi \\ &+ \frac{i}{2}(g_P + g_N)\bar{\psi}\phi_0\gamma_5\psi + \frac{i}{2}(g_P - g_N)\bar{\psi}\tau_3\phi_0\gamma_5\psi.\end{aligned}\right\} \quad (11.28)$$

We can now think of $\vec{\tau} = (\tau_1, \tau_2, \tau_3)$ as being a vector in a 3-dimensional *isobaric space*, just as $\boldsymbol{\sigma}$ is a vector in ordinary space. Under rotation of axes in this isobaric space, $\vec{\tau}$ will transform like a vector and this will induce corresponding transformations of the isobaric spin functions (11.17). If we write

$$\phi_3 = \phi_0 \quad (11.29)$$

and define $\vec{\phi} = (\phi_1, \phi_2, \phi_3)$ also to be a vector in isobaric space, then eq. (11.28) is seen to be invariant under rotations of axes about the 3-axis in isobaric space. This, it can be shown, expresses the conservation of charge which we have built into the theory*).

The theory acquires a much greater symmetry, if we demand that the interaction (11.28) should be an *invariant under rotations in isobaric space.* It can thus only depend on the scalar product $\vec{\tau}\cdot\vec{\phi}$, i.e. we require

$$g_P + g_N = 0, \ \tfrac{1}{2}(g_P - g_N) = \frac{1}{\sqrt{2}} g_c; \quad (11.31)$$

whence

$$g_P = -g_N = \frac{1}{\sqrt{2}} g_c \equiv g \quad (11.32)$$

and the interaction (11.28) becomes

$$\mathscr{H}_I(x) = ig\bar{\psi}(\vec{\tau}\cdot\vec{\phi})\gamma_5\psi. \quad (11.33)$$

*) In fact, we have seen that the conservation of charge, i.e. the existence of a continuity equation, is a result of the invariance of the theory under gauge transformations of the first kind. But this gauge transformation (7.4), expressed in terms of the real fields ϕ_1 and ϕ_2:

$$\left.\begin{aligned}\phi_1 \to \phi_1' &= \phi_1 \cos\alpha + \phi_2 \sin\alpha \\ \phi_2 \to \phi_2' &= -\phi_1 \sin\alpha + \phi_2 \cos\alpha,\end{aligned}\right\} \quad (11.30)$$

is seen to be a rotation about the 3-axis in isobaric space.

This interaction leads to the so-called *symmetric ps(ps)*-meson theory. It gives rise to a charge-independent nucleon-nucleon interaction and was introduced for this purpose by Kemmer*). It of course similarly implies an additional symmetry for meson-nucleon processes, also known as charge-independence: we have only one coupling constant (g) instead of three independent ones (g_c, g_P, g_N). Charge-independence is established with pretty good probability both for meson-nucleon processes and nuclear interactions.

The fact that charge independence is expressed mathematically by the rotational invariance in isobaric space enables one to make deductions about 'conservation of isobaric spin', very similar to those for conservation of angular momentum, leading to isobaric spin selection rules, etc., for meson-nucleon processes and nuclear reactions. For example, a pion has isobaric spin 1 (corresponding to its three possible charge states). For a system consisting of a nucleon and a pion, the total isobaric spin T can then only have the two values $\frac{1}{2}$ and $\frac{3}{2}$, obtained by vectorial addition of the pion isobaric spin 1 and the nucleon isobaric spin $\frac{1}{2}$. These questions are discussed fully in the references quoted above.

*) Kemmer, N. *Proc. Camb. phil. Soc.* **34**, 354, 1938. For more recent discussions of the symmetric meson theory and charge-independence, particularly also for meson-nucleon phenomena, cf. Wick, G. C. *Rev. mod. Phys.* **27**, 339, 1955, appendix A, and Bethe and de Hoffmann (see bibliography), vol. II, § 31.

CHAPTER 12

The Scattering Matrix

In this chapter we return to the equation of motion of a coupled interacting system, eq. (5.8):

$$i\,\frac{\partial \Phi(t)}{\partial t} = H_I(t)\Phi(t). \tag{12.1}$$

We wish to obtain a solution of this equation particularly suited to describing scattering processes. We are here given the initial state, at time $t = -\infty$, of the system

$$\Phi(-\infty) = \Phi_i. \tag{12.2}$$

This state vector will specify completely the particles present initially, i.e. long before scattering occurs when all particles are still far apart. In electrodynamics, for example, it will enumerate the electrons, positrons and photons, giving their momenta, spins and polarizations. Eq. (12.1) then tells us how the state vector (12.2) changes with time. In particular, it gives us the final state $\Phi(+\infty)$, at time $t = +\infty$, long after the scattering is over and all particles are far apart again. The scattering-matrix or S-matrix is defined as the operator which transforms $\Phi(-\infty)$ into $\Phi(+\infty)$:

$$\Phi(+\infty) = S\Phi(-\infty), \tag{12.3}$$

so that finding the S-matrix is equivalent to solving eq. (12.1).

Eq. (12.1) transforms into the integral equation

$$\Phi(t) = \Phi(-\infty)+(-i)\int_{-\infty}^{t} dt_1\, H_I(t_1)\Phi(t_1). \tag{12.4}$$

Solving this equation by iteration,

$$\Phi(t) = \Phi(-\infty)+(-i)\int_{-\infty}^{t} dt_1\, H_I(t_1) \cdot \Big\{\Phi(-\infty)+(-i)\int_{-\infty}^{t_1} dt_2\, H_I(t_2)\Phi(t_2)\Big\}, \tag{12.5}$$

and so on, we obtain the S-matrix

$$S = 1+(-i)\int_{-\infty}^{\infty} dt_1 H_I(t_1)+(-i)^2\int_{-\infty}^{\infty} dt_1 \int_{-\infty}^{t_1} dt_2 H_I(t_1)H_I(t_2)+\dots$$
$$= \sum_{n=0}^{\infty}(-i)^n\int_{-\infty}^{\infty} dt_1 \int_{-\infty}^{t_1} dt_2 \dots \int_{-\infty}^{t_{n-1}} dt_n\{H_I(t_1)\dots H_I(t_n)\}, \quad (12.6)$$

which can be rewritten as

$$S = \sum_{n=0}^{\infty}\frac{(-i)^n}{n!}\int_{-\infty}^{\infty}\int_{-\infty}^{\infty}\dots\int_{-\infty}^{\infty} dt_1\dots dt_n P\{H_I(t_1)\dots H_I(t_n)\}. \quad (12.7)$$

Here the Dyson C. P. $P\{\dots\}$ of n factors is the obvious generalization of the definition (6.13) for two factors; i.e. the factors are not to be taken in the order in which they are written in the P-bracket but so that later times stand to the left of earlier times: *earlier operators operate first.* The equivalence of eqs. (12.6) and (12.7) holds for each term n separately and is easily verified. Finally we rewrite eq. (12.7) in terms of the interaction density $\mathscr{H}_I$:

$$S = \sum_{n=0}^{\infty}\frac{(-i)^n}{n!}\int\dots\int d^4x_1\dots d^4x_n P\{\mathscr{H}_I(x_1)\dots\mathscr{H}_I(x_n)\}, \quad (12.8)$$

the integrations being over all space-time, ($d^4x = d^3x\,dt$).

Given two state-vectors Φ_i and Φ_j (these fully specify the particles present and their properties), the amplitude for a transition $\Phi_i \to \Phi_j$ is given by

$$(\Phi_j, S\Phi_i). \quad (12.9)$$

For a given initial state Φ_i, transitions to many different final states Φ_j may occur in general. For example, a state consisting of one electron and one positron may go over into a similar state (elastic scattering), it may lead to Bremsstrahlung (scattering with emission of one or more photons), the electron-positron pair may annihilate with emission of two gamma-rays, and so on. To pick out the appropriate part from the expansion (12.8), which causes a particular transition, will form the task of the next chapter but we must discuss first two points arising out of the above treatment.

In ordinary quantum mechanics, we use unperturbed wave functions to specify initial and final states in scattering problems.

This is permissible when considering short-range potentials; in this case the particles do not interact when far apart. In field theory this description appears wrong, for we are dealing with real physical particles, even when far apart, not with bare particles. An electron, even if far away from other electrons, is surrounded by its photon cloud. Hence the use in eq. (12.9) of bare particle states to specify initial and final states requires justification. One possible procedure is to appeal to the adiabatic hypothesis which affords the following description of a scattering process. Initially, at time $t = -\infty$, we may describe the system in terms of bare particles*). At a time $t = -T$, long before the scattering takes place, the particles are still far apart but during the interval $-\infty < t \leqq -T$ the equation of motion (12.1) has generated the real physical particles from the bare particles. Thus at $t = -T$ we have real particles present. This corresponds to an 'adiabatic switching on' of the coupling constant. It was zero at $t = -\infty$; it increases monotonically to its full value g which is attained at $t = -T$. The coupling constant retains its full value g during the interval $-T \leqq t \leqq T$ and, in particular, during the much shorter interval $-\tau \leqq t \leqq \tau$ during which the particles are actually close together and scattering occurs (i.e. $\tau \ll T$). Subsequently, for $t \geqq T$, the coupling constant is again switched off adiabatically, decreasing monotonically to zero. At $t = +\infty$, we again deal with bare particles. The essence of the adiabatic hypothesis is that the scattering, which actually occurs during the interval $-\tau \leqq t \leqq \tau$, cannot depend on our description of the system a long time before the scattering ($t \ll -\tau$) or a long time after the scattering ($t \gg +\tau$). Mathematically, this adiabatic cut-off procedure corresponds to replacing the coupling constant g in the interaction density $\mathscr{H}_I$, in eq. (12.8) by a time-dependent coupling constant as described above. This procedure avoids certain divergence difficulties which may arise from the interactions of a particle with its own field (e.g. of an electron with its photon cloud). Only at the end of a calculation do we go to

*) We are here considering the particles as localized, i.e. described by wave packets. In calculations it will, of course, be more convenient to adopt the more idealized description in terms of plane waves.

the limit $T \to \infty$. Of course, if we calculate a process in lowest order perturbation theory (i.e. use only the term of lowest order n in eq. (12.8) which gives a non-vanishing result) then the interaction is exclusively used to cause the transition (and not also to convert bare into real particles), so that we are dealing with bare particles initially and finally and so we may straightaway take the limit $T \to \infty$, i.e. work with the constant coupling constant without encountering divergence difficulties. A discussion of the adiabatic hypothesis, quoting further references, is given by Jauch and Rohrlich*).

The expansion (12.8) was derived purely formally and nothing will here be said about its convergence. It is a power series in the coupling constant g. For small coupling constants (so-called weak interactions) one may expect that the lowest order perturbation-theoretic calculations will give good results. This is indeed the case for electrodynamics. Here the coupling constant is simply e and $e^2/4\pi = 1/137$, the fine structure constant. Perturbation theory affords a good description of electrodynamics**). It is even outstandingly successful in the calculation of higher order corrections, the so-called radiative corrections, which are of the order of the fine structure constant. We shall return to these later. Perturbation theory fails of course for the strong interactions, e.g. for $ps(ps)$-meson theory for which, from nuclear forces, one finds $g^2/4\pi \sim 10$. One must then attempt a more ambitious procedure for solving the equations of motion. Nevertheless we shall, for two reasons, at times use meson theory to illustrate 'weak interaction' arguments. Firstly, these more ambitious 'strong interaction' methods usually presuppose familiarity with the weak coupling approach. Secondly, we have seen that mesons are in some respects much simpler than photons. Hence many of the basic ideas can be explained without introducing irrelevant complications (associated purely with photons).

*) Jauch and Rohrlich (see bibliography), p. 134.

**) Cf. Heitler (see bibliography), where a detailed comparison of theory and experiment is given.

CHAPTER 13

The S-Matrix Expansion

We must now see how to calculate the S-matrix element (12.9) in perturbation theory (i.e. up to a given order g^n in the coupling constant) for a definite transition $\Phi_i \to \Phi_j$, from the expansion (12.8) and the interaction $\mathscr{H}_I$. For electrodynamics $\mathscr{H}_I$ is given by eq. (11.1) together with eq. (8.32), for $ps(ps)$-meson theory by eq. (11.12).

In chapter 11 the interaction of electrodynamics was analysed in terms of creation and absorption operators and found to lead to various processes. Correspondingly the S-matrix expansion (12.8) will effect many more complicated transitions. However, only certain terms of the S-matrix will contribute to a given transition $\Phi_i \to \Phi_j$. For these terms must contain just the right absorption operators to destroy the particles present in Φ_i and they must contain just the right creation operators to emit the particles present in Φ_j. They may also contain additional creation and absorption operators which create particles which are subsequently reabsorbed. These particles are only present in intermediate states.

Calculations can be simplified greatly by avoiding the explicit introduction of virtual intermediate particles. An operator O which is a product of creation and absorption operators is called a *normal product* if *all* absorption operators stand to the *right* of *all* creation operators. Such an operator first absorbs a certain number of particles and then emits some particles. It does not cause emission and reabsorption of intermediate particles. Thus our object is to write each term in the S-matrix expansion (12.8) as a sum of normal products, using the method of Dyson and Wick. Each of these normal products will effect a particular transition $\Phi_i \to \Phi_j$ which can be represented by a Feynman graph, similar to those used in chapter 11.

Let $A, B, \ldots L$ be operators of the type $\psi_\alpha^\pm$, $\bar{\psi}_\alpha^\pm$, $A_\lambda^\pm$, $\phi^\pm$, i.e. each is linear in either creation or destruction operators only. We define the normal product

$$N(AB\ldots L) = (-1)^P(QR\ldots W). \tag{13.1}$$

Here $Q, R, \ldots W$ are the operators $A, B, \ldots L$ reordered so that all absorption operators (i.e. positive frequency parts) stand to the right of all creation operators (i.e. negative frequency parts). The exponent P is the number of interchanges of pairs of fermion operators required to change the order $(AB\ldots L)$ to $(QR\ldots W)$, i.e. the sign in eq. (13.1) is chosen as though, in going from the order $(AB\ldots L)$ to $(QR\ldots W)$, all fermion operators anti-commute with each other whereas two boson operators or a boson and a fermion operator commute with each other.

In the following examples of normal products we shall, for brevity, omit the arguments of the fields, that is, write $A_\lambda \equiv A_\lambda(x_1)$, $A_\mu \equiv A_\mu(x_2)$, etc., and similarly $\psi_\alpha \equiv \psi_\alpha(x_1)$, etc. Then

$$N(A_\lambda^+ A_\mu^- A_\nu^+ A_\sigma^-) = A_\sigma^- A_\mu^- A_\nu^+ A_\lambda^+, \tag{13.2}$$

but

$$N(\psi_\alpha^+ \bar{\psi}_\beta^- \bar{\psi}_\gamma^+ \psi_\delta^-) = -\,\psi_\delta^- \bar{\psi}_\beta^- \bar{\psi}_\gamma^+ \psi_\alpha^+, \tag{13.3}$$

the minus sign resulting from the interchange $\psi_\alpha^+ \leftrightarrow \psi_\delta^-$. Whether the fermion operators are 'barred' or 'unbarred' does not matter for these purposes, it being merely a question of positive and negative frequency parts. The definition (13.1) does not fix the order of the absorption or creation operators, each amongst themselves. Since both the positive and the negative frequency parts of the fields each commute amongst themselves for bosons [cf. eq. (6.11), similar relations hold for photons] and each anti-commute amongst themselves for fermion operators [cf. the remark following eq. (8.48)], these different ways of writing a normal product are, in fact, equal. For example, in eq. (13.3) we could first have interchanged ψ_α^+ and $\bar{\psi}_\beta^-$ and then ψ_α^+ and ψ_δ^- giving

$$+\,\bar{\psi}_\beta^- \psi_\delta^- \bar{\psi}_\gamma^+ \psi_\alpha^+, \tag{13.4}$$

which equals eq. (13.3).

The normal product (13.1) has the important property that its vacuum expectation value vanishes:

$$(\Phi_0, N(AB\ldots L)\Phi_0) = 0. \tag{13.5}$$

For, either $A, B, \ldots L$ contain at least one absorption operator, i.e. W is an absorption operator so that $W\Phi_0 = 0$, or $A, B, \ldots L$ are all creation operators, then the state $(AB\ldots L)\Phi_0$ is orthogonal to the vacuum*).

We generalize the definition (13.1) by requiring the normal product to obey the distributive law:

$$N(AB\ldots + RS\ldots) = N(AB\ldots) + N(RS\ldots). \tag{13.6}$$

Thus,

$$N(A_\lambda A_\mu) = A_\lambda^+ A_\mu^+ + A_\lambda^- A_\mu^- + A_\lambda^- A_\mu^+ + A_\mu^- A_\lambda^+ \tag{13.7}$$

and

$$N(\psi_\alpha \psi_\beta) = \psi_\alpha^+ \psi_\beta^+ + \psi_\alpha^- \psi_\beta^- + \psi_\alpha^- \psi_\beta^+ - \psi_\beta^- \psi_\alpha^+, \tag{13.8}$$

as well as corresponding relations with one or both fermion fields replaced by the 'barred' fields.

We can now express the interaction densities for $ps(ps)$-meson theory, eq. (11.12), and for quantum electrodynamics, eqs. (11.1) and (8.32), in terms of normal products:

$$\mathscr{H}_I(x) = igN(\bar{\psi}(x)\gamma_5\phi(x)\psi(x)) \tag{13.9}$$

for meson theory, and

$$\mathscr{H}_I(x) = ieN(\bar{\psi}(x)A\!\!\!/(x)\psi(x)) \tag{13.10}$$

for electrodynamics. We shall omit the derivations of eqs. (13.9—10) (cf. exercises 13.1—2) which are straightforward algebra using the anticommutation rules of the fermion fields, eqs. (8.42) and (8.48).

In chapter 8 the Wick C. P. was defined for two operators [eqs. (8.49—50)]. For any number of field operators $A(x_1)$, $B(x_2), \ldots$ (these stand for any of the fields $\psi_\alpha(x)$, $\bar{\psi}_\alpha(x)$, $\phi(x)$, $A_\mu(x)$), the T-product is defined in terms of the P-product by

$$T\{A(x_1)B(x_2)\ldots\} = (-1)^P P\{A(x_1)B(x_2)\ldots\}, \tag{13.11}$$

*) $A^\dagger$ is now an absorption operator, so that $A^\dagger\Phi_0 = 0$.

where the exponent P is the number of interchanges of pairs of fermion fields required to change from $\{A(x_1)B(x_2)\ldots\}$ to the chronological order.

For theories in which the interaction density $\mathscr{H}_I(x)$ is bilinear in the fermion fields (such as $ps(ps)$-meson theory or electrodynamics) we can simply replace the P-products in the S-matrix expansion (12.8) by T-products, since only even numbers of interchanges of pairs of fermion fields are involved. For quantum electrodynamics, the S-matrix (12.8) becomes

$$S = \sum_{n=0}^{\infty} \frac{e^n}{n!} \int \ldots \int d^4x_1 \ldots d^4x_n \, T\{N(\bar{\psi}\not{A}\psi)_{x_1} \ldots N(\bar{\psi}\not{A}\psi)_{x_n}\} \quad (13.12)$$

where the subscript x_i denotes the argument of all the fields in the corresponding normal product.

We must now consider the expansion of a 'mixed' T-product (i.e. a T-product whose factors are normal products), such as occurs in eq. (13.12), into a sum of normal products.

From the definition (13.1) of the normal product [cf. also eqs. (13.7—8)], we have for two operators $A = A(x_1)$ and $B = B(x_2)$,

$$AB = N(AB) + c \quad (13.13)$$

where c is a c-number*). Hence, taking the vacuum expectation value of eq. (13.13),

$$c = (\Phi_0, AB\Phi_0), \quad (13.14)$$

by eq. (13.5). Since

$$N(AB) = \pm N(BA) \quad (13.15)$$

the minus sign applying in the case of two fermion fields, the plus sign in all other cases, it follows from eqs. (13.13—15) that for $x_{10} \neq x_{20}$ ('equal times' operators will be considered below)

$$T\{A(x_1)B(x_2)\} = N\{A(x_1)B(x_2)\} + (\Phi_0, T\{A(x_1)B(x_2)\}\Phi_0). \quad (13.16)$$

*) For two boson operators $c = [A^+, B^-]$; for two fermion operators $c = [A^+, B^-]_+$; for one boson and one fermion operator $c = 0$. That c is a c-number in the function space of the state vectors, (for two fermion fields it is of course still a 4×4 matrix in spinor space), then follows from eqs. (6.11) and (8.48).

The special notation

$$\underbrace{A(x_1)B(x_2)} \equiv (\Phi_0, T\{A(x_1)B(x_2)\}\Phi_0) \qquad (13.17)$$

will be convenient for this vacuum expectation value which will be called the *contraction* of $A(x_1)$ and $B(x_2)$. Being a vacuum expectation value, it can only be different from zero if one of the operators A and B creates particles which the other absorbs. For electrodynamics, all the non-vanishing contractions have already been given explicitly in eqs. (9.14—15) and eqs. (8.51) and (8.46a):

$$\underbrace{A_\nu(x_2)A_\mu(x_1)} = \tfrac{1}{2}\delta_{\nu\mu}D_F(x_2 - x_1) \qquad (9.14)$$

and

$$\underbrace{\psi_\beta(x_2)\bar{\psi}_\alpha(x_1)} = -\underbrace{\bar{\psi}_\alpha(x_1)\psi_\beta(x_2)} = -\tfrac{1}{2}S_{F\beta\alpha}(x_2 - x_1). \qquad (8.51)$$

In eq. (9.14) each field involves photon absorption and creation operators and in eq. (8.51) $\bar{\psi}_\alpha$ involves electron emission and positron absorption operators, ψ_β just the inverse operators. But

$$\underbrace{\psi_\beta(x_2)\psi_\alpha(x_1)} = \underbrace{\bar{\psi}_\beta(x_2)\bar{\psi}_\alpha(x_1)} = \underbrace{\psi_\beta(x_2)A_\mu(x_1)} = \underbrace{\bar{\psi}_\beta(x_2)A_\mu(x_1)} = 0. \qquad (13.18)$$

To generalize eq. (13.16) to several operators $A = A(x_1), \ldots M = M(x_m), \ldots$, the generalized normal product is defined by

$$N(\underset{1}{A}\,\underset{2}{B}\,C\,\underbrace{D\,E\,F}\ldots J\,\underset{1}{K}\,L\,\underset{2}{M}\ldots) = (-1)^P \underbrace{AK}\,\underbrace{BM}\,\underbrace{DF}\ldots N(CE\ldots JL\ldots), \qquad (13.19)$$

where P denotes the number of interchanges of neighbouring fermion operators required to change the order $(ABC\ldots)$ to $(AKB\ldots)$; for example,

$$N(\psi_\alpha(x_1)\underbrace{\psi_\beta(x_2)A_\mu(x_3)\bar{\psi}_\sigma(x_4)\bar{\psi}_\tau(x_5)})$$
$$= (-1)\underbrace{\psi_\beta(x_2)\bar{\psi}_\tau(x_5)}N(\psi_\alpha(x_1)A_\mu(x_3)\bar{\psi}_\sigma(x_4)).$$

For the case of 'unequal times' (i.e. $x_{i0} \neq x_{j0}$ for $i \neq j$) Wick proves the following generalization of eq. (13.16):

$$
\begin{aligned}
T(ABCD\ldots WXYZ) &\\
&= N(ABCD\ldots WXYZ)\\
&+ N(\underbrace{AB}CD\ldots WXYZ) + N(\underbrace{ABC}D\ldots WXYZ) + \ldots\\
&\qquad\qquad + N(AB\ldots X\underbrace{YZ})\\
&+ N(\underbrace{AB}\,\underbrace{CD}\ldots WXYZ) + \ldots + N(AB\ldots \underbrace{WX}\,\underbrace{YZ})\\
&+ \ldots\\
&+ N(\underbrace{ABCD\ldots XYZ}) + \ldots . \qquad (13.20)
\end{aligned}
$$

On the right hand side of this equation appears the sum of all possible generalized normal products which can be formed from $(AB\ldots YZ)$, the second, third and fourth lines representing all terms with nil, one and two contractions, and so on.

We shall not reproduce the proof of eq. (13.20) which is by induction and so not very illuminating*).

The case of the mixed T-product

$$T\{N(\bar{\psi}\not{A}\psi)_{x_1}\ldots N(\bar{\psi}\not{A}\psi)_{x_n}\} \tag{13.21}$$

which occurs in eq. (13.12) is now easily derived. In each factor of $N(\bar{\psi}\not{A}\psi)_{x_r}$, we replace $x_r = (\mathbf{x}_r, ix_{r0})$ by $\xi_r = (\mathbf{x}_r, ix_{r0} \pm i\varepsilon)$, $(\varepsilon > 0)$, according as to whether the substitution is made in the creation or absorption part of the field. Hence

$$T\{N(\bar{\psi}\not{A}\psi)_{x_1}\ldots N(\bar{\psi}\not{A}\psi)_{x_n}\} = \lim_{\varepsilon\to 0} T\{(\bar{\psi}\not{A}\psi)_{\xi_1}\ldots(\bar{\psi}\not{A}\psi)_{\xi_n}\}, \tag{13.22}$$

the normal and chronological orderings within each group $(\bar{\psi}\not{A}\psi)$ being the same on account of the $\pm\varepsilon$ in ξ_{r0}. In expanding the right hand side of eq. (13.22) by Wick's theorem (13.20), *before* going to the limit $\varepsilon \to 0$, contractions within one group $(\bar{\psi}\not{A}\psi)$, i.e. over equal times operators, vanish as these are in normal order. Thus we have the final result: the mixed T-product (13.21) can be expanded by eq. (13.20), provided contractions over equal times operators are omitted:

$$T\{N(\bar{\psi}\not{A}\psi)_{x_1}\ldots N(\bar{\psi}\not{A}\psi)_{x_n}\} = T\{(\bar{\psi}\not{A}\psi)_{x_1}\ldots(\bar{\psi}\not{A}\psi)_{x_n}\}\big|_{\text{no e.t.c.}} \tag{13.23}$$

where 'no e.t.c.' stands for 'no equal times contractions'.

*) Wick, G. C. *Phys. Rev.* **80**, 268, 1950.

Eqs. (13.20) and (13.23) represent the desired result: an expansion of the mixed T-products, occurring in the S-matrix (13.12), into a sum of normal products. Each of these corresponds to a definite process, characterized by the operators not contracted. These operators absorb initial and create final particles. In the next chapter we shall see that the contractions can be interpreted in terms of virtual particles in intermediate states.

The above development for electrodynamics can of course equally well be carried out for $ps(ps)$-meson theory.

CHAPTER 14

Feynman Graphs

On account of the diversity of possible processes, the expansion of the S-matrix into normal products is quite complex, even for terms of low order n. The interpretations of these various terms is greatly facilitated by the use of Feynman graphs, introduced in chapter 11. Feynman arrived at these by a quite different, strongly intuitive approach. We shall follow the more conventional method, due to Dyson, which does not tax the intuitive powers of the reader unduly. Instead, everything is obtained from the mathematics. In this spirit we shall look on Feynman graphs merely as a most useful aid to interpreting the mathematics.

Postponing the quantitative details to the following chapters, we shall in this chapter give a mainly qualitative discussion of the basic ideas using the $n = 2$ term in eq. (13.12) as example. Expanded into normal products by means of eqs. (13.20) and (13.23), it becomes

$$S^{(2)} = \sum_{i=A}^{F} S_i^{(2)} = \frac{e^2}{2!}\iint d^4x_1\, d^4x_2\, T\{N(\bar{\psi}\not{A}\psi)_{x_2} N(\bar{\psi}\not{A}\psi)_{x_1}\} \quad (14.1)$$

where

$$S_A^{(2)} = \frac{e^2}{2!}\iint d^4x_1\, d^4x_2 N\{(\bar{\psi}\not{A}\psi)_{x_2}(\bar{\psi}\not{A}\psi)_{x_1}\} \quad (14.2a)$$

$$S_B^{(2)} = \frac{e^2}{2!}\iint d^4x_1\, d^4x_2\, [N\{(\bar{\psi}\not{A}\underbrace{\psi)_{x_2}(\bar{\psi}}\not{A}\psi)_{x_1}\} + N\{(\underbrace{\bar{\psi}\not{A}\psi)_{x_2}(\bar{\psi}\not{A}\psi}_{})_{x_1}\}] \quad (14.2b)$$

$$S_C^{(2)} = \frac{e^2}{2!}\iint d^4x_1\, d^4x_2 N\{(\bar{\psi}\gamma_\nu \underbrace{A_\nu\psi)_{x_2}(\bar{\psi}\gamma_\mu A_\mu}\psi)_{x_1}\} \quad (14.2c)$$

$$S_D^{(2)} = \frac{e^2}{2!}\iint d^4x_1 d^4x_2 \,[N\{(\bar{\psi}\gamma_\nu A_\nu \psi)_{x_2}(\bar{\psi}\gamma_\mu A_\mu \psi)_{x_1}\} + N\{(\bar{\psi}\gamma_\nu A_\nu \psi)_{x_2}(\bar{\psi}\gamma_\mu A_\mu \psi)_{x_1}\}] \tag{14.2d}$$

$$S_E^{(2)} = \frac{e^2}{2!}\iint d^4x_1 d^4x_2 N\{(\bar{\psi}A\!\!\!/\psi)_{x_2}(\bar{\psi}A\!\!\!/\psi)_{x_1}\} \tag{14.2e}$$

$$S_F^{(2)} = \frac{e^2}{2!}\iint d^4x_1 d^4x_2 N\{(\bar{\psi}\gamma_\nu A_\nu \psi)_{x_2}(\bar{\psi}\gamma_\mu A_\mu \psi)_{x_1}\}. \tag{14.2f}$$

In the expansion (14.1—2) contractions over equal times operators have been omitted as well as contractions which obviously vanish [eq. (13.18)].

We saw in chapter 11 that the interaction $\mathscr{H}_I$ is represented by a graph consisting of a vertex with two fermion lines and one boson line (figs. 9 and 10). We shall call this a *basic vertex part*. The second-order terms (14.2a—f) will be described by graphs involving two basic vertex parts, suitably joined together. What transitions a particular term $S_i^{(2)}$ can effect, depends on the external fields (i.e. those which are not contracted over) in this operator, for it is these external fields which are responsible for absorbing initial and creating final particles.

The term $S_A^{(2)}$, eq. (14.2a), is not very interesting. Involving only external lines, it corresponds to two processes of the types illustrated in fig. 10 going on independently of each other.

The two terms in eq. (14.2b) are identically equal to each other, as is seen by permuting the operators. This requires care on two accounts. The fermion fields are spinors as well as being non-commuting operators in virtue of their dependence on creation and absorption operators. However, the spinor indices of each group $(\bar{\psi}A\!\!\!/\psi)$ are self-contained so that these are not affected by interchanging whole groups. Furthermore this always involves an even permutation of fermion fields*) so that

$$N\{(\bar{\psi}A\!\!\!/\psi)_{x_2}(\bar{\psi}A\!\!\!/\psi)_{x_1}\} = N\{(\bar{\psi}A\!\!\!/\psi)_{x_1}(\bar{\psi}A\!\!\!/\psi)_{x_2}\}. \tag{14.3}$$

*) The reader can always resolve any cases of doubt by writing out explicitly the spinor indices.

Interchanging the variables of integration $x_1 \leftrightarrow x_2$ in the second term in eq. (14.2b) one obtains

$$S_B^{(2)} = e^2 \iint d^4x_1 d^4x_2 N\{(\bar{\psi}A\!\!\!/\underbrace{\psi)_{x_2}(\bar{\psi}}A\!\!\!/\psi)_{x_1}\}. \tag{14.4}$$

This expression we can write more fully as

$$S_B^{(2)} = e^2 \iint d^4x_1 d^4x_2 N\{(\bar{\psi}^+(x_2) + \bar{\psi}^-(x_2))\gamma_\nu(A_\nu^+(x_2) + A_\nu^-(x_2)) \times \underbrace{\psi(x_2)\bar{\psi}(x_1)}\gamma_\mu(A_\mu^+(x_1) + A_\mu^-(x_1))(\psi^+(x_1) + \psi^-(x_1))\}. \tag{14.5}$$

This operator describes, amongst other processes, Compton scattering, i.e. an incident photon is scattered by an electron which itself experiences a recoil. The operator $\psi^+(x_1)$ must absorb the electron present initially, and the operator $\bar{\psi}^-(x_2)$ must emit the final electron. But either $A_\mu^+(x_1)$ or $A_\nu^+(x_2)$ can absorb the initial photon and correspondingly $A_\nu^-(x_2)$ or $A_\mu^-(x_1)$ must emit the final photon. Thus the part of eq. (14.5) which causes Compton scattering is

$$S_{\text{c.s.}}^{(2)} = S_a^{(2)} + S_b^{(2)} \tag{14.6}$$

where

$$S_a^{(2)} = e^2 \iint d^4x_1 d^4x_2 \{\bar{\psi}^-(x_2)\gamma_\nu A_\nu^-(x_2)\underbrace{\psi(x_2)\bar{\psi}(x_1)}\gamma_\mu A_\mu^+(x_1)\psi^+(x_1)\} \tag{14.7a}$$

$$S_b^{(2)} = e^2 \iint d^4x_1 d^4x_2 \{\bar{\psi}^-(x_2)\gamma_\nu A_\nu^+(x_2)\underbrace{\psi(x_2)\bar{\psi}(x_1)}\gamma_\mu A_\mu^-(x_1)\psi^+(x_1)\}. \tag{14.7b}$$

The representation by Feynman graphs of these two terms is shown in figs. 11(a) and (b) using the conventions introduced in chapter 11. Fig. 11(a) represents the initial photon, labelled i, absorbed at x_1 and the final photon, labelled f, created at x_2. In fig. 11(b) the final photon f is created at x_1 and the initial photon i is absorbed at x_2.

On the fermion lines arrows pointing towards a vertex are associated with the operator ψ (e.g. $\psi(x_1)$ absorbs the incident electron) and arrows pointing away from a vertex with $\bar{\psi}$ (e.g. $\bar{\psi}(x_2)$ creates the emitted electron). The contraction $\underbrace{\psi(x_2)\bar{\psi}(x_1)}$ is described by the line from the vertex x_1 to x_2. In view of eq. (8.51), the following interpretation suggests itself for this con-

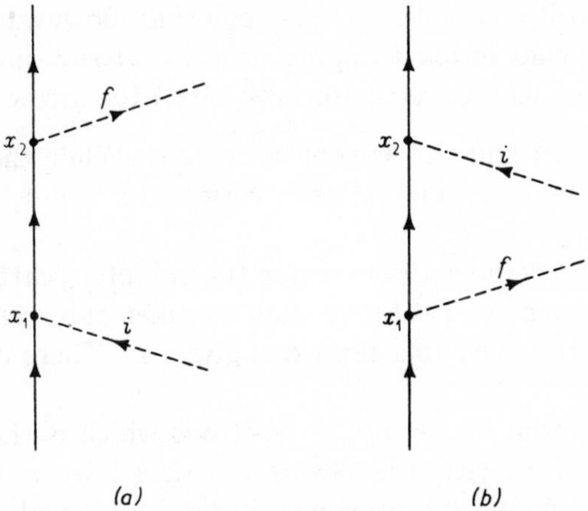

Fig. 11. Compton scattering by electrons.

traction. For $x_{10} < x_{20}$, it describes the emission of a virtual electron at x_1, its propagation to x_2 and its absorption there. For $x_{20} < x_{10}$, it describes the emission of a positron at x_2, its propagation to and absorption at x_1. In other words, if $x_{20} < x_{10}$, we can think of fig. 11(a) [fig. 11(b)] as describing the creation of an electron-positron pair at x_2 with emission of a photon f [absorption of a photon i], the positron being propagated to x_1 where it annihilates with the incident electron absorbing the initial photon [emitting the final photon]. Thus we call $\underbrace{\psi(x_2)\bar{\psi}(x_1)}$ a fermion *propagator*. It describes a virtual intermediate fermion: electron or positron according as $x_{20} \gtrless x_{10}$. Note that there is *no* time ordering in Feynman graphs as we draw them. Figs 11(a) and (b) each represent intermediate states of both kinds: a virtual electron or a virtual electron-positron pair. Furthermore this propagator already contains the summation over the spin states of the virtual fermion. This is in contrast to the older perturbation-theoretic treatments*) where one had to sum explicitly over the four states of the virtual fermion i.e. over electron and positron states and over spins. In chapter 11 the convention was introduced that electrons are drawn with arrows pointing up-

* Cf. Heitler (see bibliography).

wards, positrons with arrows pointing downwards. We now relax this convention to apply only to *external* lines but not to propagators. On a propagator $\underbrace{\psi(x_2)\bar{\psi}(x_1)}$ the arrow simply points from x_1 to x_2 and this covers both cases. While the above naive interpretation of propagators is very useful it must not be taken too literally.

After this detailed discussion of the Compton scattering diagram resulting from eq. (14.5) we shall consider only briefly the other processes to which this term can give rise. There are three such processes:

(1) Compton scattering by positrons which is the same as the above process with the electron replaced by a positron. The corresponding graphs are shown in figs. 12(a) and (b), the initial positron now being absorbed by the operator $\bar{\psi}^{+}(x_2)$, the final positron created by $\psi^{-}(x_1)$.

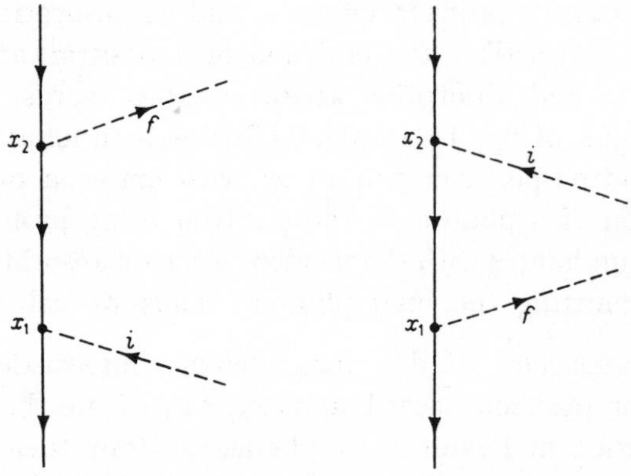

Fig. 12. Compton scattering by positrons.

(2) Two-quantum pair creation, i.e. 2 gamma rays give rise to an electron-positron pair. Fig. 13 is the typical Feynman graph for this process.

(3) The inverse process, two-quantum pair annihilation, in which an electron-positron pair annihilate each other giving rise to two gamma rays, illustrated in fig. 14.

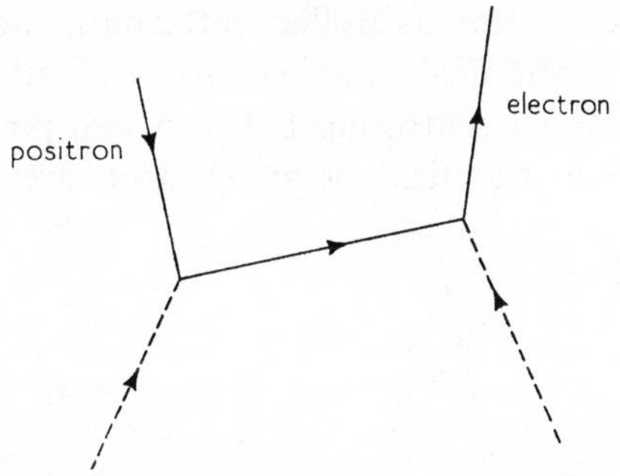

Fig. 13. Two-quantum pair creation.

That only the above four processes need to be considered in connection with eq. (14.5) is due to the fact that the S-matrix, as one might expect, only effects transitions between initial and final states which conserve energy and momentum. This point will be considered in detail in the next chapter.

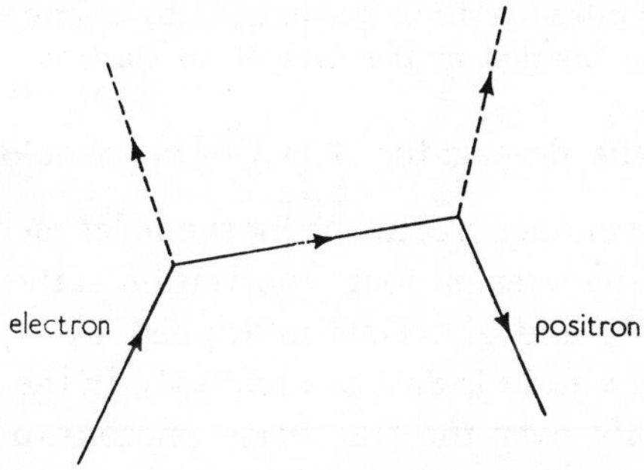

Fig. 14. Two-quantum pair annihilation.

We shall now discuss briefly the remaining terms $S_C^{(2)}$ to $S_F^{(2)}$ in eqs. (14.1—2). Taking the above treatment of Compton scattering as example, the reader should easily be able to supply the details.

In eq. (14.2c) we have four external fermion lines. The photons occur only in the contraction $\underbrace{A_\nu(x_2)A_\mu(x_1)}$ which we shall again interpret as a photon propagator. For $x_{10} < x_{20}$, a photon emitted at x_1 is propagated to x_2 where it is absorbed, and a similar interpretation for $x_{10} > x_{20}$. Thus eq. (14.2c) effects seven processes: electron-electron, positron-positron or electron-positron scattering (these processes are known as Møller scattering), and pair annihilation or creation in the field of an electron or positron. The Feynman graphs for Møller scattering between two positrons and for pair annihilation in the field of an electron are shown in figs. 15(a) and (b).

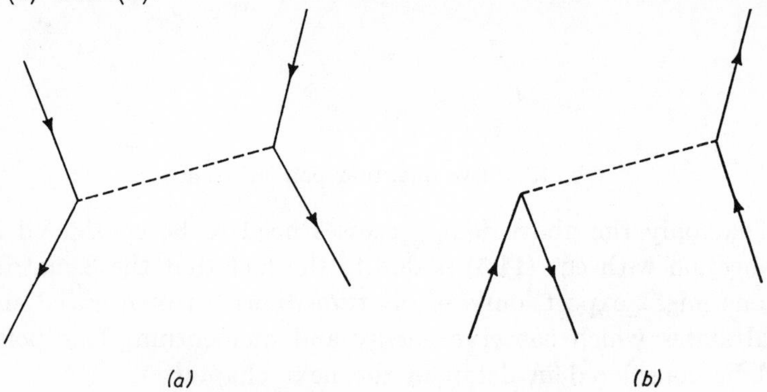

Fig. 15. (a) positron-positron scattering; (b) electron-positron pair annihilation in the field of an electron.

The role of the propagator $\underbrace{A_\nu(x_2)A_\mu(x_1)}$ should be compared with the corresponding treatment by the older methods. Here we sum automatically over all four polarization states of the virtual photon. (The A_μ and A_ν occur multiplied by γ_μ and γ_ν, with summation over μ and ν from 1 to 4 implied). In the older methods, one summed only over the transverse photons, adding to these retardation effects the instantaneous static Coulomb interaction between the charges (which is now replaced by the longitudinal and scalar photons). The present treatment is accordingly rather simpler.

Consider the Møller scattering of two electrons which have the energy-momentum vectors p_1 and p_2 initially and p_1' and p_2' finally. Eq. (14.2c) then has four terms effecting this transition. Either operator $\psi^+(x_i)$ $i = 1, 2$, can absorb the electron with four-vector p_1 or p_2 and either operator $\bar{\psi}^-(x_i)$ can emit the electron p_1' or p_2'. The two pairs of terms obtained by interchanging x_1 and x_2 are again identical and merely cancel the (2!) in the denominator in eq. (14.2c). The remaining pair of graphs are illustrated in figs. 16(a) and (b). They correspond to direct and exchange scattering. Complete analysis show that these two terms occur with opposite signs which is a consequence of the Pauli principle; we are dealing with antisymmetric states.

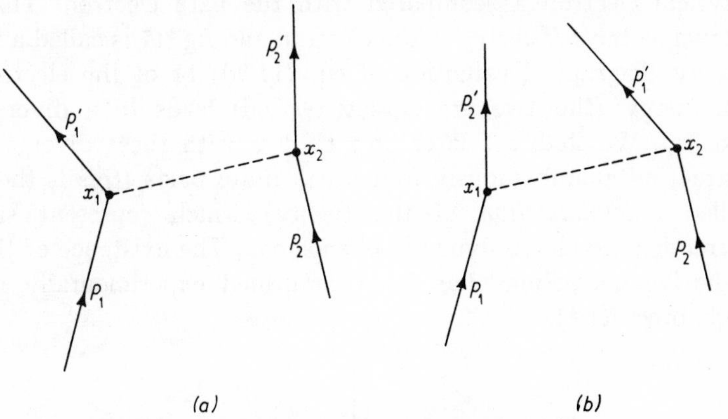

Fig. 16. Electron-electron scattering:
(a) direct scattering; (b) exchange scattering.

Turning to eq. (14.2d), the two terms are again equal. This expression gives rise to two processes according as to whether the fermion present initially and finally is an electron or a positron. Fig. 17 shows the graph for the former case. It represents a modi-

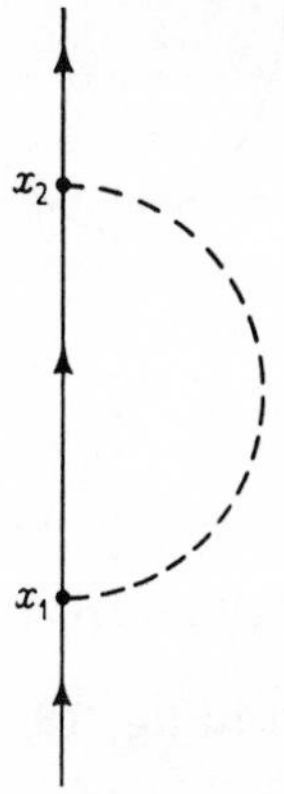

Fig. 17. Electron self-energy.

fication of the properties of a *bare* electron due to its interaction with the radiation field. It is one of the processes, in fact the simplest, which converts a bare electron into a *physical* electron, that is one surrounded by its photon cloud. This interaction causes a change in energy of the system, i.e. of the mass of the physical electron as compared with the bare electron. This is known as the *self-energy* of the electron and fig. 17 is called a self-energy diagram. Evaluation of eq. (14.2d) or of the electron's self-energy (the two are closely related) leads to a divergent integral. We shall see later how to deal with these divergences extracting unambiguously from them finite parts (this is the so-called *renormalization* of the theory) which represent small corrections to electrodynamic phenomena. The existence of these radiative corrections has been confirmed experimentally with high precision*).

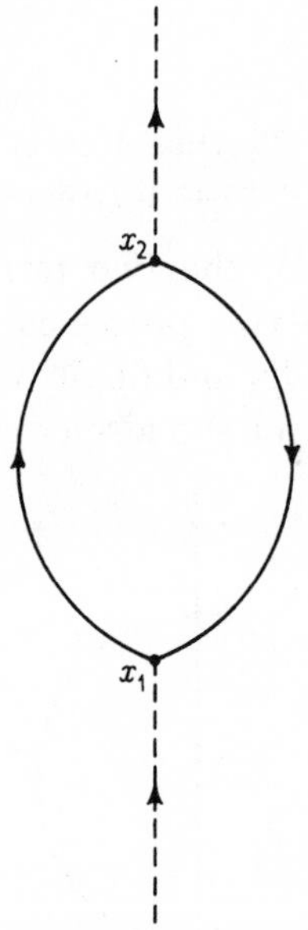

Fig. 18. Photon self-energy (vacuum polarization).

Eq. (14.2e), represented in fig. 18, similarly describes a *photon*

*) The reader may like to compare these ideas with the more naive ones of chapter 4 which, as stated at the time, however already contains many of the basic concepts. In particular figs. 16 and 17 should be compared with figs. 1, and figs. 11 with figs. 2.

self-energy, i.e. a modification of a photon due to its interaction with the electron-positron field. This interaction enables the photon to create a virtual electron-positron pair which subsequently annihilate again. An external electromagnetic field (for example the presence of a heavy nucleus) will modify the distribution of these virtual electron-positron pairs, i.e. it will polarize the vacuum, much in the same way in which an electric field polarizes a dielectric. For this reason such photon self-energy graphs are also called *vacuum polarization* diagrams. Like the electron self-energy, these also are infinite but after renormalization again give rise to finite radiative corrections which are confirmed by experiment.

The normal product in eq. (14.2e) can be written

$$N\{(\bar{\psi}A\!\!\!/\psi)_{x_2}(\bar{\psi}A\!\!\!/\psi)_{x_1}\} = (-1)\mathrm{Tr}\{\psi(x_1)\bar{\psi}(x_2)\gamma_\nu\psi(x_2)\bar{\psi}(x_1)\gamma_\mu\}N\{A_\nu(x_2)A_\mu(x_1)\}. \qquad (14.8)$$

The minus sign is characteristic of *closed fermion loops* which always involve the transposition of a single fermion operator from one end of a product of factors to the other end, i.e. an odd number of interchanges. The origin of the trace in eq. (14.8) is seen by writing out explicitly the spinor indices, using eq. (8.51). It corresponds to summing over all spin states of the virtual electron-positron pair. (Cf. the appendix, eqs. (A 28—31), where a typical spin summation, leading to a trace, is performed.)

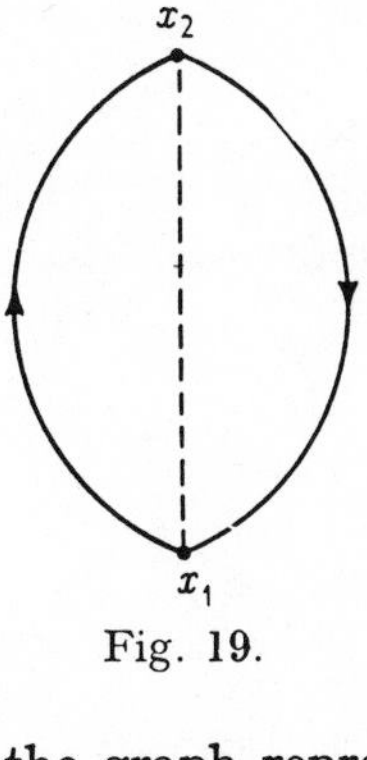

Fig. 19.

Finally, fig. 19 shows the graph representing eq. (14.2f). This has no external lines at all and consequently does not cause any transitions. One can show that such *vacuum diagrams* (as diagrams without external lines are called) may be omitted altogether, at any rate in elementary applications.

This completes the analysis of the second order part $S^{(2)}$, eq. (14.1), into normal products and the interpretation in terms of Feynman graphs. The reader should have no difficulty in similarly decomposing higher order contributions although, of course, the complexity of the analysis increases rapidly. This graphical description is a most useful way of interpreting the mathematics, particularly in complicated problems. Compared to the older type of perturbation-theoretic treatment, this analysis has two important advantages. Firstly, the analysis is in many respects simpler. Two typical simplifications were mentioned above in connection with the intermediate states in Compton and Møller scattering. Secondly, this treatment brings out particularly clearly the relativistic properties of the theory which is essential in the treatment of radiative corrections. These points will be illustrated in the following chapters in which the quantitative analysis supplementing the above discussion will be carried out for some specific problems.

CHAPTER 15

Compton Scattering

We shall now derive the cross-section for Compton scattering in lowest-order perturbation theory, i.e. taking into account the Feynman graphs in fig. **11** only. This calculation will be set out in some detail to serve as a model which should enable the reader to deal with other cases.

This type of problem subdivides into three stages: (i) the calculation of the matrix element (12.9), (ii) the derivation of the cross-section from this matrix element and (iii) summations over those spins and polarizations which are not observed in a particular experiment.

(i) *Matrix element.*

Suppose in the initial state Φ_i we have an electron of momentum $\mathbf{p}$ and energy $p_0 = E_{\mathbf{p}} \equiv (M^2 + \mathbf{p}^2)^{\frac{1}{2}}$, i.e.

$$p^2 + M^2 = 0, \qquad (15.1)$$

in the spinor state $u^{(r)}(\mathbf{p})$, $r = 1, 2$, and a photon of momentum $\mathbf{k}$ and energy $k_0 = \omega_{\mathbf{k}} = |\mathbf{k}|$, i.e.

$$k^2 = 0, \qquad (15.2)$$

and polarization vector $\varepsilon_\mu^{(m)}(\mathbf{k})$, $m = 1, 2$. (The unit vectors (9.17) are used to specify the polarization.) The restrictions $r = 1, 2$ and $m = 1, 2$ mean that we have a (negative) electron and a transversely polarized photon. Thus

$$\Phi_i = a_m^\dagger(\mathbf{k}) c_r^\dagger(\mathbf{p}) \Phi_0, \quad m = 1, 2, \quad r = 1, 2, \qquad (15.3)$$

and, with an entirely analogous notation, we write the final state Φ_j as

$$\Phi_j = a_n^\dagger(\mathbf{k}')c_s^\dagger(\mathbf{p}')\Phi_0, \quad n = 1, 2, \quad s = 1, 2. \tag{15.4}$$

The matrix element for Compton scattering is, according to eqs. (15.3—4) and (14.6—7), given by

$$M_{ji} = (\Phi_j, S_a^{(2)}\Phi_i) + (\Phi_j, S_b^{(2)}\Phi_i). \tag{15.5}$$

Consider the first of these terms, corresponding to fig. 11(a). To effect the transition $\Phi_i \to \Phi_j$ we require a term in $S_a^{(2)}$ which contains the operators $a_m(\mathbf{k})$, $c_r(\mathbf{p})$, $a_n^\dagger(\mathbf{k}')$ and $c_s^\dagger(\mathbf{p}')$, (to absorb the initial and create the final particles). From eqs. (8.37), the term in $\psi^+(x_1)$ which contains $c_r(\mathbf{p})$ is

$$\psi^+(x_1) \sim \left[\frac{1}{\sqrt{V}}\left(\frac{M}{E_\mathbf{p}}\right)^{\frac{1}{2}} u^{(r)}(\mathbf{p})\, \mathrm{e}^{ipx_1}\right] c_r(\mathbf{p}), \tag{15.6}$$

with similar expressions for the term proportional to $c_s^\dagger(\mathbf{p}')$ in $\bar{\psi}^-(x_2)$ and the terms proportional to $a_m(\mathbf{k})$ and $a_n^\dagger(\mathbf{k}')$ in $A_\mu^+(x_1)$ and $A_\nu^-(x_2)$ respectively, eq. (9.16).

For the propagator $\underbrace{\psi(x_2)\bar{\psi}(x_1)}$ we use eqs. (8.51) and (8.46a):

$$\underbrace{\psi(x_2)\bar{\psi}(x_1)} = -\tfrac{1}{2}S_F(x_2 - x_1) = -\frac{1}{(2\pi)^4}\int d^4q \frac{\mathrm{e}^{iq(x_2-x_1)}}{\not{q} - iM}. \tag{15.7}$$

We are all the time normalizing the states in a large but finite volume V [cf. eq. (15.6)]. This is most convenient in practice, particularly when calculating phase-space factors etc. [cf. (ii) below]. But in writing down the propagator (15.7) we have again approximated the sum over allowed momenta by an integral, according to eq. (3.7). The error which this introduces will vanish ultimately when we take the limit $V \to \infty$.

Now

$$(\Phi_j, a_n^\dagger(\mathbf{k}')c_s^\dagger(\mathbf{p}')a_m(\mathbf{k})c_r(\mathbf{p})\Phi_i) = (\Phi_0, \Phi_0) = 1, \tag{15.8}$$

hence*)

*) We may write $\not{\varepsilon}^{(n)}(\mathbf{k}')$ in eq. (15.9), rather than $\gamma_\mu \varepsilon_\mu^{(n)*}(\mathbf{k}')$ as expected from eq. (9.16). For the polarization vector $\varepsilon^{(n)}$ is real for transverse polarization, i.e. the $\varepsilon_4^{(n)}$-component vanishes. Cf. eqs. (9.17).

$$(\Phi_j,\ S_a^{(2)}\Phi_i)$$
$$= e^2 \int\int d^4x_1 d^4x_2 \left[\frac{1}{\sqrt{V}}\left(\frac{M}{E_{\mathbf{p}'}}\right)^{\frac{1}{2}} \bar{u}^{(s)}(\mathbf{p}')\,\mathrm{e}^{-ip'x_2}\right]$$
$$\times \left[\frac{1}{\sqrt{V}}\frac{1}{\sqrt{2\omega_{\mathbf{k}'}}}\,\not{e}^{(n)}(\mathbf{k}')\,\mathrm{e}^{-ik'x_2}\right]\left[-\frac{1}{(2\pi)^4}\int d^4q\,\frac{\mathrm{e}^{iq(x_2-x_1)}}{\not{q}-iM}\right]$$
$$\times \left[\frac{1}{\sqrt{V}}\frac{1}{\sqrt{2\omega_{\mathbf{k}}}}\,\not{e}^{(m)}(\mathbf{k})\,\mathrm{e}^{ikx_1}\right]\left[\frac{1}{\sqrt{V}}\left(\frac{M}{E_{\mathbf{p}}}\right)^{\frac{1}{2}} u^{(r)}(\mathbf{p})\,\mathrm{e}^{ipx_1}\right]. \quad (15.9)$$

Integration with respect to x_1 and x_2 can be carried out at once since these variables occur only in the exponentials and

$$\int d^4x\,\mathrm{e}^{ipx} = (2\pi)^4\,\delta^{(4)}(p) \quad (15.10)$$

where $\delta^{(4)}(p)$ is the four-dimensional Dirac δ-function, so that

$$(\Phi_j,\ S_a^{(2)}\Phi_i) = \frac{-e^2}{(2\pi)^4 V^2}\left(\frac{M^2}{4E_{\mathbf{p}}E_{\mathbf{p}'}\omega_{\mathbf{k}}\omega_{\mathbf{k}'}}\right)^{\frac{1}{2}}\int d^4q\,(2\pi)^8\,\delta^{(4)}(p+k-q)$$
$$\times\ \delta^{(4)}(q-p'-k')\,\bar{u}^{(s)}(\mathbf{p}')\left[\not{e}^{(n)}(\mathbf{k}')\,\frac{1}{\not{q}-iM}\,\not{e}^{(m)}(\mathbf{k})\right]u^{(r)}(\mathbf{p}) \quad (15.11)$$

and carrying out the integration over q,

$$(\Phi_j,\ S_a^{(2)}\Phi_i) = (2\pi)^4\,\delta^{(4)}(p+k-p'-k')\,\frac{(-e^2)}{V^2}\left(\frac{M^2}{4E_{\mathbf{p}}E_{\mathbf{p}'}\omega_{\mathbf{k}}\omega_{\mathbf{k}'}}\right)^{\frac{1}{2}}$$
$$\times\ \bar{u}^{(s)}(\mathbf{p}')\left[\not{e}^{(n)}(\mathbf{k}')\,\frac{1}{\not{p}+\not{k}-iM}\,\not{e}^{(m)}(\mathbf{k})\right]u^{(r)}(\mathbf{p}). \quad (15.12)$$

From eqs. (8.46—47), $(\not{p}+\not{k}-iM)^{-1}$ is merely an abbreviation for

$$\frac{\not{p}+\not{k}+iM}{(p+k)^2+M^2-i\varepsilon}. \quad (15.13)$$

Since by eqs. (15.1—2)

$$(p+k)^2+M^2 = 2(pk) = 2(\mathbf{pk}-E_{\mathbf{p}}\omega_{\mathbf{k}}) < 0, \quad (15.14)$$

we can already take $\varepsilon = 0$ at this stage, since it was only introduced to cope with possible zeros of the denominator in eq. (15.13).

In eq. (15.11) two δ-functions occur, one relating to each vertex.

The interpretation of the expression on the right-hand side of eq. (15.7) as the fermion propagator from x_1 to x_2 suggests interpreting

$$\frac{1}{\not{q} - iM} \tag{15.15}$$

as the fermion propagator in momentum space, representing a fermion with energy-momentum four-vector q. Thus eq. (15.12) implies that the virtual intermediate-state fermion has the energy-momentum vector q satisfying

$$p + k = q = p' + k'. \tag{15.16}$$

With this interpretation, illustrated in the Feynman graph of fig. 20(a), we have conservation of energy and momentum at

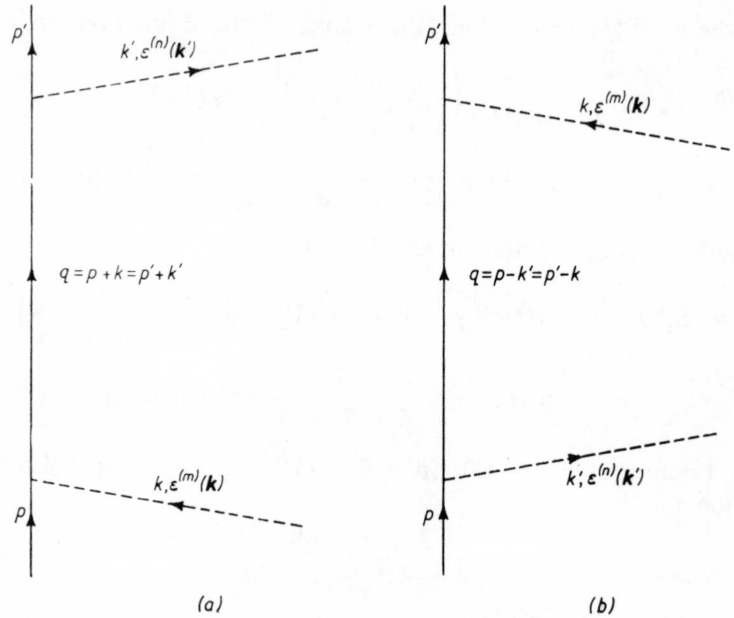

Fig. 20. Compton scattering.

each vertex, i.e. also in the intermediate state. This result apparently differs from elementary perturbation theory where energy is not conserved in virtual intermediate states. However, in the present treatment a virtual fermion of momentum p or a virtual photon of momentum k does *not* satisfy the correct energy-momentum relationship, eqs. (15.1—2). This was demonstrated explicitly for the virtual fermion of momentum $(p + k)$ in eq. (15.14). These two modes of description of virtual states are of course quite equivalent.

The second term in eq. (15.5) can be treated in exactly the same way as the first. The only difference between these terms is the order in which the two photons are emitted and absorbed resulting, for the second term, in the four-vector q of the intermediate fermion satisfying

$$p - k' = q = p' - k, \tag{15.17}$$

as shown in fig. 20(b). Hence by adding to eq. (15.12) the appropriate expression [which is simply obtained from eq. (15.12) by interchanging $\not{e}^{(m)}(\mathbf{k})$ and $\not{e}^{(n)}(\mathbf{k}')$ and replacing eq. (15.16) by eq. (15.17) in the energy denominator (15.15)], one obtains for the matrix element (15.5)

$$M_{ji} = (2\pi)^4 \delta^{(4)}(p+k-p'-k') \left(\frac{-e^2}{V^2}\right) \left(\frac{M^2}{4E_{\mathbf{p}} E_{\mathbf{p}'} \omega_{\mathbf{k}} \omega_{\mathbf{k}'}}\right)^{\frac{1}{2}} \cdot A \tag{15.18}$$

where

$$A \equiv \bar{u}^{(s)}(\mathbf{p}') \left[\not{e}^{(n)} \frac{1}{\not{p} + \not{k} - iM} \not{e}^{(m)} + \not{e}^{(m)} \frac{1}{\not{p} - \not{k}' - iM} \not{e}^{(n)} \right] u^{(r)}(\mathbf{p}). \tag{15.19}$$

Here, as throughout the following, we have abbreviated $\not{e}^{(m)} \equiv \not{e}^{(m)}(\mathbf{k})$ and $\not{e}^{(n)} \equiv \not{e}^{(n)}(\mathbf{k}')$.

(ii) *Cross-section.*

$|M_{ji}|^2$ is the total probability for all times and all space for the transition $\Phi_i \rightarrow \Phi_j$ to occur. We are here meeting difficulties of interpretation and mathematics due to the idealized description of the scattering process which has been adopted. In defining the scattering matrix, eq. (12.3), an infinite time interval was used and both incident particle and target have been described by plane waves. More realistically, one should consider finite time intervals and represent both the incident beam and the target by wave packets. Our present purpose is to show how to derive in a simple way transition probabilities, etc., from the above formalism, and not the much more difficult task of justifying this procedure in scattering theory*).

From eq. (15.18),

$$|M_{ji}|^2 = (2\pi)^8[\delta^{(4)}(p + k - p' - k')]^2 \frac{1}{V^4}\left(\frac{e^4M^2}{4E_{\mathbf{p}}E_{\mathbf{p}'}\omega_{\mathbf{k}}\omega_{\mathbf{k}'}}\right)|A|^2$$

$$= (2\pi)^4\delta^{(4)}(p + k - p' - k')\frac{1}{V^4}\left(\frac{e^4M^2}{4E_{\mathbf{p}}E_{\mathbf{p}'}\omega_{\mathbf{k}}\omega_{\mathbf{k}'}}\right)|A|^2\int d^4x \tag{15.20}$$

where the last line follows by writing one of the δ-functions as

$$(2\pi)^4\delta^{(4)}(P) = \int e^{iPx}d^4x \tag{15.21}$$

and taking $P = 0$ on account of the second delta function. The resulting integral,

$$\int d^4x,$$

represents the total space-time volume, so that the transition probability *per unit volume and per unit time* is, from eq. (15.20), given by

$$w_{ji} = (2\pi)^4\delta^{(4)}(p + k - p' - k')\frac{1}{V^4}\left(\frac{e^4M^2}{4E_{\mathbf{p}}E_{\mathbf{p}'}\omega_{\mathbf{k}}\omega_{\mathbf{k}'}}\right)|A|^2. \tag{15.22}$$

Eq. (15.22) gives the transition probability to a single final state Φ_j, eq. (15.4). In practice, we are not interested in a particle being scattered into a state with precisely defined momentum but only into one of a group of neighbouring states, say the electron should have a momentum in the range $(\mathbf{p}', \mathbf{p}' + d\mathbf{p}')$ and the photon in the range $(\mathbf{k}', \mathbf{k}' + d\mathbf{k}')$. The number of these states is

$$\frac{V^2}{(2\pi)^6}d^3p'd^3k' \tag{15.23}$$

*) For a discussion of these questions, cf. Jauch and Rohrlich, and Källén (see bibliography) and particularly also Gell-Mann, M. and Goldberger, M. L. *Phys. Rev.* **91**, 398, 1953, and Lippmann, B. A. and Schwinger, J. *Phys. Rev.* **79**, 469, 1950.

(we are still only considering definite spin and polarization states). Combining eqs. (15.22—23) one obtains for the transition probability per unit volume and unit time

$$w = \frac{1}{(2\pi)^2 V^2} \int d^3p'\, d^3k'\, \delta^{(4)}(p+k-p'-k') \left(\frac{e^4 M^2}{4E_{\mathbf{p}} E_{\mathbf{p}'} \omega_{\mathbf{k}} \omega_{\mathbf{k}'}}\right) |A|^2. \tag{15.24}$$

Which variables are integrated over (and the ranges of integration) in eq. (15.24) depends on the physical situation. If we wish to calculate the transition probability for a photon to be scattered through an angle θ into the element $d\Omega$ of solid angle oriented in the direction with polar angles (θ, ϕ), then we put

$$d^3k' = \omega_{\mathbf{k}'}^2\, d\omega_{\mathbf{k}'}\, d\Omega, \tag{15.25}$$

and integrate over $\mathbf{p}'$ and $\omega_{\mathbf{k}'}$, keeping the angles (θ, ϕ) constant. Eq. (15.24) then becomes

$$w = \frac{d\Omega}{(2\pi)^2 V^2} \int \omega_{\mathbf{k}'}^2\, d\omega_{\mathbf{k}'}\, \delta(E_{\mathbf{p}}+\omega_{\mathbf{k}}-E_{\mathbf{p}'}-\omega_{\mathbf{k}'}) \left(\frac{e^4 M^2}{4E_{\mathbf{p}} E_{\mathbf{p}'} \omega_{\mathbf{k}} \omega_{\mathbf{k}'}}\right) |A|^2$$

$$= \frac{d\Omega}{(2\pi)^2 V^2} \left\{ \omega_{\mathbf{k}'}^2 \left[\frac{\partial \omega_{\mathbf{k}'}}{\partial (E_{\mathbf{p}'} + \omega_{\mathbf{k}'})}\right]_{\theta\phi} \left(\frac{e^4 M^2}{4E_{\mathbf{p}} E_{\mathbf{p}'} \omega_{\mathbf{k}} \omega_{\mathbf{k}'}}\right) |A|^2 \right\} \tag{15.26}$$

where, throughout, $E_{\mathbf{p}}$, $\omega_{\mathbf{k}}$, θ and ϕ are to be treated as the independent variables which are kept fixed [in particular in carrying out the differentiation in eq. (15.26)] and $\omega_{\mathbf{k}'}$ is to be given the corresponding value determined by the conservation of energy.

Eq. (15.16) can be written

$$p - k' = p' - k. \tag{15.16a}$$

Squaring this equation and using eqs. (15.1—2) leads to

$$pk' = p'k = pk - k'k. \tag{15.27}$$

So far we have not assumed that the electron is initially at rest but have used a quite general frame of reference. In this way all expressions are much more symmetric between initial and final states. This will be very useful when evaluating the spin and polarization sums [cf. (iii) below]. Furthermore, when expressed in this generality, there exists a close relation between two processes A and B which differ only in that in process A a photon, electron or positron is absorbed (emitted) whereas in process B a photon, positron or electron, respectively, is emitted (absorbed). Hence the matrix elements and spin and polarization sums for process B are easily deduced from those for process A. However, to calculate the phase-space factors in eq. (15.26) we shall take the electron initially at rest,

$$p = (000,\ iM),$$

as this simplifies the analysis and represents the most important case. The conservation equations (15.16a) now become

$$E_{\mathbf{p}'} + \omega_{\mathbf{k}'} = M + \omega_{\mathbf{k}}\,, \quad \mathbf{p}' + \mathbf{k}' = \mathbf{k}, \tag{15.16b}$$

and eq. (15.27) becomes

$$\omega_{\mathbf{k}'} = \frac{M\omega_{\mathbf{k}}}{M + \omega_{\mathbf{k}}(1 - \cos\theta)}, \tag{15.28}$$

which gives the energy of a photon scattered through an angle θ off an electron at rest, its initial energy having been $\omega_{\mathbf{k}}$. As expected, it is independent of the azimuthal angle ϕ.

From $E_{\mathbf{p}'} = (M^2 + \mathbf{p}'^2)^{\frac{1}{2}}$ and the momentum equation (15.16b)

$$\omega_{\mathbf{k}'} + E_{\mathbf{p}'} = \omega_{\mathbf{k}'} + [M^2 + \omega_{\mathbf{k}'}^2 + \omega_{\mathbf{k}}^2 - 2\omega_{\mathbf{k}}\omega_{\mathbf{k}'}\cos\theta]^{\frac{1}{2}}.$$

Differentiating this equation with respect to $(\omega_{\mathbf{k}'} + E_{\mathbf{p}'})$, keeping θ and ϕ constant, one obtains

$$\left[\frac{\partial\omega_{\mathbf{k}'}}{\partial(\omega_{\mathbf{k}'} + E_{\mathbf{p}'})}\right]_{\theta\phi} = \frac{E_{\mathbf{p}'}}{E_{\mathbf{p}'} + \omega_{\mathbf{k}'} - \omega_{\mathbf{k}}\cos\theta} = \frac{E_{\mathbf{p}'}\omega_{\mathbf{k}'}}{M\omega_{\mathbf{k}}}, \tag{15.29}$$

where the last step follows from eqs. (15.16b) and (15.28).

Since we normalized our states to one particle in a volume V, wV represents the transition probability per scattering centre per unit time and $I = 1/V$ represents the intensity of the incident beam, expressed as photons per cm² per sec (remember, we have taken the velocity of light $= 1$). Hence the differential cross-section $(wV)/I$ is given from eqs. (15.26) and (15.29) as

$$\frac{wV}{I} = \left(\frac{e^2}{4\pi}\right)^2 d\Omega \left(\frac{\omega_{\mathbf{k}'}}{\omega_{\mathbf{k}}}\right)^2 |A|^2. \tag{15.30}$$

If initially the target and the incident photon beam are unpolarized and we do not observe the polarizations of the scattered photon or recoil electron, then we must average over the initial and sum over the final spin and polarization orientations. Thus the unpolarized cross-section for Compton scattering is given by

$$\sigma(\theta)d\Omega = \left(\frac{e^2}{4\pi}\right)^2 d\Omega \left(\frac{\omega_{\mathbf{k}'}}{\omega_{\mathbf{k}}}\right)^2 \{\tfrac{1}{4}\sum_{r=1}^{2}\sum_{s=1}^{2}\sum_{m=1}^{2}\sum_{n=1}^{2}|A|^2\}. \tag{15.31}$$

The normalization volume V has disappeared from the expressions (15.30—31) for the cross-sections, as is necessary for a reasonable physical interpretation: for a sufficiently large volume V, the physical process must be independent of the boundary conditions on the surface of V. The errors which were introduced by approximating momentum sums in the propagators S_F by integrals vanish in the limit as we let $V \to \infty$.

(iii) *Polarization sums.*

Finally we must carry out the polarization summations indicated in eq. (15.31). For this purpose it is convenient to introduce the abbreviations

$$\left.\begin{array}{ll} M^2\xi_1 = pk = p'k', & M^2\xi_2 = -pk' = -p'k \\ f_1 = p + k = p' + k' & f_2 = p - k' = p' - k \\ g_1 = \not{f}_1 + iM & g_2 = \not{f}_2 + iM \end{array}\right\} \tag{15.32}$$

Eq. (15.19) can then be written

$$A = \bar{u}^{(s)}(\mathbf{p}')Ou^{(r)}(\mathbf{p}) \tag{15.33}$$

with

$$O = \frac{1}{2M^2}\left[\not{e}^{(n)}\frac{g_1}{\xi_1}\not{e}^{(m)} + \not{e}^{(m)}\frac{g_2}{\xi_2}\not{e}^{(n)}\right] \tag{15.34}$$

whence one proves directly that $\tilde{O} = \gamma_4 O^\dagger \gamma_4$ is given by

$$\tilde{O} = -\frac{1}{2M^2}\left[\not{e}^{(m)}\frac{g_1}{\xi_1}\not{e}^{(n)} + \not{e}^{(n)}\frac{g_2}{\xi_2}\not{e}^{(m)}\right]. \tag{15.35}$$

The summations of the electron spins $(\frac{1}{2}\sum_{r,s=1}^{2})$ in eq. (15.31) are now at once obtained from eqs. (A28—31):

$$\tfrac{1}{4}\sum_{r,s}\sum_{m,n}|A|^2 = \tfrac{1}{4}\sum_{m,n=1}^{2}\mathrm{Tr}\,\{\tilde{O}\Lambda^+(\mathbf{p}')O\Lambda^+(\mathbf{p})\} = \frac{1}{64M^6}\cdot B \qquad (15.36)$$

where

$$B \equiv \sum_{m,n=1}^{2}\mathrm{Tr}\left\{\left[\frac{1}{\xi_1}\,\not{e}^{(m)}g_1\not{e}^{(n)} + \frac{1}{\xi_2}\,\not{e}^{(n)}g_2\not{e}^{(m)}\right](\not{p}' + iM)\right.$$
$$\left.\times\left[\frac{1}{\xi_1}\,\not{e}^{(n)}g_1\not{e}^{(m)} + \frac{1}{\xi_2}\,\not{e}^{(m)}g_2\not{e}^{(n)}\right](\not{p} + iM)\right\}. \qquad (15.37)$$

In the appendix, eqs. (A 39—47), it is shown that in eq. (15.37) we may replace $\not{e}^{(m)}(\mathbf{k})$ by γ_m and $\not{e}^{(n)}(\mathbf{k}')$ by γ_n, the summations over m and n being at the same time extended to run from 1 to 4. We have here another example of the simplicity of manipulation introduced by the covariant methods: summations of photon polarizations can be allowed for without any additional work (in fact things become simpler) rather than by explicit geometrical considerations of the vectors involved. Thus eq. (15.37) becomes

$$B = \frac{1}{\xi_1^2}T_{11} + \frac{1}{\xi_2^2}T_{22} + \frac{1}{\xi_1\xi_2}(T_{12} + T_{21}) \qquad (15.38)$$

where

$$\left.\begin{aligned} T_{11} &= \mathrm{Tr}\,\{\gamma_m g_1\gamma_n(\not{p}' + iM)\gamma_n g_1\gamma_m(\not{p} + iM)\} \\ T_{22} &= \mathrm{Tr}\,\{\gamma_n g_2\gamma_m(\not{p}' + iM)\gamma_m g_2\gamma_n(\not{p} + iM)\} \\ T_{12} &= \mathrm{Tr}\,\{\gamma_m g_1\gamma_n(\not{p}' + iM)\gamma_m g_2\gamma_n(\not{p} + iM)\} \\ T_{21} &= \mathrm{Tr}\,\{\gamma_n g_2\gamma_m(\not{p}' + iM)\gamma_n g_1\gamma_m(\not{p} + iM)\}, \end{aligned}\right\} \qquad (15.39)$$

summations over m and n from 1 to 4 being understood.

By interchanging k and $(-k')$ [which implies interchanging ξ_1, f_1 and g_1 with ξ_2, f_2 and g_2 respectively, cf. eq. (15.32)], T_{11} and T_{22} become interchanged, and similarly T_{12} and T_{21}. Thus one need only evaluate T_{11} and T_{12}. Furthermore from eqs. (15.39), $T_{12} = T_{21}$, as T_{21} is obtained from T_{12} by reversing the order of the factors — all of which are γ-matrices or c-numbers — in the trace [cf. eq. (A 35)]. Hence $T_{12} = T_{21}$ is symmetric in ξ_1 and ξ_2, which is a useful check in evaluating T_{12}.

The evaluation of T_{11} and T_{12} using the rules given in eqs.

(A 32—38) [particularly eqs. (A 38) which should be used first of all to eliminate the γ_m and γ_n] is quite straight forward and is left as an exercise to the reader. One obtains for eq. (15.38):

$$B = 32M^4 \left[\left(\frac{1}{\xi_1} + \frac{1}{\xi_2} \right)^2 - 2 \left(\frac{1}{\xi_1} + \frac{1}{\xi_2} \right) - \left(\frac{\xi_1}{\xi_2} + \frac{\xi_2}{\xi_1} \right) \right]; \qquad (15.40)$$

hence combining eqs. (15.31), (15.36) and (15.40),

$$\sigma(\theta)\, d\Omega = \tfrac{1}{2} r_0^2 d\Omega \left(\frac{\omega_{\mathbf{k}'}}{\omega_{\mathbf{k}}} \right)^2 \left[\left(\frac{1}{\xi_1} + \frac{1}{\xi_2} \right)^2 - 2 \left(\frac{1}{\xi_1} + \frac{1}{\xi_2} \right) - \left(\frac{\xi_1}{\xi_2} + \frac{\xi_2}{\xi_1} \right) \right], \qquad (15.41)$$

where $r_0 \equiv (e^2/4\pi M)$ is the classical electron radius. Finally we must substitute from eqs. (15.32) for ξ_1 and ξ_2 and specialize to the frame of axes in which the electron was initially at rest, $p = (000,\ iM)$. In this case, eqs. (15.32) give

$$M\xi_1 = -\,\omega_{\mathbf{k}}, \quad M\xi_2 = +\,\omega_{\mathbf{k}'}\,. \qquad (15.42)$$

Using eq. (15.28), the differential cross-section (15.41) becomes

$$\sigma(\theta)\, d\Omega = \tfrac{1}{2} r_0^2 d\Omega \left(\frac{\omega_{\mathbf{k}'}}{\omega_{\mathbf{k}}} \right)^2 \left[\frac{\omega_{\mathbf{k}'}}{\omega_{\mathbf{k}}} + \frac{\omega_{\mathbf{k}}}{\omega_{\mathbf{k}'}} - \sin^2\theta \right] \qquad (15.43)$$

which is the famous Klein-Nishina formula. By means of eq. (15.28), one can of course eliminate $\omega_{\mathbf{k}'}$ altogether.

CHAPTER 16

Coulomb Scattering

In treating Compton scattering, both electrons and photons were described by quantized fields involving creation and absorption operators. In some problems it may be adequate to represent only one field in this way, the other being described purely classically as a function of the space-time coordinates. For example, we may consider the scattering of electrons by a given external*) electromagnetic field $A^e_\mu(x)$, as such a field is often called, in contrast to the quantized radiation field $A_\mu(x)$ of chapter 9. In general, it will be necessary to consider both fields, for example when considering Bremsstrahlung or radiative corrections. In the S-matrix expansion (13.12), the radiation field $A_\mu(x)$ is then throughout replaced by $[A_\mu(x) + A^e_\mu(x)]$:

$$S = \sum_{n=0}^{\infty} \frac{e^n}{n!} \int \ldots \int d^4x_1 \ldots d^4x_n T\{N[\bar{\psi}(\not{A}+\not{A}^e)\psi]_{x_1} \ldots N[\bar{\psi}(\not{A}+\not{A}^e)\psi]_{x_n}\}. \tag{16.1}$$

In first Born approximation, the scattering of electrons by the external field will then be given by

$$S^{(0)} = e \int d^4x \, \bar{\psi}^-(x) \gamma_\mu A^e_\mu(x) \psi^+(x) \tag{16.2}$$

where ψ^+ and $\bar{\psi}^-$ are the quantized fermion fields, eqs. (8.37). The corresponding Feynman graph is shown in fig. 21 where the cross at the vertex indicates that an external field acts at this point. If the field is purely electrostatic, then

$$A^e_i(x) = 0, \quad i = 1, 2, 3, \tag{16.3}$$

*) The term 'external' in this context should of course not be confused with its quite different use in chapter 14.

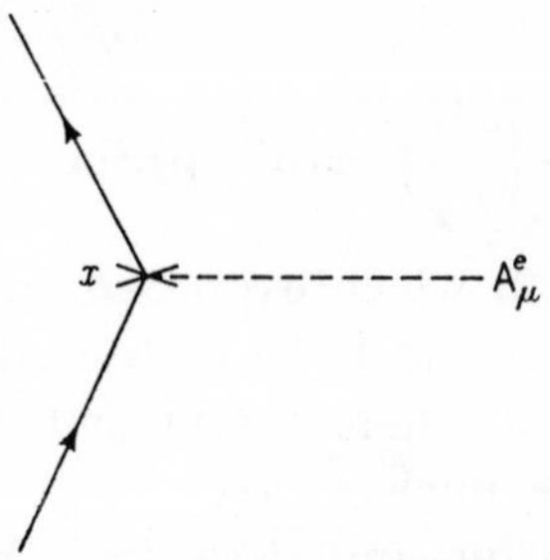

Fig. 21. Coulomb scattering.

$$A_4^e(x) = iV(\mathbf{x}) = \frac{i}{(2\pi)^3}\int \phi(\mathbf{q})e^{i\mathbf{qx}}\,d^3q, \tag{16.4}$$

i.e.

$$\phi(\mathbf{q}) = \int V(\mathbf{x})\,e^{-i\mathbf{qx}}\,d^3x. \tag{16.5}$$

We may under certain circumstances describe the scattering by the field of a heavy nucleus in this way, i.e. as scattering due to the Coulomb potential

$$V(\mathbf{x}) = Ze/(4\pi\,|\mathbf{x}|). \tag{16.6}$$

The matrix element for elastic scattering of an electron from a state (i) with four-momentum $p = (\mathbf{p}, iE_\mathbf{p})$ and spinor $u^{(r)}(\mathbf{p})$ to the state (j) with four-momentum $p' = (\mathbf{p}', iE_{\mathbf{p}'})$ and spinor $u^{(s)}(\mathbf{p}')$ is given by

$$M_{ji} = (c_s^\dagger(\mathbf{p}')\Phi_0,\ S^{(0)}c_r^\dagger(\mathbf{p})\Phi_0). \tag{16.7}$$

Using eqs. (16.2—5) and (8.37) this gives, after a short calculation which is left as an exercise to the reader,

$$M_{ji} = 2\pi\delta(E_\mathbf{p} - E_{\mathbf{p}'})\,\frac{ie}{V}\left(\frac{M}{E_\mathbf{p}}\right)\phi(\mathbf{p}' - \mathbf{p})(u^{(s)\dagger}(\mathbf{p}')u^{(r)}(\mathbf{p})). \tag{16.8}$$

The δ-function in eq. (16.8) ensures conservation of energy. We do not have conservation of momentum now corresponding to the fact that we are neglecting the sources of the external field which will of course experience a recoil; but if we are dealing with a heavy nucleus, this recoil will be negligible.

From eq. (16.8) the transition probability per unit time is obtained as

$$w_{ji} = |M_{ji}|^2/\int dt$$
$$= 2\pi\delta(E_{\mathbf{p}} - E_{\mathbf{p}'}) \frac{1}{V^2} \left(\frac{eM}{E_{\mathbf{p}}}\right)^2 |\phi(\mathbf{p}' - \mathbf{p})|^2 |u^{(s)\dagger}(\mathbf{p}') u^{(r)}(\mathbf{p})|^2. \quad (16.9)$$

Unlike eqs. (15.20—22) which expressed transition probabilities per unit volume which had to be converted to probabilities per scattering centre, we are here throughout dealing with a single scattering centre (one nucleus, say).

Let us write $P \equiv |\mathbf{p}|$ and $P' \equiv |\mathbf{p}'|$. Multiplication of eq. (16.9) by $Vd^3p'/(2\pi)^3$ gives the probability for scattering into a momentum state in the range $(\mathbf{p}', \mathbf{p}' + d\mathbf{p}')$, and division by the incident intensity $I = v/V$ (where

$$v = P/E_{\mathbf{p}} \quad (16.10)$$

is the relativistic expression for the incident velocity) gives the differential cross-section. For scattering through an angle θ into an element of solid angle $d\Omega$ we put

$$d^3p' = d\Omega (P')^2 dP' \quad (16.11)$$

and use $E^2_{\mathbf{p}'} = M^2 + P'^2$, whence $P'dP' = E_{\mathbf{p}'}dE_{\mathbf{p}'}$. Hence the cross-section for definite polarizations becomes

$$\left(\frac{VE_{\mathbf{p}}}{P}\right) \cdot \frac{Vd\Omega}{(2\pi)^3} \int P' E_{\mathbf{p}'} dE_{\mathbf{p}'} 2\pi\delta(E_{\mathbf{p}} - E_{\mathbf{p}'})$$
$$\cdot \frac{1}{V^2} \left(\frac{eM}{E_{\mathbf{p}}}\right)^2 |\phi(\mathbf{p}' - \mathbf{p})|^2 |u^{(s)\dagger}(\mathbf{p}') u^{(r)}(\mathbf{p})|^2$$
$$= \left(\frac{eM}{2\pi}\right)^2 d\Omega |\phi(\mathbf{p}' - \mathbf{p})|^2 |u^{(s)\dagger}(\mathbf{p}') u^{(r)}(\mathbf{p})|^2, \quad (16.12)$$

which is again independent of the normalization volume.

To obtain the 'unpolarized' cross-section we must replace the last factor in eq. (16.12), according to eqs. (A 28—31), by

$$\tfrac{1}{2} \sum_{r,s=1}^{2} |\bar{u}^{(s)}(\mathbf{p}') \gamma_4 u^{(r)}(\mathbf{p})|^2 = \tfrac{1}{2} \mathrm{Tr}\{\gamma_4 \Lambda^+(\mathbf{p}') \gamma_4 \Lambda^+(\mathbf{p})\}$$
$$= \frac{1}{2M^2} (M^2 + E^2_{\mathbf{p}} + \mathbf{p}\mathbf{p}') \quad (16.13)$$

where the last expression follows by means of eqs. (A 22), (A 2) and (A 33). Writing $M^2 = E_{\mathbf{p}}^2 - P^2$ and $\mathbf{pp}' = P^2 \cos\theta$ and using eq. (16.10), expression (16.13) becomes

$$\left(\frac{E_{\mathbf{p}}}{M}\right)^2 \left(1 - v^2 \sin^2 \frac{\theta}{2}\right); \tag{16.14}$$

hence the unpolarized cross-section is, by eq. (16.12), given by

$$\sigma(\theta) d\Omega = \left(\frac{eE_{\mathbf{p}}}{2\pi}\right)^2 d\Omega \, |\phi(\mathbf{p}' - \mathbf{p})|^2 \left(1 - v^2 \sin^2 \frac{\theta}{2}\right). \tag{16.15}$$

For the Coulomb potential (16.6)

$$\phi(\mathbf{p}' - \mathbf{p}) = \frac{Ze}{|\mathbf{p}' - \mathbf{p}|^2} = \frac{Ze}{(2P \sin \frac{1}{2}\theta)^2} \tag{16.16}$$

so that eq. (16.15) becomes

$$\sigma(\theta) d\Omega = \left(\frac{Ze^2}{8\pi} \frac{E_{\mathbf{p}}}{P^2} \frac{1}{\sin^2 \frac{1}{2}\theta}\right)^2 d\Omega \left(1 - v^2 \sin^2 \frac{\theta}{2}\right). \tag{16.17}$$

Eqs. (16.15) and (16.17) differ from the non-relativistic Born approximation in that they involve the relativistic energy and momentum and they contain the additional factor

$$\left(1 - v^2 \sin^2 \frac{\theta}{2}\right).$$

The non-relativistic limit $v \ll 1$, $E_{\mathbf{p}} \to M$, $P \to Mv$, is obtained at once. Eq. (16.17) reduces to the Rutherford formula for Coulomb scattering

$$\sigma(\theta) d\Omega = \left(\frac{Ze^2}{8\pi M v^2} \frac{1}{\sin^2 \frac{1}{2}\theta}\right)^2 d\Omega. \tag{16.18}$$

CHAPTER 17

Radiative Corrections

So far we have calculated matrix elements of the S-matrix in the lowest-order of perturbation theory only. We expect to obtain corrections to these results by taking into account higher order terms in the S-matrix expansion. In this and the following four chapters the calculation of these so-called *radiative corrections* are themselves considered in lowest order of perturbation theory. We shall return to higher order corrections and other general questions in chapter 22.

As a qualitative introduction to these ideas, we shall, in this chapter, consider the radiative corrections to Coulomb scattering. The lowest-order perturbation calculation of chapter 16 was based on expression (16.2) for the S-matrix and the corresponding Feynman graph, fig. 21. We now still wish to treat the external field A^e_μ linearly but consider terms in eq. (16.1) quadratic in the radiation field A_μ, corresponding to the emission and reabsorption of one virtual photon*). These e^2— or second-order corrections thus derive from the $n = 3$ term in eq. (16.1) which may be written in the form

$$S^{(2)} = \frac{e^3}{2!} \int \ldots \int d^4x\, d^4x_1\, d^4x_2\, T\{N(\bar{\psi} A\!\!\!/^e \psi)_x N(\bar{\psi} A\!\!\!/ \psi)_{x_1} N(\bar{\psi} A\!\!\!/ \psi)_{x_2}\}, \tag{17.1}$$

where the external field always operates at the vertex x, the radiation field at x_1 and x_2. The contributions to elastic scattering to which this term leads are shown in fig. 22. The external field acts at the vertex marked by a cross, the radiation field at the

*) Terms linear in A_μ in eq. (16.1) do not contribute to elastic electron scattering, as they necessarily involve the emission or absorption of a photon. They represent inelastic electron scattering, i.e. Bremsstrahlung.

other two vertices. Each of the five graphs occurs twice, corresponding to labelling the latter two vertices x_1 and x_2 or x_2 and x_1.

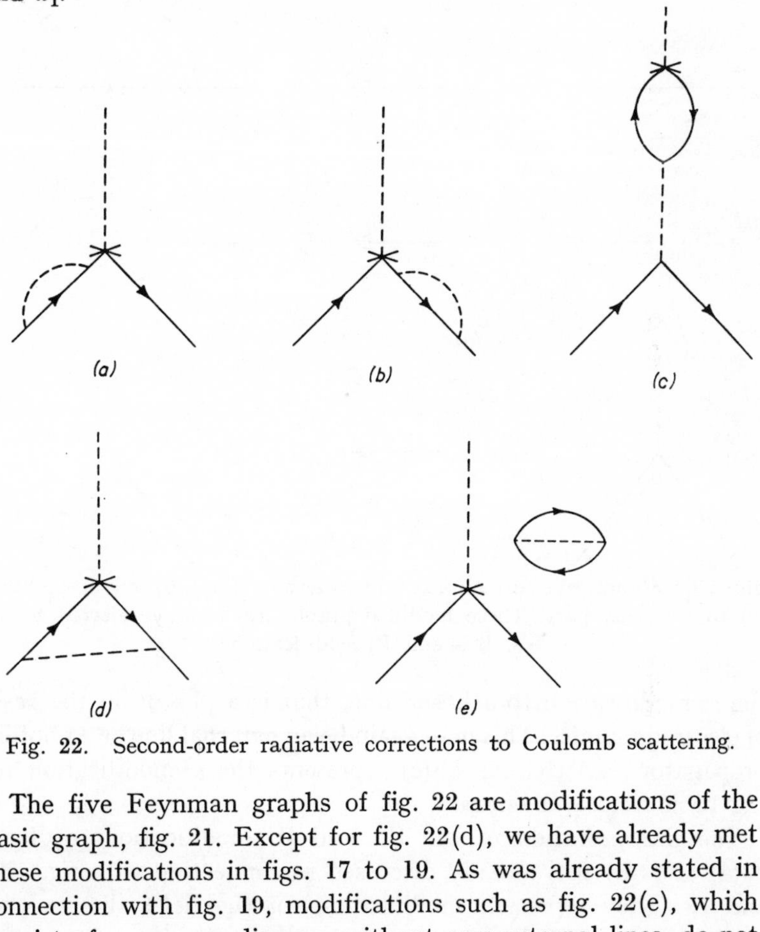

Fig. 22. Second-order radiative corrections to Coulomb scattering.

The five Feynman graphs of fig. 22 are modifications of the basic graph, fig. 21. Except for fig. 22(d), we have already met these modifications in figs. 17 to 19. As was already stated in connection with fig. 19, modifications such as fig. 22(e), which consist of a vacuum diagram without any external lines, do not produce any observable effects and may be omitted. The remaining modifications in fig. 22 divide into three types, shown in fig. 23. Fig. 23(a) represents the e^2-modification to a fermion line. This may be an external line, i.e. an incident or emitted fermion, as in figs. 22(a) and (b), or it may be an internal line, i.e. a fermion propagator. For example, in calculating second order radiative corrections to Compton scattering the modified graph shown in fig. 24 will occur, amongst others. Fig. 23(b) represents

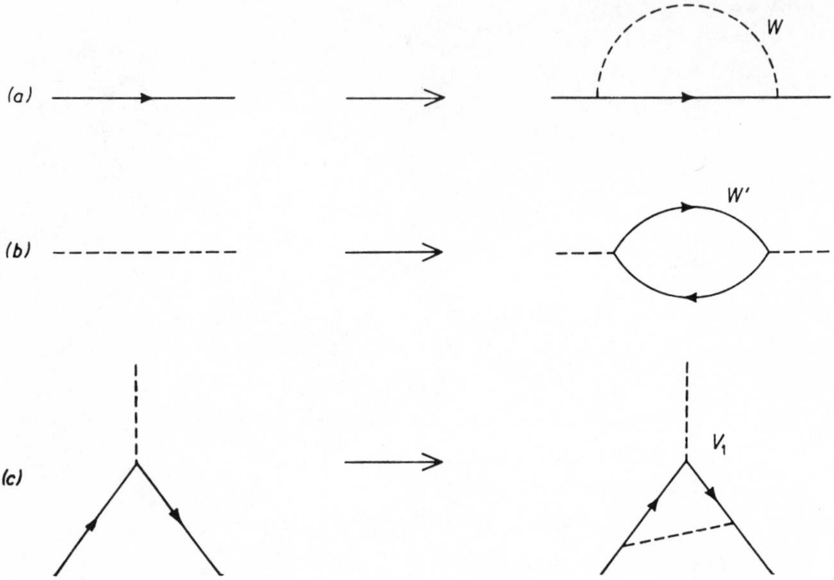

Fig. 23. e^2-radiative corrections: (a) to a fermion line; (b) to a boson line; (c) to a vertex part. These modified graphs are usually referred to as W-, W'- and V_1-modifications.

the e^2-modification to a boson line, that is a photon in the case of electrodynamics. This may again be an external line or a photon propagator. Lastly, fig. 23(c) represents the e^2-modification to the basic vertex diagram.

The interpretation of the W- and W'-modifications of figs. 23(a) and (b) was already discussed in connection with figs. **17** and 18. They represent modifications of the fields due to the interactions. Instead of bare particles we are now dealing with dressed particles (electrons surrounded by their own photon clouds, etc.). Of course the 'fully dressed' real particles are only obtained if we consider *all* radiative corrections whereas we are here only treating the e^2-modifications which will only give us a partial conversion from bare to real particles. Similarly fig. 23(b) represents a modification of the radiation field due to the possibility of forming virtual electron-positron pairs, i.e. due to the polarizability of the vacuum. These effects lead to a modification

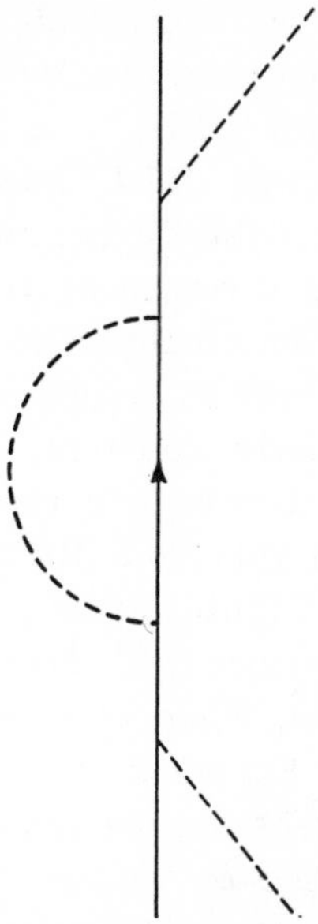

Fig. 24. An e^2-modification to Compton scattering.

of the masses of the particles (there are now self-energy effects due to the interaction of a particle with its own field) and of the coupling constant (i.e. of the electronic charge in electrodynamics) which are known as *mass* and *charge renormalizations*. Similarly fig. 23(c) represents a modification of the interaction which leads to a charge renormalization. Instead of describing the particles by the mass M and charge e associated with the non-interacting fields we now use the mass M_0 and charge e_0 of the real particles. The bare mass M has been augmented by an electromagnetic self-energy contribution to give the real mass M_0. For a single electron, self-energy effects lead only to this mass renormalization. When we consider an electron interacting with the electromagnetic field, say in Møller or Coulomb scattering, there are in addition observable radiative corrections to the lowest order calculations. The problem of how to carry out these renormalizations and calculate the radiative corrections will be discussed in the following chapters.

In the spirit of perturbation theory, one would expect the radiative corrections to represent small corrections to the lowest order calculation, for quantum electrodynamics of the order of the fine structure constant 1/137, i.e. a few per cent. Evaluation of these corrections from eq. (17.1), however, leads to divergent integrals. We shall see that there exists an unambiguous procedure for separating off these divergences and interpreting them as infinite mass and charge renormalizations. The fact that evaluation of eq. (17.1) leads to infinite results makes the necessity for renormalization particularly apparent. These infinities are due to the fact that in relativistic field theories the particles occur as point singularities of the field. By introducing form factors which give the particles a finite spread (usually this leads to other difficulties) one can construct field theories which do not involve divergences. Nevertheless, when treating such interacting fields in perturbation theory, Feynman graphs such as figs. 17 to 19 or figs. 22 will occur, representing renormalization effects, now finite, which describe the conversion of the bare to the real particles.

Serious difficulties are met in attempting to give a mathematically satisfactory derivation of the theory for interacting fields which has here been outlined. Nevertheless this approach has been outstandingly successful in quantum electrodynamics which must be considered one of the best established physical theories, having been verified experimentally with very high precision for the Lamb shift and the anomalous magnetic moment of the electron.

The detailed calculations of these radiative correction phenomena involve exceedingly heavy, if often elementary, analysis and tricks especially invented for these problems by Feynman. For this reason we shall in the following three chapters limit ourselves to an incomplete discussion of the renormalization theory associated with the three modified graphs of fig. 23. Our analysis should explain the basic ideas and methods and serve as a guide to the more complete treatments. In any case, the diagrams of fig. 23 are of particular importance for two reasons. Firstly, they play a special role in the general renormalization theory, i.e. when considering diagrams of any order. Secondly, they are the only divergent diagrams required in the calculation of second-order radiative corrections.

To illustrate the last point briefly, consider the e^2-radiative corrections to Compton scattering. The basic diagram, itself of order e^2, is shown in fig. 25. The lowest-order radiative corrections

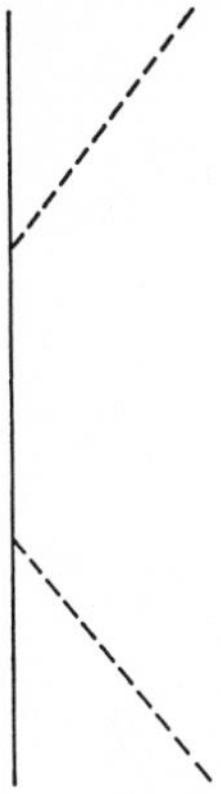

Fig. 25. Compton scattering.

stem from the e^4-terms in the S-matrix (13.12), (cf. exercise 14.1). The corresponding Feynman graphs are shown in fig. 26. Graphs (a) to (d) are all modifications of the second order graph, fig. 25, of the types shown in fig. 23. They are modifications to electron lines [graphs (a) and (b)], to photon lines [graphs (c)] and to vertices [graphs (d)]. The graph (e) turns out to give a finite contribution if calculated according to the usual rules. Graph (f), a so-called triangle diagram can be shown to give no contribution to either electrodynamics or neutral or symmetric $ps(ps)$-meson theory (cf. exercises 14.3—4). Hence if we can extract the appropriate finite contributions from the modifications in fig. 23, then the e^2-radiative corrections can be calculated.

This state of affairs, here illustrated for Compton scattering, is generally true. Given a particular Feynman graph G (representing a process in lowest order, i.e. not itself already containing radiative corrections), all divergent radiative corrections of order

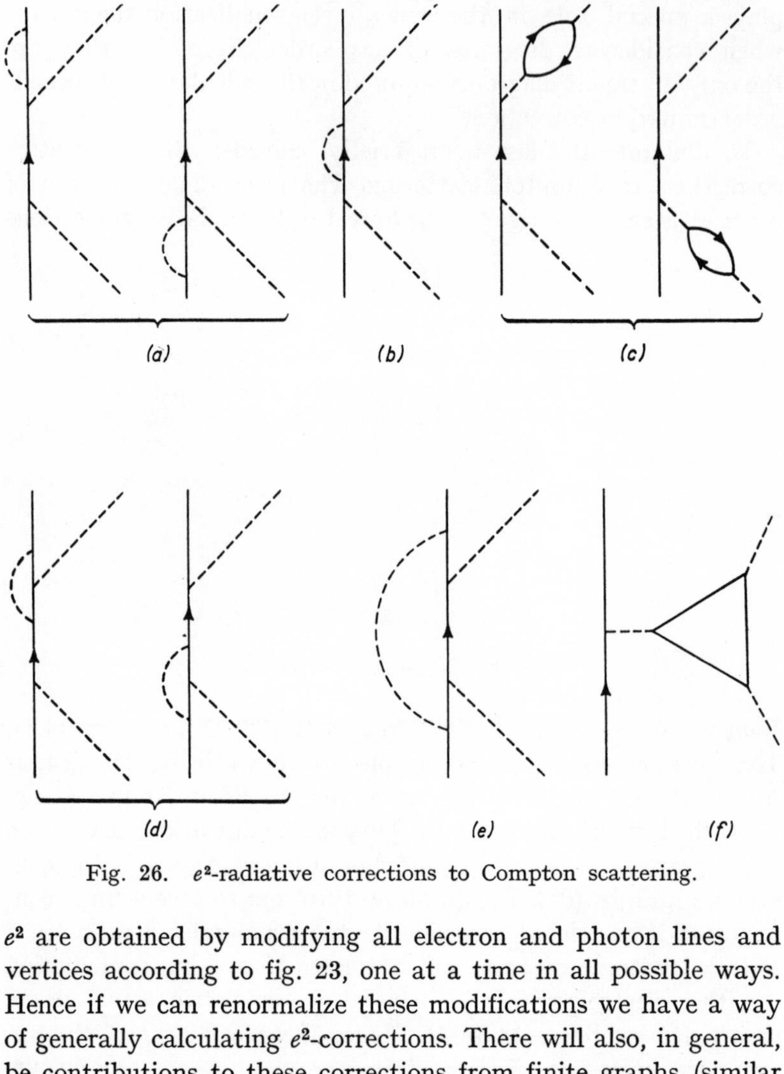

Fig. 26. e^2-radiative corrections to Compton scattering.

e^2 are obtained by modifying all electron and photon lines and vertices according to fig. 23, one at a time in all possible ways. Hence if we can renormalize these modifications we have a way of generally calculating e^2-corrections. There will also, in general, be contributions to these corrections from finite graphs (similar to fig. 26(e) for Compton scattering) which must be found from the S-matrix according to Wick's theorem and evaluated in the usual way.

CHAPTER 18

The Fermion Self-Energy

We shall now discuss the self-energy diagram W, fig. 23(a), considering electrodynamics for definiteness. Inserted into an external or internal electron line of a Feynman graph, the modification W describes a radiative correction, of the second order in the coupling constant, due to the interaction of the bare electron with the radiation field. This is the process of partly converting a bare electron into an electron surrounded by its photon cloud, i.e. a real electron.

From the general methods of evaluating Feynman graphs, it should be clear to the reader that it suffices to consider the modification W of an electron line once and for all and that this result can then be substituted into any Feynman graph. We shall hence consider the modification to an electron propagator, mentioning the other cases more briefly below.

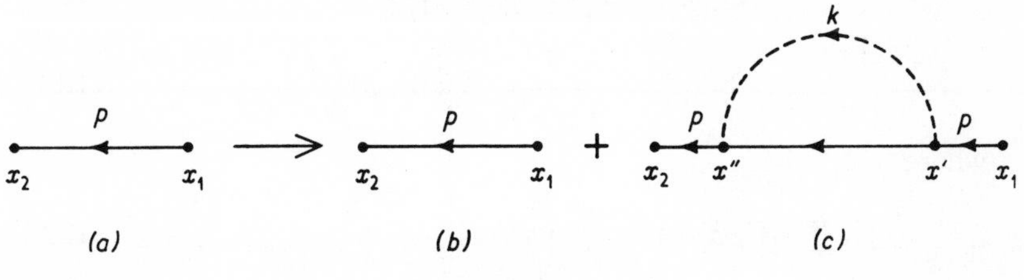

Fig. 27.

The replacement shown in fig. 27 corresponds to considering the electron propagator not in lowest order but modified by the second-order radiative corrections. Mathematically, it corresponds to replacing

$$\underbrace{\psi(x_2)\bar{\psi}(x_1)} = -\tfrac{1}{2}S_F(x_2 - x_1) \tag{18.1}$$

by

$$-\tfrac{1}{2}S'_F(x_2 - x_1) = -\tfrac{1}{2}S_F(x_2 - x_1) - \tfrac{1}{2}S_F^{(2)}(x_2 - x_1), \qquad (18.2)$$

where

$$-\tfrac{1}{2}S_F^{(2)}(x_2 - x_1) = \iint d^4x'\, d^4x''\, \underbrace{\psi(x_2)\bar{\psi}(x'')}\{e^2\gamma_\mu \underbrace{\psi(x'')\bar{\psi}(x')}\gamma_\lambda \times \underbrace{A_\mu(x'')A_\lambda(x')}\}\underbrace{\psi(x')\bar{\psi}(x_1)}. \qquad (18.3)$$

We now go over to momentum space by defining the Fourier transform of the fermion propagator by

$$\underbrace{\psi(x_2)\bar{\psi}(x_1)} = -\tfrac{1}{2}S_F(x_2 - x_1) = \frac{-1}{(2\pi)^4}\int d^4p\, e^{ip(x_2-x_1)}S_F(p), \qquad (18.4)$$

i.e. from eq. (8.46a) by

$$S_F(p) = \frac{1}{\not p - iM}. \qquad (18.5)$$

We define $S_F^{(2)}(p)$ from $S_F^{(2)}(x)$ by an equation exactly analogous to eq. (18.4) with S_F replaced by $S_F^{(2)}$, and similarly for $S'_F(p)$ and $S'_F(x)$. Eqs. (18.2—3) then become, using the momentum representations of the propagators, eqs. (8.46a) and (9.15), and carrying out the integrations over x' and x'' in eq. (18.3),

$$S'_F(p) = S_F(p) + S_F^{(2)}(p), \qquad (18.6)$$

$$S_F^{(2)}(p) = \frac{1}{\not p - iM}\Sigma(W, p)\frac{1}{\not p - iM} \qquad (18.7)$$

where

$$\Sigma(W, p) = \frac{-ie^2}{(2\pi)^4}\int d^4k\, \gamma_\mu \frac{1}{\not p - \not k - iM}\gamma_\mu \frac{1}{k^2}. \qquad (18.8)$$

Eqs. (18.7—8) are seen to be of the appropriate form to represent the Feynman graph of fig. 27(c) and, apart from numerical factors, could be written down directly.

The k-integration in eq. (18.8) extends over all values of the momentum

$$|k| = \sqrt{k^2} = \sqrt{(\mathbf{k}^2 - k_0^2)}.$$

Counting powers of $|k|$ in the numerator and denominator of the integral suggests that it diverges like

$$\int^{\infty} d|k|,$$

i.e. linearly*). This type of argument of course only gives the *maximum* possible degree of divergence of an integral. It may well happen, due to the special form of the integrand, that cancellations occur which lead to a less fiercely divergent (or even convergent) result than that predicted by the above argument. This is the case for expression (18.8) which diverges only logarithmically, i.e. like

$$\int d|k|/|k|.$$

For, the leading term, for large $|k|$, in eq. (18.8) is proportional to

$$\gamma_\mu \int d^4k\, k_\mu/(k^2)^2. \tag{18.9}$$

Since this multiple integral is not absolutely convergent, its value depends on the exact method of evaluation. However, in order to preserve the relativistic invariance the integral multiplying γ_μ would have to be a *constant four-vector*. Since no four-vector with constant components exists, we must calculate the integral in such a way that it has the value zero. This corresponds to evaluating the integral in terms of four-dimensional polar coordinates with origin at $k=0$ and carrying out the angular integration first which gives zero from symmetry considerations.

We must now see how to deal with this divergent result. (We expected a small correction, of the order of $e^2/4\pi = 1/137$.) Multiplying numerator and denominator of eq. (18.8) by $(\not{p} - \not{k} + iM)$ and using eqs. (A 38), one obtains

$$\Sigma\,(W, p) = \frac{-2ie^2}{(2\pi)^4} \int d^4k \frac{(\not{k} - \not{p} + 2iM)}{(\not{p} - \not{k} - iM)(\not{p} - \not{k} + iM)k^2}. \tag{18.10}$$

Introducing the new parameter

$$z = \not{p} - iM \tag{18.11}$$

*) We are not here dealing with an integration in a four-dimensional *Euclidean* space, for which we would have

$$|k| = \sqrt{(\mathbf{k}^2 + k_0^2)}.$$

Hence a more careful justification is required for the above argument. This has been given by Dyson, F. J. *Phys. Rev.* **75**, 1736, 1949.

(note that by eq. (18.10) $\sum(W, p)$ depends on p through $\not{p}$ only), we can write this expression as

$$\sum(W, p) = \int d^4k\, R_W(k, z) \tag{18.12}$$

where

$$R_W(k, z) = \frac{-2ie^2}{(2\pi)^4} \frac{(\not{k} - \not{p} + 2iM)}{(\not{p} - \not{k} - iM)(\not{p} - \not{k} + iM)k^2}. \tag{18.13}$$

We expand this expression into the first few terms of a Taylor series in z plus a remainder term:

$$R_W(k, z) = R_W(k, 0) + \left[\frac{\partial R_W(k, z)}{\partial z}\right]_{z=0} z + R_{W_c}(k, z)z. \tag{18.14}$$

It follows from dimensional arguments that successive terms in the Taylor expansion (18.14) contain extra factors of k in the denominator: we are really expanding in powers of $(z/\not{k})$. Hence substituting eq. (18.14) in eq. (18.12), the degree of divergence of successive terms will decrease:

$$\sum(W, p) = A + B(\not{p} - iM) + S_c(W, p)(\not{p} - iM), \tag{18.15}$$

where

$$A = \int d^4k\, R_W(k, 0) \tag{18.16}$$

is an at most linearly divergent (in k) constant,

$$B = \int d^4k \left[\frac{\partial R_W(k, z)}{\partial z}\right]_{z=0} \tag{18.17}$$

is an at most logarithmically divergent constant and

$$S_c(W, p) = \int d^4k\, R_{W_c}(k, z) \tag{18.18}$$

is a finite function of the four-momentum p.

The separation of $\sum(W, p)$ into terms of different degrees of divergence has here been carried out in a relativistically invariant manner. Remembering that all the expressions which have been written down above are spinor operators (i.e. functions of γ-matrices) which occur between two spinors and the way such expressions transform under Lorentz transformations, it follows that z and $R_W(k, z)$, and hence A, B and $S_c(W, p)$ in eq. (18.15), are relativistically invariant quantities. They are of the second order in e.

To illustrate the Feynman techniques for evaluating the momentum integrals which occur in field theory, we shall briefly indicate how to calculate the constant A from eqs. (18.10—16). From eq. (18.15) it follows that evaluating A is equivalent to evaluating $\sum(W, p)$ taking $\not{p} - iM = 0$, i.e. $p^2 + M^2 = 0$, i.e. for the free-particle state, and we shall, in the following, repeatedly use these 'free-particle conditions' without saying so explicitly. Eq. (18.10) then becomes

$$A = \frac{-2ie^2}{(2\pi)^4} \int d^4k \frac{\not{k} + iM}{k^2(k^2 - 2pk)}. \tag{18.19}$$

Using Feynman's identity

$$\frac{1}{ab} = \int_0^1 dt \frac{1}{[at + b(1-t)]^2},$$

with $a = (k^2 - 2pk)$ and $b = k^2$, eq. (18.19) becomes

$$A = \frac{-2ie^2}{(2\pi)^4} \int_0^1 dt \int d^4k \frac{\not{k} + iM}{(k^2 - 2pkt)^2}. \tag{18.20}$$

Writing

$$k = q + tp,$$

the expression (18.20) transforms into

$$\begin{aligned} A &= \frac{-2ie^2}{(2\pi)^4} \int_0^1 dt \int d^4q \frac{\not{q} + t\not{p} + iM}{(q^2 - t^2p^2)^2} \\ &= \frac{2e^2M}{(2\pi)^4} \int_0^1 dt(1+t) \int d^4q \frac{1}{(q^2 + M^2t^2)^2}. \end{aligned} \tag{18.21}$$

Here the last line follows from the previous one, since, by symmetry arguments, the term linear in $\not{q}$ in the numerator does not contribute to the q-integration. It is this fact which reduces the divergence of the q-integral in eq. (18.21) from a linear to a logarithmic one, as stated before.

Using four-dimensional polar coordinates*), one finds, on evaluating the q-integral in eq. (18.21), that

$$\int \frac{d^4q}{(q^2 + M^2t^2)^2} = \lim_{K\to\infty} 2i\pi^2 \ln\left(\frac{K}{Mt}\right). \tag{18.22}$$

The limit as $K \to \infty$ in the last expression does, of course, not exist; rather the expression diverges logarithmically. Defining the logarithmically divergent constant

$$R = \lim_{K\to\infty} \ln\left(\frac{K}{M}\right) + \tfrac{5}{6}, \tag{18.23}$$

one obtains from eq. (18.21), by substituting eqs. (18.22—23) and carrying out the t-integration,

$$A = \frac{3i}{2\pi}\left(\frac{e^2}{4\pi}\right) MR = \frac{3i}{2\pi}\left(\frac{MR}{137}\right). \tag{18.24}$$

We must now interpret the coefficients A, B and $S_c(W, p)$ in the decomposition (18.15).

To interpret A, we consider the modification W not between two propagators but between two external electron lines, i.e. fig. 17, represented by the operator $S_D^{(2)}$, eq. (14.2d),

$$S_D^{(2)} = \iint d^4x'\, d^4x''\, \bar{\psi}(x'')\, \{e^2 \gamma_\mu \underbrace{\psi(x'')\bar{\psi}(x')}\gamma_\lambda \underbrace{A_\mu(x'')A_\lambda(x')}\}\psi(x'), \tag{18.25}$$

evaluated between two single electron states. Eq. (18.25) is, as expected, closely similar to eq. (18.3). Defining Fourier transforms of the electron fields by

$$\psi(x) = \frac{-1}{(2\pi)^4}\int d^4p\, e^{ipx}\psi(p), \tag{18.26}$$

etc., eq. (18.25) becomes

$$S_D^{(2)} = \frac{-1}{(2\pi)^4}\int d^4p\, \bar{\psi}(p) \sum (W, p)\psi(p), \tag{18.27}$$

which should be compared with eqs. (18.7—8).

*) Cf. Jauch and Rohrlich (see bibliography), appendix A5.

Now ψ and $\bar{\psi}$ satisfy the Dirac equation for the non-interacting field (we are, of course, using the interaction picture),

$$(\not{p} - iM)\psi(p) = 0, \ \bar{\psi}(p)(\not{p} - iM) = 0. \tag{18.28}$$

Hence substituting eq. (18.15) in eq. (18.27), this reduces to

$$S_D^{(2)} = \frac{-A}{(2\pi)^4}\int d^4p\,\bar{\psi}(p)\psi(p). \tag{18.29}$$

This last term, containing the infinite constant A, can be removed altogether from the scattering matrix by a process of *mass renormalization*, i.e. by replacing the bare mass M by the physical observable mass M_0 of the electron,

$$M \to M_0 = M + \delta M, \tag{18.30}$$

where δM represents the change in energy, i.e. mass, of the electron, due to its interaction with the radiation field. If the bare mass M is eliminated from the Lagrangian (8.19) by means of eq. (18.30), we obtain the following additional term in the Hamiltonian density of the non-interacting electron field (cf. exercise 18.1)

$$\mathscr{H}'(x) = -\tfrac{1}{2}\delta M\{\psi^\dagger\gamma_4\psi + \psi\gamma_4\psi^\dagger\} = -\delta M\bar{\psi}(x)\psi(x). \tag{18.31}$$

Since the mass correction δM is due to the interaction with the photons (it goes to zero if we let $e \to 0$), the term (18.31) is more appropriately incorporated with the interaction Hamiltonian density (13.10), rather than the free field part, giving

$$\mathscr{H}_I(x) = ieN(\bar{\psi}(x)\not{A}(x)\psi(x)) - \delta M\bar{\psi}(x)\psi(x). \tag{18.32}$$

Correspondingly we shall, in future, use this modified interaction in the S-matrix expansion (12.8), denoting the *modified* scattering matrix by S, as before.

If we recalculate the electron self-energy in lowest order of perturbation theory, using the modified S-matrix, we obtain as additional contribution to eq. (18.29), due to the second term in eq. (18.32),

$$(-i)\int d^4x\{-\delta M\bar{\psi}(x)\psi(x)\} = \frac{i\delta M}{(2\pi)^4}\int d^4p\,\bar{\psi}(p)\psi(p). \tag{18.33}$$

Combining eqs. (18.29) and (18.33), we obtain for the modified S-matrix operator

$$S_D^{(2)} = \frac{-1}{(2\pi)^4}(A - i\delta M)\int d^4p\,\bar{\psi}(p)\,\psi(p). \tag{18.34}$$

The constant A is determined by eq. (18.16), and has been evaluated in eq. (18.24). On the other hand, the δM which was introduced in eqs. (18.30—31) is so far quite arbitrary: we could give it any value. We now decide on the particular choice for which

$$A - i\delta M = 0. \tag{18.35}$$

As a result the S-operator, eq. (18.34), vanishes. There are now no self-energy effects for a single electron, apart from using its physical mass M_0 instead of its bare mass M.

In general, for example when considering an electron propagator, the above procedure of using the "counter term" δM in the interaction (18.32) and in the S-matrix has two effects. Firstly, wherever the bare particle mass M has been used (e.g. in the propagators in eqs. (18.5—7), etc.), the real mass M_0 should be used. Secondly, the effect of the counter term is to give an additional contribution; eq. (18.15) is to be replaced everywhere by

$$\Sigma(W, p) - i\delta M = B(\not{p} - iM_0) + S_c(W, p)(\not{p} - iM_0), \tag{18.36}$$

where we have used eq. (18.35). This replacement is just what was done in going from eq. (18.29) to eq. (18.34).

The electron propagator is now given by eq. (18.6) with

$$S_F(p) = \frac{1}{\not{p} - iM_0} \tag{18.37}$$

and

$$S_F^{(2)}(p) = \frac{1}{\not{p} - iM_0}\{\Sigma(W, p) - i\delta M\}\frac{1}{\not{p} - iM_0}, \tag{18.38}$$

so that

$$S'_F(p) = S_F(p)(1 + B) + S_F(p)S_c(W, p). \tag{18.39}$$

Similarly, inserting a W-modification into an external electron line, modifies the operators $\psi(p)$ or $\bar{\psi}(p)$ which now replace the propagator $S_F(p)$. Thus $\psi(p)$ becomes

$$\begin{aligned}\psi'(p) &= \psi(p) + \frac{1}{\not p - iM_0}\{\Sigma(W, p) - i\delta M\}\psi(p)\\ &= \psi(p) + \frac{1}{\not p - iM_0}\{B(\not p - iM_0) + S_c(W, p)(\not p - iM_0)\}\psi(p).\end{aligned} \tag{18.40}$$

Now as one sees from eq. (18.14), S_c is itself proportional to $\not p - iM_0$. Hence, on account of eq. (18.28), the last term in eq. (18.40) vanishes. The coefficient of B in this equation, however, is indeterminate, since

$$(\not p - iM_0)^{-1}[(\not p - iM_0)\psi(p)] = 0$$

by eq. (18.28), but

$$[(\not p - iM_0)^{-1}(\not p - iM_0)]\psi(p) = \psi(p).$$

A proper analysis*) of this term shows that the correct form for eq. (18.40) is

$$\psi'(p) = (1 + B)^{\frac{1}{2}}\psi(p) = (1 + \tfrac{1}{2}B)\psi(p), \tag{18.41a}$$

where we have expanded the factor $\sqrt{(1 + B)}$ to the term linear in B. Similarly one shows that

$$\bar\psi'(p) = (1 + B)^{\frac{1}{2}}\bar\psi(p) = (1 + \tfrac{1}{2}B)\bar\psi(p). \tag{18.41b}$$

The whole analysis in this chapter is based on a perturbation approach. The fermion self-energy effects have been calculated to second order in the coupling constant e; A (and thus δM), B and $S_c(W, p)$ have been regarded as small quantities of order e^2 [e.g. in eqs. (18.41) we replaced $\sqrt{(1 + B)}$ by $(1 + \frac{1}{2}B)$]. Since the results of the analysis are not only not small but actually divergent, this procedure cannot be justified mathematically. Nevertheless, we shall calculate formally as though δM, A and B are small quantities. The justification of this procedure must be sought in the astounding success achieved in practice.

In addition to these radiative corrections of order e^2, there are of course also higher-order effects and corresponding higher-order

*) Cf. Dyson, F. J. *Phys. Rev.* **83**, 608, 1951.

contributions to δM which is thus to be thought of as a power series expansion in e. As for the e^2-terms above, the higher order contributions to the counter term δM are so chosen that for a single electron there are no self-energy effects, apart from using its physical mass M_0 instead of its bare mass M.

We must now interpret the other terms, B and $S_c(W, p)$, which derive from the self-energy loop W when inserted in an electron line. From eqs. (18.39) and (18.41) it follows that S_c does not contribute to a modification of an external line but only of an electron propagator. It corresponds in this case to a finite radiative correction of order e^2 relative to the original Feynman graph into which W was inserted. To obtain all second-order radiative corrections (due to electron self-energies) we must of course insert W into each electron propagator in turn.

The B-term in eq. (18.39) has the effect of multiplying the original matrix element by $(1 + B)$ when any one propagator S_F is replaced by S'_F in a Feynman graph. Since the corresponding S-matrix element is proportional to a power of the coupling constant e, we can absorb this factor $(1 + B)$ into the coupling constant. This is the process of *charge* or *coupling constant renormalization*. To show the consistency of this procedure, we must consider *all* possible W-modifications of the graph. For a graph G with F_i internal and F_e external electron lines, it follows from eqs. (18.39) and (18.41) that the effect of adding all W-modifications to G is to multiply the original matrix element by

$$1 + (F_i + \tfrac{1}{2}F_e)B. \tag{18.42}$$

Now

$$F_i + \tfrac{1}{2}F_e = n,$$

the number of vertices of the graph G. Hence we can write the factor (18.42) as

$$(1 + nB) = (1 + B)^n,$$

to second order in e. Since the matrix element of G is itself proportional to e^n, this factor can be incorporated into the charge, by defining the renormalized charge

$$e_0 = e(1 + B), \tag{18.43}$$

which is to be thought of as the observable charge of a physical electron. As in the case of mass renormalization so here, too, eq. (18.43) represents the first two terms of a power series expansion of the real charge in terms of the bare charge.

To sum up the results of this chapter. The effects of taking into account the second-order radiative corrections due to the electron self-energy are threefold.

(i) It implies a renormalization of the electron's mass, eq. (18.30).

(ii) It implies a renormalization of the electron's charge, eq. (18.43).

From the practical point of view, these two effects merely imply that we use the physical rather than the bare mass and charge of the electron. The above analysis involving δM and B can be forgotten. It was required for the purpose of showing the consistency of the scheme, e.g. to derive eq. (18.43) which shows that the charge renormalization is independent of the graph G under consideration.

(iii) Lastly, the W-modifications inserted into internal electron lines give rise to finite observable radiative corrections of order e_0^2 (to second order we of course now replace e by e_0 everywhere). To calculate these radiative corrections, one replaces each electron propagator S_F by the convergent part of eq. (18.39),

$$S'_{F_c}(p) = S_F(p)[1 + S_c(W, p)], \qquad (18.44)$$

in the expression for the graph G. The term independent of S_c then gives the original nth order matrix element; the term linear in S_c is the second-order radiative correction, due to electron self-energy effects, of this matrix element.

The radiative corrections due to the electron's self-energy are mainly responsible for the *Lamb shift*. According to the Dirac theory of the hydrogen atom, the $2s$ and $2p_{1/2}$ levels are degenerate. The effect of radiative corrections is to cause a shift of the energy levels, by different amounts for different states, leading to a splitting of the $2s - 2p_{1/2}$ levels. It is this phenomenon which is known as the *Lamb shift* of the hydrogen atom. In fig.22 the Feynman graphs were given which are responsible for the second-order radiative corrections to the scattering of an electron by an external electromagnetic field. We can think of the Lamb shift as being due to the same types of diagrams, with the electron lines not representing plane wave states but electrons bound in a Bohr orbit. As we are now dealing with a bound state problem the calculations become much more complicated. The bibliography at the end of this book contains references which give different approaches to the Lamb shift calculation and the reader is referred to these.

High precision measurements, by Lamb and collaborators, of the Lamb shift in hydrogen give the value*)

$$\Delta E \equiv \Delta E(2s) - \Delta E(2p_{1/2}) = (1057{\cdot}77 \pm 0{\cdot}10)\text{Mc/sec.} \tag{18.45}$$

Calculations of the second-order radiative corrections due to the electron self-energy (i.e. the graphs of figs. 22(a) and (b) only) give a contribution of 1011·45 Mc/sec to ΔE, showing that the Lamb shift is mainly due to electron self-energy effects. The other graphs also contribute, the vacuum polarization (fig. 22(c)) and the vertex modification (fig. 22(d)) contributing —27·13 Mc/sec and 67·82 Mc/sec, respectively. Thus combining these results, one obtains for the Lamb shift, derived theoretically in second-order perturbation theory,

$$\Delta E = 1052{\cdot}14 \text{ Mc/sec.} \tag{18.46}$$

The agreement between the experimental and theoretical values (18.45—46) is sufficiently good to give one considerable confidence in the renormalization theory, outlined above, which leads to these finite radiative corrections. The remaining discrepancy can be removed if one takes into account fourth-order radiative corrections, small corrections due to the finite mass of the proton, etc. In this way, one obtains for the best theoretical value of the Lamb shift**)

$$\Delta E = (1058{\cdot}03 \pm 0{\cdot}15)\text{Mc/sec,} \tag{18.47}$$

*) Dayhoff, E. S., Triebwasser, S. and Lamb, W. E. *Phys. Rev.* **89**, 98, 1953.

**) Bethe, H. A. and Salpeter, E. E. *Quantum mechanics of the one and two electron systems* Vienna; Springer Verlag, 1958; addendum to § 21.

in excellent agreement with the experimental value. Similarly striking agreement has also been obtained for the $2s - 2p_{1/2}$ line shift in deuterium and in singly-ionized helium and for the $3s - 3p_{1/2}$ shift in hydrogen*).

*) For a discussion and references, cf. Bethe and Salpeter, loc. cit., and Lamb, W. F. *Yearbook of the Physical Society*, 1958, p. 1.

CHAPTER 19

Vacuum Polarization

We shall now consider the boson self-energy modification W', fig. 23(b). The analysis and interpretation are very similar to the fermion case treated in the last chapter, so that we shall be quite brief, leaving details to the reader.

In electrodynamics, the W'-diagram represents the creation and subsequent annihilation of a virtual electron-positron pair. In general, for example if an external electromagnetic field is present, these virtual pairs are 'polarized', much in the same way in which a dielectric is polarized by an applied electric field. For this reason, the W'-graph is called a vacuum polarization diagram. Its effect is to lead to a modification of the electromagnetic interaction, i.e. it gives rise to radiative corrections.

We shall, to begin with, consider *ps*(*ps*)-meson theory so as to avoid the special features peculiar to photons. Inserting a W'-modification into a meson line then leads to three effects: it gives rise to renormalizations of the meson mass and of the coupling constant and to finite radiative corrections.

The mass renormalization we take into account at once by using the real meson mass m_0 instead of the bare mass m in the free field Hamiltonian density (2.20) where

$$m_0^2 = m^2 + \delta(m^2) \tag{19.1}$$

and introducing a counter term into the interaction Hamiltonian density (13.9) which now becomes

$$\mathscr{H}_I(x) = igN(\bar{\psi}\gamma_5\phi\psi) - \tfrac{1}{2}\delta(m^2)\phi^2 - \delta M\bar{\psi}\psi. \tag{19.2}$$

We shall not be concerned with the nucleon mass renormalization (which was discussed in the last chapter) and shall therefore omit the last term in eq. (19.2).

Let us consider inserting the vacuum polarization part W' in a meson propagator, i.e. the replacement shown in fig. 28. We

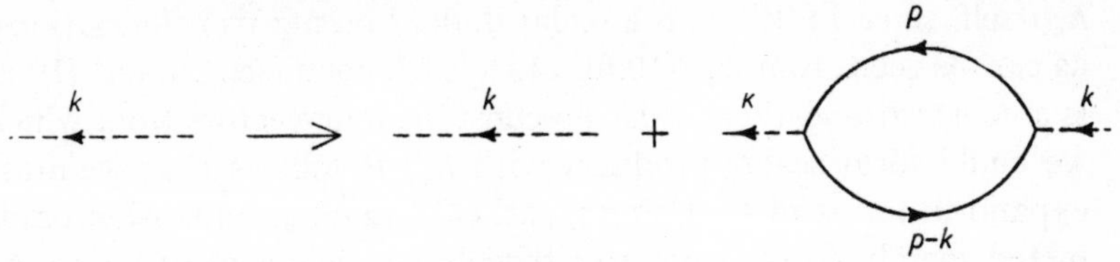

Fig. 28.

proceed as in chapter 18, eqs. (18.1—8). Defining the boson propagator in momentum space, $\Delta_F(k)$, by

$$\underbrace{\phi(x_2)\phi(x_1)} = \tfrac{1}{2}\Delta_F(x_2 - x_1) = \frac{-1}{(2\pi)^4}\int d^4k\, e^{ik(x_2-x_1)}\Delta_F(k),$$

i.e. from eqs. (6.15—18) by

$$\Delta_F(k) = \frac{i}{k^2 + m_0^2}, \tag{19.3}$$

the replacement shown in fig. 28 corresponds to replacing $\Delta_F(k)$ by

$$\Delta_F'(k) = \Delta_F(k) + \Delta_F^{(2)}(k) \tag{19.4}$$

where

$$\Delta_F^{(2)}(k) = \frac{i}{k^2 + m_0^2}\left\{\prod(W', k) - \frac{i}{2}\delta(m^2)\right\}\frac{i}{k^2 + m_0^2}, \tag{19.5}$$

and

$$\prod(W', k) = \frac{g^2}{(2\pi)^4}\int d^4p \,\mathrm{Tr}\left[\gamma_5 \frac{1}{\not p - iM_0}\gamma_5 \frac{1}{\not p - \not k - iM_0}\right]. \tag{19.6}$$

This integral diverges quadratically, behaving like

$$\int d^4p/p^2$$

for large p. We proceed as in the fermion case in the last chapter. The integrand in eq. (19.6) is finite and we can therefore expand it in powers of

$$z = -i(k^2 + m_0^2) \tag{19.7}$$

into the first two terms of a Taylor series plus a remainder term, giving, on integration with respect to p,

$$\prod(W', k) = A' + B'z + \Delta_c(W', k)z. \tag{19.8}$$

We have expanded in powers of k^2, rather than the four-vector k_μ itself, since $\prod(W', k)$ is a scalar under Lorentz transformations, as can be seen from eq. (19.6). Since each coefficient in eq. (19.8) is a constant and there exist no constant four-vectors from which we could form scalar products with k_μ, it follows that we must expand in terms of k^2. Using z, rather than k^2, as expansion parameter, merely corresponds to a trivial rearrangement of terms. As a result

$$z = 0 \tag{19.9}$$

for a free meson. The factor $(-i)$ in eq. (19.7) makes z equal to the inverse of the propagator (19.3) which is convenient in practice [cf. eqs. (18.5) and (18.11)].

From dimensional arguments it follows that the constants A', B' and the function $\Delta_c(W', k)$ are at most (and in fact turn out to be) quadratically divergent, logarithmically divergent and finite, respectively. The development from here runs in exact parallel to that in the last chapter. We again choose the counter term $\delta(m^2)$ in eq. (19.5) so that

$$A' - \frac{i}{2}\,\delta(m^2) = 0. \tag{19.10}$$

The propagator (19.4) then becomes

$$\Delta'_F(k) = \Delta_F(k)(1 + B') + \Delta_F(k)\Delta_c(W', k), \tag{19.11}$$

which is to be compared with eq. (18.39). Similarly, one obtains equations analogous to eqs. (18.41) for external boson lines

$$\phi'(x) = (1 + B')^{\frac{1}{2}}\phi(x) = (1 + \tfrac{1}{2}B')\phi(x). \tag{19.12}$$

Here we are throughout again adopting a perturbation approach, treating B' (and of course A' and $\delta(m^2)$) as small quantities. Inserted into the meson lines of a graph G, the last term in eq. (19.11) then gives finite second-order radiative corrections. The first term in eq. (19.11) together with eq. (19.12) can again be reinterpreted as leading to a coupling constant renormalization. The effect of these terms is, to second order, to multiply the matrix element representing G by

$$1 + (B_i + \tfrac{1}{2}B_e)B' = (1 + \tfrac{1}{2}nB') = (1 + B')^{n/2}, \qquad (19.13)$$

where B_i, B_e and n are, respectively, the number of internal and external boson lines and of vertices of G. The logarithmically divergent constant B' can again be eliminated by means of the coupling constant renormalization

$$g \to g_0 = g(1 + B')^{\frac{1}{2}}, \qquad (19.14)$$

which is of course to be taken in conjunction with the previous renormalization (18.43), originating from the fermion self-energy*).

Turning now to electrodynamics, the meson counter term in eq. (19.2) would have to be replaced by

$$-\tfrac{1}{2}\delta(m^2)A_\mu^2. \qquad (19.15)$$

For the pure radiation field (i.e. no interaction) the mass of the bare photon must vanish in order that the theory be gauge invariant. By using symmetry arguments similar to those used in connection with the integral (18.9), but now appealing to gauge invariance instead of Lorentz invariance, one can show that in the case of interacting fields the requirement of gauge invariance also implies that the mass of the physical photon be zero, i.e. the counter term $\delta(m^2)$ in eq. (19.15) is zero. The equations for the modified propagator and field, eqs. (19.11—12), from which the boson mass renormalization has already been eliminated, are of course, with the appropriate changes, applicable to the case of photons. This leads to a corresponding interpretation in terms of charge renormalization and radiative corrections of the order of the fine structure constant.

The existence of these vacuum polarization effects is well established by the Lamb shift. As stated in the last chapter, vacuum polarization effects contribute about 27 Mc/sec to the $2s - 2p_{\frac{1}{2}}$ Lamb shift in hydrogen whereas the calculations are in complete agreement with experiments accurate to 0·1 Mc/sec. We can think of this effect as a modification of the Coulomb field of the

*) In eq. (18.43) we wrote e instead of g, etc., as we were discussing electrodynamics at that time. But all the considerations of the previous chapter also apply to $ps(ps)$-meson theory, with the appropriate modifications to details.

nucleus. The presence of the protons polarizes the virtual electron-positron pairs, the protons attracting the electrons and repelling the positrons. The atomic electron then experiences this modified field.

CHAPTER 20

The Vertex Modification

We shall now analyse the vertex modification V_1, fig. 23(c), for electrodynamics. We define the Fourier transform $F(p_1, p_2)$ of a function of two four-vectors x_1 and x_2 by

$$F(x_1, x_2) = \frac{1}{(2\pi)^8} \int d^4 p_1 d^4 p_2 \, e^{i(p_1 x_1 + p_2 x_2)} F(p_1, p_2). \quad (20.1)$$

The modification of the basic vertex part shown in fig. 29 cor-

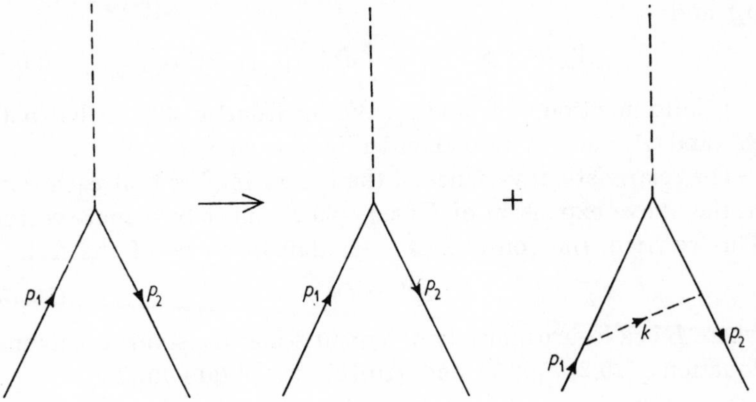

Fig. 29.

responds to the replacement of γ_μ by

$$\Gamma_\mu(V_1, p_2, p_1) = \gamma_\mu + \Lambda_\mu(V_1, p_2, p_1) \quad (20.2)$$

where

$$\Lambda_\mu(V_1, p_2, p_1) = \frac{-ie^2}{(2\pi)^4} \int d^4 k \, \gamma_\lambda \frac{1}{\not{p}_2 - \not{k} - iM_0} \gamma_\mu \frac{1}{\not{p}_1 - \not{k} - iM_0} \gamma_\lambda \frac{1}{k^2}. \quad (20.3)$$

This integral behaves like

$$\int d^4 k/(k^2)^2$$

for large k, i.e. it is logarithmically divergent. Writing

$$\Lambda_\mu(V_1, p_2, p_1) = \int d^4 k\, R_{V_1}(k, z_2, z_1), \tag{20.4}$$

where

$$z_1 = \not{p}_1 - iM_0,\ z_2 = \not{p}_2 - iM_0, \tag{20.5}$$

we expand the integrand in the form

$$R_{V_1}(k, z_2, z_1) = R_{V_1}(k, 0, 0) + R_{V_{1c}}(k, z_2, z_1). \tag{20.6}$$

Hence

$$\Lambda_\mu(V_1, p_2, p_1) = A'' + \Lambda_{\mu c}(V_1, p_2, p_1), \tag{20.7}$$

where

$$A'' = \int d^4 k R_{V_1}(k, 0, 0) \tag{20.8}$$

is a logarithmically divergent constant (i.e. independent of p_1 and p_2) and

$$\Lambda_{\mu c}(V_1, p_2, p_1) = \int d^4 k\, R_{V_{1c}}(k, z_2, z_1) \tag{20.9}$$

is a finite function of p_1 and p_2. We see from eq. (20.3) that both A'' and $\Lambda_{\mu c}$ are of second order in the charge e.

The relativistic invariance of the theory implies that each term in the above expansion of Γ_μ, eq. (20.2), must be a four- vector. This restricts the constant A'', eq. (20.8), to be of the form

$$A'' = L\gamma_\mu \tag{20.10}$$

where L is a logarithmically divergent scalar constant. Combining equations (20.2), (20.7) and (20.10), we obtain finally

$$\Gamma_\mu(V_1, p_2, p_1) = \gamma_\mu(1 + L) + \Lambda_{\mu c}(V_1, p_2, p_1). \tag{20.11}$$

On substituting Γ_μ for γ_μ at each vertex, in turn, of a Feynman graph G, the second term $\Lambda_{\mu c}$ in eq. (20.11) will give finite radiative corrections of order e^2, whereas the first term can again be interpreted as a charge renormalization

$$e \to e_0 = e(1 + L), \tag{20.12}$$

applied to the matrix element of the graph G. This charge renormalization must of course be combined with the charge renormalizations originating from the electron and photon self-energy effects, eqs. (18.43) and (19.14), giving

$$e_0 = e(1 + B)(1 + L)(1 + B')^{\frac{1}{2}}. \tag{20.13}$$

If one evaluates the logarithmically divergent constants B and L, much in the same way in which we calculated the divergent constant A, eq. (18.19), one finds that

$$B = -L, \tag{20.14}$$

i.e. the two constants B and $(-L)$ are given by the *same* divergent integral expression (cf. exercise 20.3). Hence, to second order in e, we can write eq. (20.13) as

$$e_0 = e(1 + B')^{\frac{1}{2}}. \tag{20.15}$$

This equation implies that the charge renormalization stems entirely from the vacuum polarization; not from the fermion self-energy or vertex modifications. This result is true generally, not only in second-order perturbation theory discussed above; furthermore it holds for particles of spin 0, not only of spin $\frac{1}{2}$. This has the important consequence that the charge renormalization depends exclusively on self-energy effects of the photon, i.e. on vacuum polarization modifications inserted into photon lines. Hence the charge renormalization is the same for all elementary particles. It follows that the experimentally observed equality of the charges of the elementary particles implies the equality of their bare charges.

The existence of the above radiative corrections is again demonstrated by the excellent agreement between the measured and calculated values of the Lamb shift, as discussed at the end of chapter 18.

CHAPTER 21

The Anomalous Magnetic Moment of the Electron

To illustrate the results of the last three chapters, we shall in this chapter briefly discuss the simplest problem involving radiative corrections, namely the calculation of the anomalous magnetic moment of the electron. According to the Dirac theory, the electron possesses a magnetic moment

$$\mu = \left(\frac{-e_0}{2M_0}\right). \tag{21.1}$$

One way in which this magnetic moment manifests itself is in the scattering of electrons by an external electromagnetic field $A^e_\mu(x)$. The matrix element for this process, shown in the Feynman graph of fig. 21, follows in lowest-order perturbation theory from eq. (16.2). For the scattering from an electron state with four-momentum p and spinor $u(\mathbf{p})$ to an electron state with four-momentum p' and spinor $u'(\mathbf{p}')$, eq. (16.2) gives the matrix element

$$\frac{M_0}{V(E_\mathbf{p} E_{\mathbf{p}'})^{\frac{1}{2}}} e_0 \bar{u}'(\mathbf{p}')\gamma_\alpha u(\mathbf{p}) A^e_\alpha(q) \tag{21.2}$$

where

$$A^e_\alpha(x) = \frac{1}{(2\pi)^4}\int d^4q \, e^{iqx} A^e_\alpha(q) \tag{21.3}$$

and

$$q = p' - p \tag{21.4}$$

is the momentum transfer in the scattering. Using the Dirac equations

$$(\not{p} - iM_0)u(\mathbf{p}) = 0, \qquad \bar{u}'(\mathbf{p}')(\not{p}' - iM_0) = 0,$$

and the definition of the spin matrix $\sigma_{\alpha\beta}$, eq. (A 6), the matrix element (21.2) can be rewritten in the form

$$-\frac{M_0}{V(E_{\mathbf{p}}E_{\mathbf{p}'})^{\frac{1}{2}}}\frac{\mu}{2}\{-2i\bar{u}'(\mathbf{p}')[(p+p')A^e(q)]u(\mathbf{p})$$
$$+\bar{u}'(\mathbf{p}')\sigma_{\alpha\beta}u(\mathbf{p})[q_\alpha A^e_\beta(q)-q_\beta A^e_\alpha(q)]\}. \quad (21.5)$$

If we consider the limiting case of a slowly moving electron (i.e. we take the non-relativistic limit) and a static magnetic field **H**, then the second term in eq. (21.5) becomes identical with the matrix element for the scattering of a particle of magnetic moment μ in a static external magnetic field **H**, as given by the non-relativistic Pauli theory.

Let us now also take into account the second-order radiative corrections to electron scattering, shown in figs. 22(a) to (d). As we saw in chapter 18, the electron self-energy parts W inserted in the external electron lines, figs. 22(a) and (b), lead only to charge renormalizations. These cancel a charge renormalization stemming from the vertex modification V_1 in fig. 22(d). This modification also gives a finite radiative correction, obtained by replacing γ_α in the matrix element (21.2) by $\Lambda_{\alpha c}(V_1, p', p)$, eq. (20.9). Finally, the vacuum polarization graph, fig. 22(c), leads to a charge renormalization plus a finite second-order radiative correction*).

*) In chapter 19, we considered the insertion of a vacuum polarization part W' between two operators of the quantized boson field, e.g. in eq. (19.11) for a meson propagator. The modification of fig. 22(c) involves the external electromagnetic field A^e_α which is not quantized but treated classically. One easily finds for this case that the modification of fig. 22(c) corresponds to replacing $A^e_\alpha(q)$ in the matrix element (21.2) by

$$D_F(q)\,\Pi(W', q)A^e_\alpha(q) = [B'+D_c(W', q)]A^e_\alpha(q). \quad (21.6)$$

Apart from the appropriate changes to allow for the fact that we are here dealing with photons, this expression is closely analogous to the second-order modification $\Delta_F^{(2)}(q)$ of a meson propagator given by eqs. (19.4) and (19.11).

Strictly speaking we should, in order to be consistent, have written e rather than e_0 in eq. (21.2). Only after incorporating the matrix element arising from the B' term in eq. (21.6) in the zero-order matrix element (21.2) should we write e_0. This corresponds, according to eq. (20.15), to a renormalization of the charge of the electron which is being scattered, as well as a renormalization of the charges which are the sources of the

Combining the contributions from these graphs, figs. 22(a) to (d), we can write the corresponding matrix element for the second-order radiative corrections again in the form of eq. (21.5), that is, as the sum of two terms, one independent of the spin matrix $\sigma_{\alpha\beta}$ and one proportional to $\sigma_{\alpha\beta}$. The latter term stems entirely from the vertex modification, fig. 22(d), and, in the non-relativistic limit of a slowly moving electron, is identical with the second term in eq. (21.5), except that the constant μ is replaced by*)

$$\delta\mu = \frac{1}{2\pi}\left(\frac{e_0^2}{4\pi}\right)\mu = 0{\cdot}0011614\,\mu. \tag{21.8}$$

Thus the electron's magnetic moment is augmented by an anomalous contribution $\delta\mu$ due to the second-order radiative corrections. This result, first derived by Schwinger**) is in excellent agreement with the best experimental value of

$$\delta\mu = (0{\cdot}001165 \pm 0{\cdot}000011)\,\mu, \tag{21.9}$$

due to Franken and Liebes†). The fourth-order radiative correction to the magnetic moment has also been calculated††) giving the value

$$\delta\mu = 0{\cdot}0011596\,\mu$$

but the errors on the experimental result are too large to be able to say that the existence of this term is verified.

---

external field A^e_α. We may, if we wish, call this a renormalization of the external field

$$(A^e_\alpha)_0 = A^e_\alpha(1 + B')^{\frac{1}{2}}. \tag{21.7}$$

*) The value of the fine structure constant taken is 1/137·04.

) Schwinger, J. *Phys. Rev.* **73, 416, 1948 and *Phys. Rev.* **76**, 790, 1949.

†) Franken, P. and Liebes, S. *Phys. Rev.* **104**, 1197, 1956.

††) Sommerfield, C. M. *Phys. Rev.* **107**, 328, 1957, and *Annals of Physics* **5**, 26, 1958; Petermann, A. *Helv. phys. Acta* **30**, 407, 1957.

CHAPTER 22

Renormalization

So far we have considered second-order modifications to fermion and boson lines and to vertex parts. There exist, of course, an infinite set of higher-order modifications; some typical fourth-order ones are shown in fig. 30. The theory of how to deal with

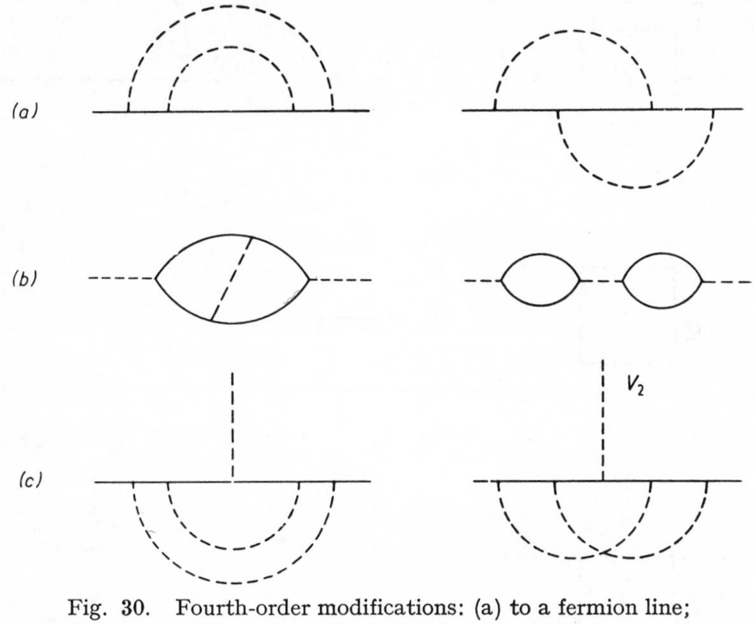

Fig. 30. Fourth-order modifications: (a) to a fermion line; (b) to a boson line; (c) to a vertex.

these higher order graphs systematically is due to Dyson, Salam, Ward and others. The main result of this analysis is that for certain types of field theory, known as *renormalizable*, the approach indicated for second-order corrections in the previous chapters goes through for modifications of *any finite* order; that is, if for a particular process one considers all graphs up to some finite order n, then these are equivalent to the lowest-order graph plus some finite radiative corrections, mass and charge renormalization having been applied to eliminate all divergences. Typical examples of such theories are electrodynamics and neutral or symmetric $ps(ps)$-meson theory. We shall take electrodynamics as an example in the following discussion of higher-order radiative corrections which will be quite incomplete, merely illuminating some interesting features and serving as an introduction to the more complete accounts.

In previous chapters we saw how to modify a Feynman graph by inserting self-energy or vertex parts; cf. fig. 23. We now

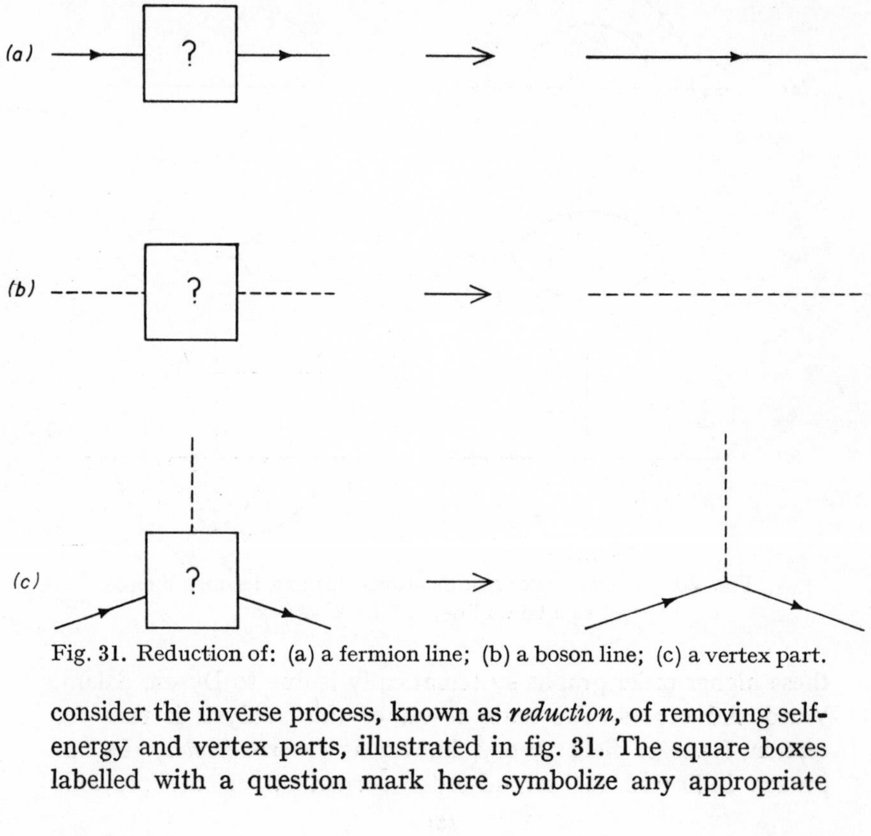

Fig. 31. Reduction of: (a) a fermion line; (b) a boson line; (c) a vertex part.

consider the inverse process, known as *reduction*, of removing self-energy and vertex parts, illustrated in fig. 31. The square boxes labelled with a question mark here symbolize any appropriate self-energy or vertex part, for example those shown in fig. 30. By repeatedly applying the substitutions of fig. 31 to a graph G we finally obtain a graph which cannot be reduced any further. Such a graph is called *irreducible*. The irreducible second- and

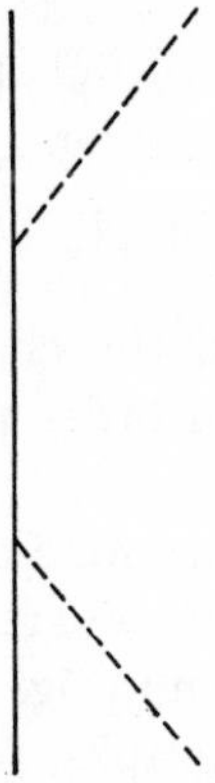

Fig. 32. Irreducible e^2-graph for Compton scattering.

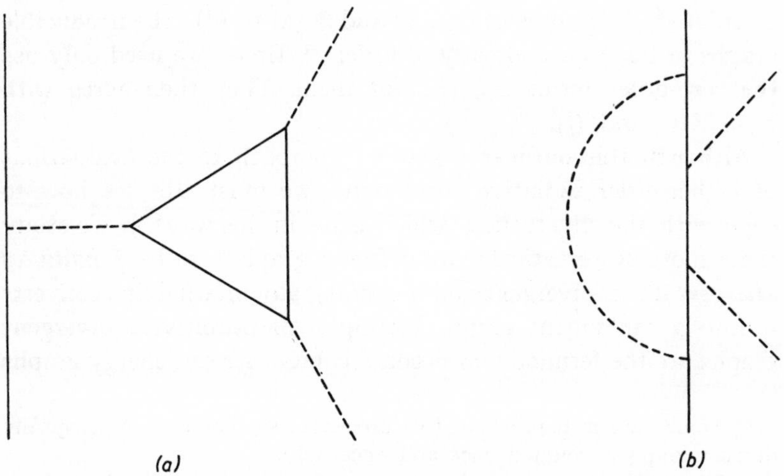

Fig. 33. Irreducible e^4-graphs for Compton scattering.

fourth-order graphs for Compton scattering are shown in figs. 32 and 33. The triangle diagram, fig. 33(a), gives no contribution (cf. exercise 14.3).

To calculate a particular process to nth order, we no longer consider all appropriate graphs up to this order. Instead, we only consider the irreducible ones, inserting into them not the zero-order terms S_F, D_F and γ_μ but the modified propagators and vertex parts

$$\left.\begin{aligned} S'_F &= S_F + S_F^{(2)} + \dots, \\ D'_F &= D_F + D_F^{(2)} + \dots, \\ \Gamma_\mu &= \gamma_\mu + \Lambda_\mu + \dots, \end{aligned}\right\} \tag{22.1}$$

expanded as power series in the charge up to e^n *). This gives all corrections up to the nth order plus some higher ones to be neglected.

We illustrate this procedure for Compton scattering up to the fourth-order graphs. The only e^2-graph is shown in fig. 32, the fourth-order ones being shown in fig. 26. Alternatively we restrict ourselves to the irreducible graphs, figs. 32 and 33. Inserting the second-order modifications of figs. 27 to 29 into the internal and external electron and photon lines and vertices of fig. 32 gives, to order e^4, the graphs of figs. 32 and 26(a) to (d). The irreducible graphs of fig. 33 are already of order e^4. Hence we need only use the zero-order terms S_F, etc., in them. They then agree with figs. 26(e) and (f).

Although this outlines a general approach to the evaluations of higher-order radiative corrections, we must still see how to cope with the divergences which arise in this way**). To study these more systematically we define a graph G to be *primitively divergent* if it is divergent and if opening any internal line converts it into a convergent graph. Examples of primitively divergent graphs are the fermion and boson second-order self-energy graphs

*) Some care is required in this procedure so that each topologically distinct graph is counted once and once only.

**) We shall only consider divergences arising from large values of the momentum four-vectors of virtual particles, i.e. of propagators. These are the kind of divergences treated in the previous chapters and are the only ones which lead to serious difficulties. Other kinds of divergences do occur, such as the infra-red divergence in electrodynamics, but these can be disposed of.

W and W' and the second-order vertex modification V_1. For example, opening either fermion propagator of the vacuum polarization diagram W' gives the finite Compton-scattering graph, fig. 32. Whilst W and W' are the only primitively divergent self-energy modifications, there are infinitely many primitively divergent vertex modifications of higher order; a fourth-order one is shown in fig. 30(c), graph V_2. In a primitively divergent graph G, the momentum of any internal line is a variable of integration; otherwise, opening this line would not convert G into a convergent graph. For a primitively divergent graph the corresponding integrand is finite. Hence the same procedure of expanding the integrand into a Taylor series, successive terms of which are decreasingly divergent, which was applied to the e^2-modifications in earlier chapters, can generally be used for primitively divergent graphs. The importance of primitively divergent graphs is due to the fact that we can deal with any divergent graph G by successively dealing with the primitively divergent bits occurring in G.

We shall now enumerate the different kinds of primitively divergent graphs. For this purpose we can restrict ourselves to graphs G with these properties:

(i) G possesses no primitively divergent subgraphs*) (if G does possess primitively divergent subgraphs, it is certainly not *primitively* divergent itself), i.e. G is either finite or primitively divergent;

(ii) we exclude graphs containing internal lines whose momenta are not variables of integration but fixed (e.g. the Compton diagram, fig. 32); for such graphs are certainly not primitively divergent.

For a graph with these properties we then obtain a criterion as to whether it is finite or primitively divergent by counting up the momentum factors in the numerator and denominator of the expression representing G, just as was done in chapters

*) Any graph which can be obtained from G by opening one or more internal lines and discarding the rest of G is called a subgraph of G. For example, the triangle diagram, fig. 34, is a subgraph of fig. 33(a).

18 to 20*). We obtain in this way an expression of the form**)

$$\int^{\infty} d^4p\, p^{K-4} \sim p^K. \tag{22.2}$$

This will be necessarily convergent if $K < 0$, it *may* diverge at most logarithmically if $K = 0$ and it *may* diverge at most like p^K if $K > 0$.

Let G have n vertices, F_i internal fermion lines and B_i internal boson lines. If F_e and B_e are the number of external fermion and boson lines, then

$$F_e + 2F_i = 2n, \qquad B_e + 2B_i = n. \tag{22.3}$$

To find K, we note that there are $4(F_i + B_i)$ variables of integration. These are not independent but are restricted by the n four-dimensional delta functions arising from the vertices. One of these delta functions expresses the over-all conservation of energy and momentum, i.e. it involves only external momenta but not integration variables. Hence it does not reduce the number of independent variables of integration. The propagators contribute $(F_i + 2B_i)$ factors linear in momentum to the denominator, while the vertices are momentum-independent in a theory not involving derivative coupling in the interaction. Combining these results, one obtains

$$\begin{aligned} K &= 4(F_i+B_i)-4(n-1)-(F_i+2B_i) \\ &= 4-\tfrac{3}{2}F_e-B_e. \end{aligned} \tag{22.4}$$

We see from this relation that whether the graph G is primitively divergent depends *only* on the numbers of external fermion and boson lines. Furthermore, G will certainly be convergent if it contains sufficiently many external lines. In other words, there are only a finite number of different *types* of primitively divergent graphs, specified by the number of external fermion and boson lines. We briefly enumerate these.

*) This naive procedure has been justified by Dyson, F. J. *Phys. Rev.* **75**, 1736, 1949.

**) It is only for a graph G possessing no primitively divergent subgraph (i.e. satisfying restriction (i) above) that the matrix element is of this form. If G possesses primitively divergent subgraphs, then each of these will lead to a "self-contained" divergent integral.

(i) The vacuum polarization graph ($F_e = 0$, $B_e = 2$, $K = 2$), shown in fig. 31(b). The only primitively divergent graph is the second-order W'-loop, fig. 23(b). For meson theory this graph does lead to a quadratic divergence, for electrodynamics gauge invariance reduces it to a logarithmic one.

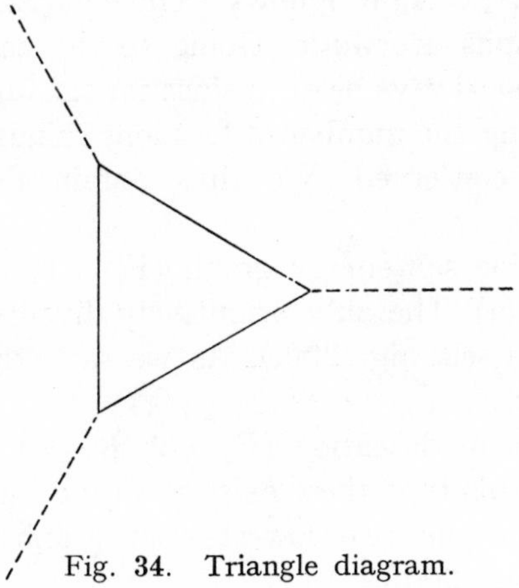

Fig. 34. Triangle diagram.

(ii) The triangle diagram, fig. 34, ($F_e = 0$, $B_e = 3$, $K = 1$). For electrodynamics and $ps(ps)$-meson theory, this diagram gives no contribution (cf exercises 14.3—4). In general (e.g. in $s(s)$-meson theory) it will lead to a divergence which then requires special consideration.

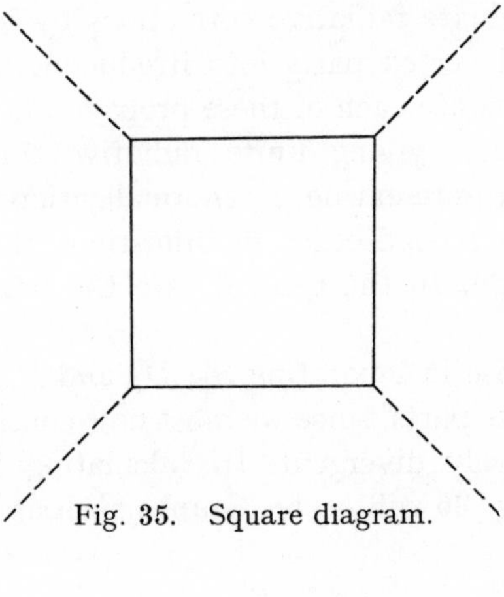

Fig. 35. Square diagram.

(iii) The square diagram, fig. 35, ($F_e = 0$, $B_e = 4$, $K = 0$). In general this will be logarithmically divergent. In electrodynamics, where it represents the scattering of light by light, it is strongly convergent on account of gauge-invariance requirements.

For $F_e = 0$, $B_e > 4$, it follows from eq. (22.4) that $K < 0$, i.e. all such graphs are finite. Going to the cases $F_e > 0$, we note that F_e must always be even since for the interactions which we are considering the number of fermions minus the number of antifermions is conserved. We thus obtain these primitively divergent graphs:

(iv) The fermion self-energy graph ($F_e = 2$, $B_e = 0$, $K = 1$), shown in fig. 31(a). The only primitively divergent graph is the W-modification itself, fig. 23(a). As we saw, the divergence is only logarithmic.

(v) The vertex modification ($F_e = 2$, $B_e = 1$, $K = 0$), shown in fig. 31(c). Of this type these exist an infinite set of primitively divergent graphs, the two lowest-order graphs being V_1, fig. 23(c), and V_2, fig. 30(c).

This exhausts the different types of primitively divergent graphs. For quantum electrodynamics there are only three possibilities: the self-energy loops W and W' and the vertex modifications, fig 31(c). Since an irreducible graph contains no self-energy or vertex modifications, it follows that all irreducible graphs are finite.

Hence, to evaluate radiative corrections by inserting modified propagators and vertex parts into irreducible graphs, one must show how to separate each of these propagators and vertex parts into a finite part (giving finite radiative corrections) plus a divergent part (representing a renormalization of a lower-order graph). For the second-order modifications this was shown in chapters 18 to 20. In the general case the proof is much more intricate.

Difficulties arise in separating S'_F, D'_F and Γ_μ, eqs. (22.1), into finite plus infinite parts, since we must now consider graphs which are not primitively divergent. In calculating S'_F, for example, the graphs of fig. 36 will occur. Graphs such as figs. 36(a) or (b) cause no trouble. In (a) we deal with each W-loop by itself, in (b) we deal with the inner loop first and then the outer one. In this way we have at each stage a single divergent integral whose

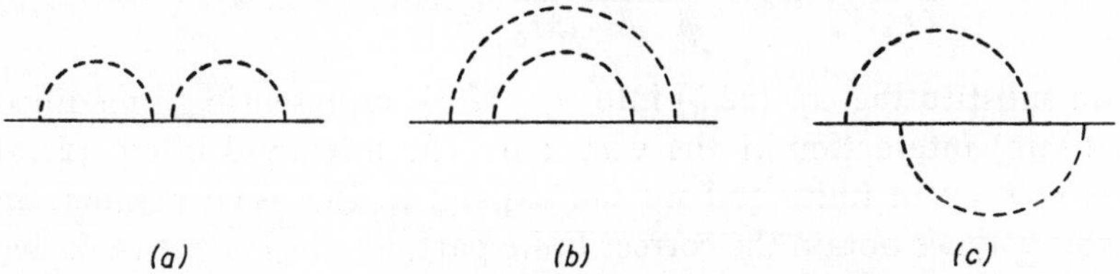

Fig. 36. e^4-modifications to the fermion propagator.

integrand, however, is finite so that the usual expansion procedure can be employed. The difficulties arise from graphs like fig. 36(c), known as *overlapping* divergences. One here deals with multiple integrals which are divergent when the integration is performed with respect to one variable while keeping the others fixed. Hence we can carry out the first integration, using a Taylor expansion, but cannot go further since the integrand for further integrations is divergent. A more sophisticated approach is needed.

For practical purposes a simple approach fortunately exists. We consider, for example, the graph in fig. 36(c) as a V_1 vertex modification of the vertex labelled A in the graph of fig. 37, i.e.

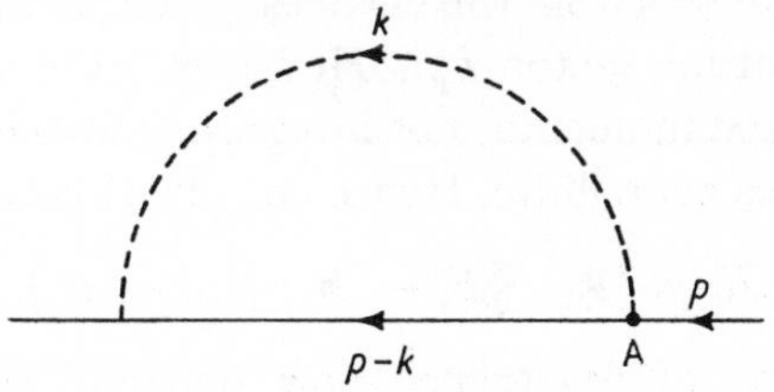

Fig. 37.

the usual W-loop. This graph is represented by eqs. (18.8) and (18.38). To obtain the overlapping graph, fig. 36(c), we replace the second factor γ_μ in eq. (18.8) by

$$\Lambda_\mu(V_1, p-k, p) = L\gamma_\mu + \Lambda_{\mu c}(V_1, p-k, p) \qquad (22.5)$$

[cf. eqs. (20.7) and (20.10)]. The first of these terms gives merely an infinite multiple of the original W-loop and we drop it as a renormalization effect. The second term in eq. (22.5) will lead to the integral

$$\frac{-ie_0^2}{(2\pi)^4}\int d^4k\,\gamma_\mu\,\frac{1}{\not p-\not k-iM_0}\,\Lambda_{\mu c}(V_1,\,p-k,\,p)\,\frac{1}{k^2} \qquad (22.6)$$

on substituting eq. (22.5) into eq. (18.8), representing a modified (finite) interaction at the vertex A. The integrand in eq. (22.6) is now again finite and we can expand in the usual manner. In this way we obtain the correct finite part, i.e. the correct radiative correction. However, the infinite part which was dropped was 'wrong', i.e. it is not true that it corresponds to a renormalization. To prove the renormalizability one must use a more sophisticated procedure which leads to the *same* finite part but a different divergent term. The latter then can be shown to represent a renormalization effect only. The sort of approach which has here been outlined works quite generally for calculating the finite parts of overlapping divergences.

Finally, we consider briefly how the above arguments are to be modified if we are dealing with an interaction involving gradient coupling, for example $ps(pv)$-meson theory, eq. (11.13), involving the gradient of the meson field $\partial\phi/\partial x_\lambda$. In the argument leading to eq. (22.4) we then get additional contributions to the number of momentum factors from the vertices. ($\partial/\partial x_\mu$ in momentum space gives a momentum factor k_μ). However, external meson lines involve only fixed momenta, not integration variables, hence only the internal lines contribute. Hence eq. (22.4) is to be replaced by

$$K = (4-\tfrac{3}{2}F_e - B_e)+(n - B_e). \qquad (22.7)$$

Thus the degree of divergence now depends not only on the external lines but also on the complexity of the graph G, i.e. on the number of vertices n. As we go to higher approximations new primitively divergent graphs appear all the time: there are now infinitely many of them. It is this feature which distinguishes non-renormalizable theories from renormalizable ones which contain only a finite number of types of primitively divergent graphs. In the latter case a finite number of experiments are required to determine the renormalized constants; thereafter one can use the theory to make predictions. For a non-renormalizable theory, on the other hand, each higher approximation brings in its own new renormalization constants, showing this approach futile in this case.

By systematically considering radiative corrections of all orders for a particular process for a renormalizable theory one obtains, for the corresponding matrix element, a series expansion in powers of the renormalized coupling constant, the expansion coefficients being finite now. Nothing has here been said about the convergence of this series and this question is so far quite unsolved. By considering simplified models of a quantized field theory, Edwards*) has shown that in the case of two interacting scalar fields the series diverges, whereas in the case of a boson field interacting with a fermion field (as in electrodynamics or meson theory) one cannot draw a general conclusion: the series may converge or diverge. Edwards's general results are in agreement with particular calculations by various authors. Caianiello**) has constructed a particular model, involving fermions and bosons, which leads to a convergent series, while other authors†) have explicitly proved the divergence for the idealized boson-boson case.

A related problem, so far unsolved, is that of the self-consistency of quantum field theory. Again, the study of idealized models has led to serious difficulties in this respect which may also occur for more realistic theories, such as electrodynamics. However, the great practical success of the perturbation-theoretic approach to electrodynamics suggests that any future electrodynamic theory, free from these difficulties, will bear a close relation to the above formulation. For meson theory where the coupling constant is large no such success is to be expected or, indeed, found. An approach not based on a perturbation expansion seems essential in this case. Attempts at a development in this direction have so far met with very limited success only.

*) Edwards, S. F. *Phil. Mag.* **46**, 569, 1955.

) Caianiello, E. R. *Nuovo Cim.* **3, 223, 1956.

†) Hurst, C. A. *Proc. Camb. phil. Soc.* **48**, 625, 1952; Thirring, W. *Helv. phys. Acta* **26**, 33, 1953; Petermann, A. *Helv. phys. Acta* **26**, 291, 1953; Utiyama, R. and Imamura, T. *Prog. theor. Phys. Osaka* **9**, 431, 1953.

Exercises *

1.1 Derive eq. (1.11) from eq. (1.10).

1.2 Derive eq. (1.12) from eqs. (1.10—11).

1.3 Derive the commutation relations (1.13) from eqs. (1.10—11).

2.1 Derive the Euler equations for the four fields $A_\mu(x)$, $\mu = 1, \ldots 4$, which result from the variational principle (2.4) with the Lagrangian density

$$\mathscr{L}(x) = -\tfrac{1}{2} \sum_{\mu=1}^{4} \sum_{\nu=1}^{4} \frac{\partial A_\mu}{\partial x_\nu} \frac{\partial A_\mu}{\partial x_\nu}. \tag{1}$$

2.2 Show that replacing the Lagrangian density $\mathscr{L}(\phi^\alpha, \phi^\alpha_{,\nu})$, eq. (2.1), by

$$\mathscr{L}' = \mathscr{L} + \frac{\partial \Lambda_\nu}{\partial x_\nu},$$

where $\Lambda_1, \ldots, \Lambda_4$ are functions of the fields $\phi^\alpha(x)$, does not alter the field equations.

2.3 Show that, in virtue of the field equations (2.8), the tensor

$$T_{\mu\nu} = -\phi^\alpha_{,\nu} \frac{\partial \mathscr{L}}{\partial \phi^\alpha_{,\mu}} + \mathscr{L} \delta_{\mu\nu} \tag{1}$$

$[\mathscr{L} = \mathscr{L}(\phi^\alpha, \phi^\alpha_{,\nu})]$ satisfies the equations

$$\frac{\partial T_{\mu\nu}}{\partial x_\mu} = 0, \qquad (\nu = 1, \ldots 4). \tag{2}$$

* Exercises are numbered according to chapters.
Hints for solving the more difficult exercises will be found on pp. 168–189.

2.4 Derive the tensor $T_{\mu\nu}$, defined in exercise 2.3, for the meson field specified by the Lagrangian density (2.18), and show that $(-T_{44}) = \mathscr{H}$, the Hamiltonian density, eq. (2.20).

2.5 Define

$$P_\lambda(t) = -i \int d^3x \, T_{4\lambda}$$

where $T_{\mu\nu}$ is the tensor given by eqs. (1) and (2) of exercise 2.3 and the integration is over all 3-space at the instant of time t. Show that $P_\lambda(t)$ is constant in time, provided the fields $\phi^\alpha(\mathbf{x}, t)$ go to zero sufficiently rapidly as $|\mathbf{x}| \to \infty$, and interpret the result.

2.6 Show that if the energy-momentum tensor $T_{\mu\nu}$ is symmetric,

$$\frac{\partial \mathscr{M}_{\lambda\mu\nu}}{\partial x_\lambda} = 0 \tag{1}$$

where

$$\mathscr{M}_{\lambda\mu\nu} = T_{\lambda\mu} x_\nu - T_{\lambda\nu} x_\mu,$$

and hence that the angular momentum of the field is conserved.

3.1 Derive the commutation rules (3.5) from those for the fields, eqs. (3.2).

3.2 Derive eq. (3.6).

3.3 If the energy-momentum tensor of the quantized meson field is given by the operator

$$T_{\mu\nu} = \frac{1}{2}\left\{ \frac{\partial\phi}{\partial x_\mu}\frac{\partial\phi}{\partial x_\nu} + \frac{\partial\phi}{\partial x_\nu}\frac{\partial\phi}{\partial x_\mu} \right\} + \mathscr{L}\delta_{\mu\nu} \tag{1}$$

(with $\mathscr{L}$ given by eq. (2.18)), show that the momentum of the field is given by

$$\mathbf{P} = \sum_{\mathbf{k}} a^\dagger(\mathbf{k})\, a(\mathbf{k})\, \mathbf{k}, \tag{2}$$

(cf. solution of exercise 2.5).

6.1 Derive eq. (6.3).

6.2 Derive eqs. (6.11).

6.3 Prove that $\Delta(x)$ is a solution of the Klein-Gordon equation.

7.1 If the Lagrangian density $\mathscr{L}(\phi^\alpha, \phi^\alpha_{,\nu})$ is invariant under the variation $\phi^\alpha \to \phi^\alpha + \delta\phi^\alpha$, show that the resulting invariance of the action integral (2.3) leads to the conservation equation

$$\frac{\partial j_\nu}{\partial x_\nu} = 0, \tag{1}$$

where

$$j_\nu = \frac{\partial \mathscr{L}}{\partial \phi^\alpha_{,\nu}} \delta\phi^\alpha, \tag{2}$$

the ϕ^α being solutions of the field equations.

Assuming the Lagrangian density (7.2) to be invariant under the gauge transformation (7.11), show that the above procedure leads to the continuity equation for the charge-current four-vector.

7.2 Derive eq. (7.23) and show that it commutes with the Hamiltonian, eq. (7.21).

8.1 Derive eq. (8.15).

8.2 Justify the use of the Lagrangian density (8.19), although this is not a Hermitian operator.

8.3 Derive eq. (8.22).

8.4 Show that in virtue of the field equations the four-current (8.32) satisfies the continuity equation.

8.5 Derive eq. (8.34).

8.6 Derive the anticommutation relations (8.42).

8.7 Show that the function $S(x)$ is a solution of the Dirac equation.

8.8 Prove that

$$S(x)|_{x_0=0} = i\gamma_4 \delta(\mathbf{x}).$$

8.9 Derive the 'equal-times' anticommutation relations

$$\left.\begin{aligned} [\psi_\alpha(\mathbf{x}, t), \psi_\beta(\mathbf{x}', t)]_+ = [\psi^\dagger_\alpha(\mathbf{x}, t), \psi^\dagger_\beta(\mathbf{x}', t)]_+ = 0 \\ [\psi_\alpha(\mathbf{x}, t), \psi^\dagger_\beta(\mathbf{x}', t)]_+ = \delta_{\alpha\beta}\delta(\mathbf{x} - \mathbf{x}'). \end{aligned}\right\} \tag{1}$$

8.10 Show that the commutator

$$[s_\mu(x),\ s_\nu(x')]$$

vanishes if $(x - x')$ is a space-like vector (i.e. $(x - x')^2 > 0$).

8.11 Prove eq. (A 32).

8.12 If A and B are anticommuting operators, prove that

$$\mathrm{Tr}\,(AB) = 0. \tag{1}$$

8.13 Derive eqs. (A 33—38).

9.1 Prove that

$$D(x) = \frac{1}{4\pi r}\{\delta(x_0 + r) - \delta(x_0 - r)\},$$

where $r = |\mathbf{x}|$.

10.1 Derive eqs. (10.25—26).

11.1 Derive eq. (11.12).

11.2 Derive the non-relativistic $ps(pv)$-interaction (11.14) from the relativistic interaction (11.13).

11.3 Show that the Lagrangian density of quantum electrodynamics is invariant under gauge transformations and under charge conjugation.

11.4 What is the most general form of the interaction Hamiltonian density $\mathscr{H}$ for the β-decay processes

$$N \rightarrow P + e^- + \bar{\nu},\ P \rightarrow N + e^+ + \nu,$$

if $\mathscr{H}$ is: (i) linear in each of the four spinor fields,
(ii) does not involve any derivatives of the fields, and
(iii) is invariant under proper Lorentz transformations but need not conserve parity?

12.1 Derive eq. (12.7) from eq. (12.6).

13.1 Derive eq. (13.9).

13.2 Derive eq. (13.10).

14.1 Obtain the fourth-order Feynman graphs for Compton scattering.

14.2 Obtain the fourth-order Feynman graphs for electron-positron Møller scattering.

14.3 Show that the total e^3-contribution to the S-matrix of electrodynamics, eq. (13.12), due to Feynman graphs having three external photon lines and no external fermion lines, vanishes.

14.4 Show that the third-order contribution to the S-matrix in neutral $ps(ps)$-meson theory, having three external meson lines and no external nucleon lines, vanishes.

15.1 Derive eq. (15.40).

15.2 Obtain the differential and total cross-sections for Compton scattering in the non-relativistic limit of low energy photons.

16.1 Derive eq. (16.8).

16.2 Show that the elastic scattering of light by the Coulomb field $A_\mu^e(x)$ of a heavy nucleus calculated in first Born approximation in the external field $A_\mu^e(x)$ vanishes.

16.3 Show that the annihilation of a free electron-positron pair (i.e. there is no external field present) with emission of a single photon cannot occur.

16.4 Obtain the differential cross-sections, in the centre-of-momentum system and in the laboratory system in which the electron is initially at rest, for the annihilation of an electron and positron, colliding in flight, with emission of two photons:

$$e^+ + e^- \to \gamma + \gamma.$$

16.5 Obtain the differential cross-sections, in an arbitrary coordinate system and in the centre-of-momentum system, for elastic electron-electron scattering (Møller scattering).

16.6 Obtain the non-relativistic limit of the differential cross-section for Møller scattering [cf. exercise 16.5] in the centre-of-mass system of the two electrons and in the laboratory system in which one electron is at rest.

18.1 Derive eq. (18.31).

19.1 Derive eqs. (19.4—6).

20.1 Derive eqs. (20.2—3).

20.2 Prove the identity

$$\frac{\partial \Sigma(W, p)}{\partial p_\lambda} = - \Lambda_\lambda(V_1, p, p). \tag{1}$$

20.3 Prove, to order e^2, eq. (20.14); i.e. prove the equality of the renormalization constants B and $(-L)$ due to the second-order electron self-energy and vertex modifications. (Cf. exercise 20.2.)

21.1 Derive eq. (21.5).

Hints for Solving Exercises

2.1 Eqs. (2.8) give the Euler equations

$$\Box^2 A_\mu(x) = 0, \qquad \mu = 1, \ldots 4.$$

These are the equations for the four-vector potential $A_\mu(x) = (\mathbf{A}, iV)$ of an electromagnetic field which, together with the Lorentz condition

$$\frac{\partial A_\mu}{\partial x_\mu} = 0,$$

are equivalent to Maxwell's equations (cf. chapter IX).

2.2 Replacing $\mathscr{L}$ by $\mathscr{L}'$ changes the action integral (2.3) by

$$J = \int_\Omega d^4x \frac{\partial A_\nu}{\partial x_\nu} = \int_\Gamma dS_\nu A_\nu(\phi^\alpha),$$

by Gauss's theorem, and the variation $\delta J \equiv 0$, since $\delta\phi^\alpha = 0$ on Γ. Thus two Lagrangian densities differing by a four-dimensional divergence, of the above form, lead to the same field equations; we say the field equations are invariant under the transformation $\mathscr{L} \to \mathscr{L}'$.

2.4

$$T_{\mu\nu} = \phi_{,\mu}\phi_{,\nu} + \mathscr{L}\delta_{\mu\nu}$$

2.5

$$\frac{dP_\lambda}{dt} = \int d^3x \frac{\partial T_{4\lambda}}{\partial x_4} = -\int d^3x \sum_{r=1}^{3} \left(\frac{\partial T_{r\lambda}}{\partial x_r}\right).$$

Using Gauss's theorem, this three-dimensional volume integral of a divergence may be written as a two-dimensional surface integral, over the surface at infinity, of the normal component of the vector $\mathbf{T}_\lambda(\equiv T_{1\lambda}, T_{2\lambda}, T_{3\lambda})$, i.e.

$$\frac{dP_\lambda}{dt} = -\int \mathbf{T}_\lambda d\mathbf{S}, \qquad (\lambda = 1, \dots 4).$$

This integral vanishes if the fields vanish sufficiently rapidly at infinity (e.g. if the fields are different from zero in a finite region only).

We shall now briefly show that eqs. (2), exercise 2.3, state the laws of conservation of energy and momentum in differential form, whereas in this example these laws have been transformed to the integral form.

We saw in exercise 2.4 that, for the meson field, $T_{44} = -\mathscr{H}$. This relation is generally true. Hence

$$P_4(t) = -i \int d^3x\, T_{44} = i \int d^3x\, \mathscr{H} = iH(t),$$

and the constancy of $P_4(t)$ simply states the conservation of energy.

Defining the three-vector

$$\mathscr{S}_r = -i\, T_{r4}, \qquad r = 1, \dots 3,$$

we can write eq. (2), exercise 2.3, for $\nu = 4$, as

$$\frac{\partial \mathscr{H}}{\partial t} + \sum_{r=1}^{3} \left(\frac{\partial \mathscr{S}_r}{\partial x_r} \right) = 0.$$

This equation shows that the vector $\mathscr{S}_r$ ($r = 1, \dots 3$) is to be interpreted as the energy flux of the field.

The three other equations

$$\frac{\partial T_{\mu r}}{\partial x_\mu} = 0, \qquad (r = 1, \dots 3),$$

can similarly be interpreted as expressing conservation of momentum, the vector

$$\mathscr{G}_r = -iT_{4r}, \qquad (r = 1, \dots 3),$$

representing the momentum density of the field and the tensor T_{rs} (r, $s = 1, \dots 3$) the stress tensor of the field*).

*) For a more detailed discussion of these questions, cf. the books by Heitler or Wentzel (see bibliography), or Landau and Lifschitz, *Classical Theory of Fields*, Cambridge, Mass.; Addison-Wesley, 1951. An excellent account for the case of the electromagnetic field will be found in Becker, R. *Theorie der Elektrizität*, vol. II, § 57; 6th ed. Teubner 1933.

The tensor $T_{\mu\nu}$, defined by eq. (1) of exercise 2.3, is called the *canonical* energy-momentum tensor.

The conservation equations (2), exercise 2.3, do not determine the energy-momentum tensor uniquely, since they are unaltered if we replace $T_{\mu\nu}$ by

$$\tilde{T}_{\mu\nu} = T_{\mu\nu} + \frac{\partial}{\partial x_\lambda} G_{\lambda\mu\nu},$$

where $G_{\lambda\mu\nu}$ is a tensor of the third rank with

$$G_{\lambda\mu\nu} = - G_{\mu\lambda\nu}.$$

In general, the canonical energy-momentum tensor will not be symmetric, i.e.

$$T_{\nu\mu} \neq T_{\mu\nu}.$$

It is then possible to choose the third rank tensor $G_{\lambda\mu\nu}$ in such a way that the resultant energy-momentum tensor $\tilde{T}_{\mu\nu}$ is symmetric*)

$$\tilde{T}_{\mu\nu} = \tilde{T}_{\nu\mu}.$$

2.6 From the definition of $\mathscr{M}_{\lambda\mu\nu}$ and eq. (2), exercise 2.3,

$$\frac{\partial \mathscr{M}_{\lambda\mu\nu}}{\partial x_\lambda} = T_{\nu\mu} - T_{\mu\nu} = 0$$

if $T_{\mu\nu}$ is symmetric.

By comparison with exercise 2.5 it is clear that we have here derived another conservation law, the conserved quantity being

$$M_{\mu\nu} = - i \int d^3x \, \mathscr{M}_{4\mu\nu}.$$

In particular,

$$\begin{aligned} M_{rs} &= - i \int d^3x (T_{4r} x_s - T_{4s} x_r) \\ &= \int d^3x (\mathscr{G}_r x_s - \mathscr{G}_s x_r), \qquad r, s = 1, \ldots 3, \end{aligned}$$

where $\mathscr{G}_r$ is the momentum density of the field, defined in exercise 2.5, so that $(\mathscr{G}_r x_s - \mathscr{G}_s x_r)$ can be interpreted as the angular momentum density of the field and M_{rs} as the total angular momentum of the field.

*) Cf. Jauch and Rohrlich (see bibliography), § 1–11.

3.3 The energy-momentum tensor $T_{\mu\nu}$ given in eq. (1) of this exercise is of course identical with the energy-momentum tensor derived in exercise 2.4, provided we are dealing with a classical, i.e. unquantized field. The two expressions differ if we are dealing with a quantized theory, i.e. the ϕ and $\phi_{,\nu}$ are operators which in general do not commute. In this case the tensor $T_{\mu\nu}$ given in eq. (1) of this exercise is the correct energy-momentum tensor; it is symmetric and also has the required reality properties: T_{rs} and T_{44} are Hermitian, and T_{4r} and T_{r4} are anti-Hermitian, corresponding to the former quantities being observables (stress tensor and energy density), the latter observables (momentum density and energy flux) multiplied by i.

The momentum $\mathbf{P}$ of the field is given by

$$P_r = \int d^3x\, \mathscr{G}_r = -i \int d^3x\, T_{4r}$$

$$= -i \int d^3x \frac{1}{2} \left\{ \frac{\partial\phi}{\partial x_4} \frac{\partial\phi}{\partial x_r} + \frac{\partial\phi}{\partial x_r} \frac{\partial\phi}{\partial x_4} \right\}$$

$$= -\frac{1}{2} \int d^3x \left\{ \pi \frac{\partial\phi}{\partial x_r} + \frac{\partial\phi}{\partial x_r} \pi \right\},$$

where $\pi = \dot{\phi}$ (cf. eq. (2.19)), and we now interpret this equation as an operator equation in the Schrödinger representation. We see from this equation that $P_r^\dagger = P_r$, as required. Substituting eqs. (3.4), carrying out the integration and using the commutation relations (3.5), the result

$$\mathbf{P} = \sum_{\mathbf{k}} a^\dagger(\mathbf{k})\, a(\mathbf{k})\, \mathbf{k}$$

follows. It again illustrates the interpretation of $a^\dagger(\mathbf{k})a(\mathbf{k})$ as the occupation number operator for the state of a meson with momentum $\mathbf{k}$, the total momentum $\mathbf{P}$ being the sum of the contributions from the individual mesons.

7.1 Varying the action integral gives

$$\delta I = \int_\Omega d^4x \frac{\partial}{\partial x_\nu} \left\{ \frac{\partial \mathscr{L}}{\partial \phi^\alpha_{,\nu}} \delta\phi^\alpha \right\} = 0. \tag{1}$$

This follows from eq. (2.5), the first term on the right-hand side of this equation vanishing since the ϕ^α satisfy the field equations. Since eq. (1) holds for any four-volume Ω, the integrand must vanish identically, giving eqs. (1—2) of exercise 7.1.

For the density (7.2),

$$j_\nu = \frac{\partial \mathscr{L}}{\partial \phi_{,\nu}} \delta\phi + \frac{\partial \mathscr{L}}{\partial \phi^*_{,\nu}} \delta\phi^*$$
$$= i\alpha \left\{ \frac{\partial \mathscr{L}}{\partial \phi_{,\nu}} \phi - \frac{\partial \mathscr{L}}{\partial \phi^*_{,\nu}} \phi^* \right\},$$

where the last line follows from eq. (7.11), agreeing with eq. (7.8). Hence eq. (1) of exercise 7.1 in this case reduces to eq. (7.9), expressing the conservation of charge.

8.2 The Lagrangian density $\mathscr{L}$, eq. (8.19), differs from the Hermitian $\frac{1}{2}(\mathscr{L} + \mathscr{L}^\dagger)$ only by a divergence which, according to exercise 2.2, does not affect the field equations.

8.6 The first two relations (8.42) follow at once since they only involve anticommutators which vanish by eqs. (8.20b).

Similarly,

$$[\psi_\alpha(x),\ \bar\psi_\beta(x')]_+ = [\psi_\alpha^+(x),\ \bar\psi_\beta^-(x')]_+ + [\psi_\alpha^-(x),\ \bar\psi_\beta^+(x')]_+. \quad (1)$$

Using eqs. (8.37), the first anticommutator on the right-hand side of this equation becomes

$$[\psi_\alpha^+(x),\ \bar\psi_\beta^-(x')]_+$$
$$= \frac{1}{V} \sum_{\substack{p_0=E_{\mathbf{p}} \\ p'_0=E_{\mathbf{p}'}}} \sum \frac{M}{(p_0 p'_0)^{\frac{1}{2}}} \sum_{r=1}^{2} \sum_{s=1}^{2} [c_r(\mathbf{p}),\ c_s^\dagger(\mathbf{p}')]_+ u_\alpha^{(r)}(\mathbf{p}) \bar u_\beta^{(s)}(\mathbf{p}') e^{i(px-p'x')}.$$

Using successively eqs. (8.20a), (A 27), (A 22) and (3.7), this can be written

$$\frac{-1}{(2\pi)^3 2} \int_{p_0=E_{\mathbf{p}}} \frac{d^3p}{p_0} (i\not p - M)_{\alpha\beta} e^{ip(x-x')}$$
$$= \left(\gamma_\mu \frac{\partial}{\partial x_\mu} - M\right)_{\alpha\beta} \{-i\Delta^+(x-x',\ M)\} = -iS_{\alpha\beta}^+(x-x'),$$

by eqs. (6.9) and (8.44). This proves the first of the relations (8.48). The second one is derived similarly and hence the last of eqs. (8.42) follows.

8.7 From eq. (8.44),

$$\left(\gamma_\mu \frac{\partial}{\partial x_\mu} + M\right) S(x) = (\Box^2 - M^2)\Delta(x, M) = 0,$$

by exercise 6.3.

8.8 This follows either directly from eq. (8.43) or from

$$S(x) = \left(\gamma_\mu \frac{\partial}{\partial x_\mu} - M\right) \Delta(x, M).$$

8.9 These follow from eqs. (8.42) and exercise 8.8.

8.10 For $(x - x')$ a non-zero space-like vector, $\Delta(x - x', M)$ vanishes (cf. eq. (5.22)). From eqs. (8.44) and (8.42) it follows that in this case *all* components of the fields ψ and $\bar{\psi}$ anticommute. As a result all components of the four-current, which is bilinear in the spinor fields, commute.

8.13 (a) To obtain eq. (A 34): Using the anticommutation relations (A 2), a product of an odd number of γ-matrices can be reduced to $\pm\gamma_\lambda$ or to $\gamma_\lambda\gamma_\mu\gamma_\nu$ (λ, μ, ν different); and

$$\mathrm{Tr}\,\gamma_\lambda = \mathrm{Tr}\,\gamma_\lambda\gamma_\mu\gamma_\nu = 0$$

as follows from exercise 8.12 by writing $\gamma_\lambda = (\gamma_\lambda\gamma_\mu)\gamma_\mu$, with $\mu \neq \lambda$ and no summation over μ, and by writing $\gamma_\lambda\gamma_\mu\gamma_\nu = (\gamma_\lambda\gamma_\mu\gamma_\nu\gamma_\sigma)\gamma_\sigma$, with $\lambda, \mu, \nu, \sigma$ all different and no summation over σ.

(b) To obtain eq. (A 35): Using the anticommutation rules (A 2) we can write $(\gamma_\lambda\gamma_\mu \cdots \gamma_\sigma\gamma_\tau)$ as a multiple of the unit matrix or as a product of *different* γ-matrices only. Hence

$$\mathrm{Tr}\,(\gamma_\lambda\gamma_\mu \cdots \gamma_\sigma\gamma_\tau) \neq 0 \tag{1}$$

only if

$$(\gamma_\lambda\gamma_\mu \cdots \gamma_\sigma\gamma_\tau) = (-1)^P\, 1 \tag{2}$$

where P is the number of interchanges of neighbouring γ-matrices involved in going from the left-hand to the right-hand side of eq. (2). The same number P of interchanges is then required to write

$$(\gamma_\tau \gamma_\sigma \ldots \gamma_\mu \gamma_\lambda) = (-1)^P 1. \tag{3}$$

Hence eq. (A 35) follows.

9.1 This follows, for example, from eq. (5.18) by carrying out the $\mathbf{k}$-integration, writing $\mathbf{kx} = \omega r \cos\theta$, with $\omega = |\mathbf{k}|$, $r = |\mathbf{x}|$ and θ the angle between the vectors $\mathbf{k}$ and $\mathbf{x}$.

10.1 From eq. (9.16),

$$\langle A_\mu(x)\rangle = \frac{1}{\sqrt{V}} \sum_{\substack{s \\ (k_0=|\mathbf{k}_s|)}} \frac{1}{\sqrt{2k_0}} \sum_{m=1}^{4} \{\varepsilon_\mu^{(m)}(\mathbf{k}_s)\, e^{ik_s x}(\Phi,\ \eta a_m(\mathbf{k}_s)\Phi) + \varepsilon_\mu^{(m)*}(\mathbf{k}_s)\, e^{-ik_s x}(\Phi,\ \eta a_m^\dagger(\mathbf{k}_s)\Phi)\}. \tag{1}$$

From eqs. (10.24), (10.9), (10.17—23):

$$(\Phi,\ \eta a_m(\mathbf{k}_s)\Phi) = (\Phi,\ \eta a_m^\dagger(\mathbf{k}_s)\Phi) = 0, \qquad (m = 1,\ 2) \tag{2}$$

and

$$(\Phi,\ \eta a_m(\mathbf{k}_s)\Phi) = c_1(\mathbf{k}_s), \qquad (m = 3,\ 4) \tag{3}$$

where $c_1(\mathbf{k}_s)$ is the coefficient $c(\nu_1, \nu_2, \ldots)$ defined in eqs. (10.24) and (10.27).

From eq. (3) and eqs. (10.7)

$$(\Phi,\ \eta a_m^\dagger(\mathbf{k}_s)\Phi) = \pm c_1^*(\mathbf{k}_s), \qquad \left(m = \begin{Bmatrix} 3 \\ 4 \end{Bmatrix}\right). \tag{4}$$

Combining eqs. (1)—(4), the result, eqs. (10.25—26), follows since $\varepsilon_\mu^{(3)*} = \varepsilon_\mu^{(3)}$, $\varepsilon_\mu^{(4)*} = -\varepsilon_\mu^{(4)}$, and $\varepsilon_\mu^{(3)}(\mathbf{k}_s) + \varepsilon_\mu^{(4)}(\mathbf{k}_s) = (\mathbf{k}_s)_\mu/|\mathbf{k}_s|$.

11.1 The difference of eqs. (11.11) and (11.12) involves

$$\bar\psi\gamma_5\psi - \tfrac{1}{2}[\bar\psi,\ \gamma_5\psi] = \tfrac{1}{2}[\bar\psi,\ \gamma_5\psi]_+ = \left(\frac{-i}{2}\right) \mathrm{Tr}\,[\gamma_5 S(0)]$$

by eq. (8.42); and

$$\mathrm{Tr}\,[\gamma_5 S(0)] = \mathrm{Tr}\left[\gamma_5 \left(\gamma_\mu \frac{\partial}{\partial x_\mu} - M\right) \Delta(x,\ M)\right]_{x=0} = 0,$$

since $\mathrm{Tr}\,\gamma_5 = \mathrm{Tr}\,\gamma_5\gamma_\mu = 0$ (cf. exercises 8.12 and 8.13).

11.2 Using eq. (A 6a), eq. (11.13) becomes

$$\frac{f}{m}\{\psi^\dagger \boldsymbol{\sigma}\,\mathrm{grad}\,\phi\psi\} - \frac{f}{m}\psi^\dagger\gamma_5\psi\frac{\partial\phi}{\partial t}$$

and the second term is of order (v/c) in the non-relativistic limit.

11.3 The Lagrangian density is

$$\mathscr{L} = \mathscr{L}_{ph} + \mathscr{L}_f + \mathscr{L}_I \tag{1}$$

where $\mathscr{L}_{ph}$, $\mathscr{L}_f$ and $\mathscr{L}_I$ are respectively the Lagrangian densities of the free photon field, the free electron-positron (i.e. fermion) field and the interaction, and are respectively given by eq. (1) of exercise 2.1, eq. (8.19) and

$$\mathscr{L}_I = -\frac{ie}{2}[\bar{\psi}, \gamma_\mu\psi]A_\mu. \tag{2}$$

(The last equation follows from eqs. (11.7), (11.1) and (8.32)).

Under the gauge transformation (11.16), $(\mathscr{L}_f + \mathscr{L}_I)$ remains invariant. $\mathscr{L}_{ph}$ transforms into

$$\mathscr{L}_{ph} + \frac{\partial}{\partial x_\nu}\left\{A_\mu\frac{\partial^2\Lambda}{\partial x_\nu \partial x_\mu}\right\} - A_\mu\frac{\partial}{\partial x_\mu}(\Box^2\Lambda) - \tfrac{1}{2}\sum_{\mu,\nu}\frac{\partial^2\Lambda}{\partial x_\nu\partial x_\mu}. \tag{3}$$

Here the last term, being independent of the fields $A_\mu(x)$, and the second term, being a divergence, are not significant. Hence $\mathscr{L}_{ph}$, and consequently the total Lagrangian $\mathscr{L}$, are gauge-invariant provided $\Box^2\Lambda = 0$. This is just the condition that the transformed potential A'_μ should also satisfy the Lorentz condition (cf. eq. (9.6)).

The invariance under charge conjugation of the Lagrangian (1) follows from that of each term in eq. (1) separately. Under charge conjugation the fermion fields transform according to

$$\psi \to \psi^\dagger, \; \psi^\dagger \to \psi. \tag{4}$$

$\mathscr{L}_f$, eq. (8.19), was deliberately constructed to be invariant under this transformation while from eq. (8.29) $s_\mu \to -s_\mu$. Corresponding to this change in sign of charges and currents, the electromagnetic field must also change sign: $A_\mu(x) \to -A_\mu(x)$. Hence $\mathscr{L}_{ph}$ and $\mathscr{L}_I$ are also invariant with respect to the transformation of charge conjugation.

11.4 We must form all possible scalars and pseudoscalars which can be obtained by contraction from the five basic covariants eqs. (A 11). Taking ψ_N together with $\bar{\psi}_P$, and ψ_ν with $\bar{\psi}_e$, (where ψ_N is the operator which absorbs neutrons and emits antineutrons, etc.) one finds in this way for the interaction Hamiltonian density

$$\left.\begin{aligned}\mathscr{H} = \sum_i (\bar{\psi}_P O_i \psi_N)\,\{C_i(\bar{\psi}_e O_i \psi_\nu) + C_i'(\bar{\psi}_e O_i \gamma_5 \psi_\nu)\}\\ + \text{ Hermitian conjugate.}\end{aligned}\right\} \quad (1)$$

Here $i = S, V, T, A$ and P corresponds to the five possible covariants, eq. (A 11), with

$$O_S = 1,\ O_V = \gamma_\mu,\ O_T = \sigma_{\mu\nu},\ O_A = \gamma_\mu\gamma_5,\ O_P = \gamma_5.$$

The Hermitian conjugate is added so that $\mathscr{H}$ be a Hermitian operator. C_i and C_i' denote the 10 coupling constants; the terms proportional to C_i conserve parity, those linear in C_i' violate parity conservation.

At first sight, it may appear as though further interaction terms can be constructed by pairing the fermion operators differently. However, it can be shown that such terms are merely linear combinations of the ten interactions which occur in eq. (1)*).

13.1 One can write

$$N(\bar{\psi}\gamma_5\psi) = (\gamma_5)_{\alpha\beta}\{\bar{\psi}_\alpha\psi_\beta - [\psi_{\bar{\beta}}^-,\ \bar{\psi}_\alpha^+]_+\} \quad (1)$$

and

$$\tfrac{1}{2}[\bar{\psi},\ \gamma_5\psi] = \tfrac{1}{2}(\gamma_5)_{\alpha\beta}[\bar{\psi}_\alpha,\ \psi_\beta]. \quad (2)$$

Hence the difference of these expressions [(2)—(1)] gives

$$\tfrac{1}{2}(\gamma_5)_{\alpha\beta}\{-[\psi_\beta,\ \bar{\psi}_\alpha]_+ + 2[\psi_{\bar{\beta}}^-,\ \bar{\psi}_\alpha^+]_+\} = \tfrac{1}{2}\,\mathrm{Tr}\,\{\gamma_5 S^{(1)}(0)\},$$

by eqs. (8.42), (8.48) and (6.8); and

$$\mathrm{Tr}\,\{\gamma_5 S^{(1)}(0)\} = \mathrm{Tr}\left\{\gamma_5\left(\gamma_\mu\frac{\partial}{\partial x_\mu} - M\right)\Delta^{(1)}(x, M)\right\}_{x=0} = 0.$$

13.2 Compared with $ps(ps)$-meson theory one now finds that the difference of the two Hamiltonians (13.10) and (11.1) is

*) Fierz, M. *Z. Phys.* **104**, 553, 1937; Michel, L. *Proc. phys. Soc.* A **63**, 514, 1950; Case, K. M. *Phys. Rev.* **97**, 810, 1955.

proportional to $\mathrm{Tr}\,\{\gamma_\mu S^{(1)}(0)\}$. On account of eq. (A 33) one cannot at once say that this trace vanishes. However, using the integral representation (6.7—8) to express $S^{(1)}(0)$, one obtains,

$$\mathrm{Tr}\,\{\gamma_\mu S^{(1)}(0)\} = \frac{i}{(2\pi)^3}\int \frac{d^3p}{2E_{\mathbf{p}}}\{2iM\,\mathrm{Tr}\,\gamma_\mu + 2p_r\,\mathrm{Tr}\,\gamma_\mu\gamma_r\} = 0,$$

since $\mathrm{Tr}\,\gamma_\mu = 0$ and the momentum integrals in the second term vanish from symmetry considerations.

14.1 These graphs are obtained by expanding by Wick's theorem the e^4-term in eq. (13.12),

$$S^{(4)} = \frac{e^4}{4!}\int\ldots\int d^4x_1\ldots d^4x_4\,T\{N(\bar\psi A\!\!\!/\psi)_{x_4}\ldots N(\bar\psi A\!\!\!/\psi)_{x_1}\}, \tag{1}$$

picking out the terms involving three fermion propagators and one photon propagator. In this way two photon operators and two fermion operators (ψ and $\bar\psi$) are left which are not contracted over and which absorb the initial photon and electron and emit the final ones. The (4!) in the denominator of eq. (1) again cancels against the (4!) possible permutations of labelling vertices. Since we are dealing with electron scattering, we pick out the parts ψ^+ and $\bar\psi^-$ from the uncontracted fermion fields. (For positrons, $\bar\psi^+$ and ψ^- would occur.) For the photons we similarly require an A^+ and an A^- but now *either* photon field can supply the absorption or creation part. As a result each topologically distinct Feynman graph gives two contributions, as we already found in eqs. (14.6—7) and figs. 11(a) and (b).

The e^4-graphs are shown in fig. 26: each graph represents two contributions according to which photon line represents the incident and which the scattered photon, as just discussed. The first of the two graphs, fig. 26(a), originates from the following contribution to eq. (1):

$$\begin{aligned} e^4 &\int\ldots\int d^4x_1\ldots d^4x_4 \\ &\times N\{\bar\psi^-(x_4)\gamma_\sigma\underbrace{\psi(x_4)\bar\psi(x_3)}\gamma_\nu\underbrace{\psi(x_3)\bar\psi(x_2)}\gamma_\mu\underbrace{\psi(x_2)\bar\psi(x_1)}\gamma_\lambda\psi^+(x_1)\} \\ &\times N\{\underbrace{A_\sigma(x_4)A_\nu(x_3)}A_\mu^-(x_2)A_\lambda^+(x_1)\} \end{aligned}$$

and a similar term with $A_\mu^-(x_2)A_\lambda^+(x_1)$ replaced by $A_\mu^+(x_2)A_\lambda^-(x_1)$. Similarly one obtains the expressions corresponding to the other Feynman graphs in fig. 26. Fig. 26(f) contains a further two-fold multiplicity according as to whether the arrows on the three fermion propagators forming the triangle run in clockwise or anticlockwise direction. The contributions from these two graphs cancel as can be shown quite generally (cf. exercise 14.3—4).

14.3 These contributions arise from the graphs shown in fig. 38, known as triangle diagrams. If the contribution due to graph (a) is $S_a = e^3M$, that due to (b) will be

$$S_b = (-e)^3M = -S_a. \tag{1}$$

For the two graphs differ only in the senses of the fermion lines, i.e. electrons and positrons have been interchanged. This is the same as replacing e by $(-e)$ in the interaction, leading to the above result.

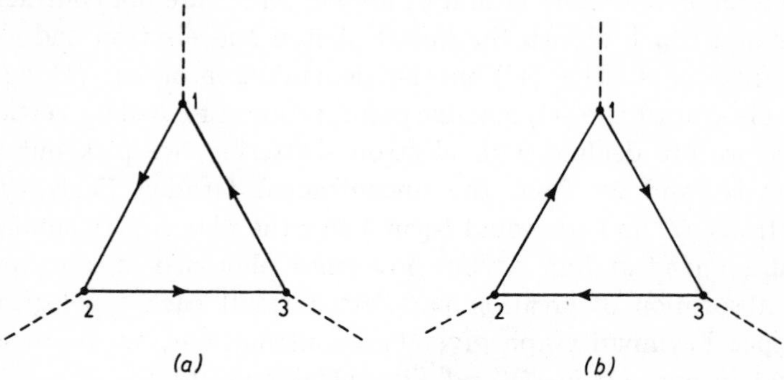

Fig. 38. Triangle diagrams.

The above general argument is easily verified in detail from the S-matrix. Writing ψ_n and $\bar{\psi}_n$ for $\psi(x_n)$ and $\bar{\psi}(x_n)$:

$$S^{(3)} = e^3 \int \ldots \int d^4x_1 \ldots d^4x_3 N\{A_\nu(x_3)A_\mu(x_2)A_\lambda(x_1)$$

$$\times [\bar{\psi}_3\gamma_\nu\psi_3\bar{\psi}_2\gamma_\mu\psi_2\bar{\psi}_1\gamma_\lambda\psi_1 + \bar{\psi}_3\gamma_\nu\psi_3\bar{\psi}_2\gamma_\mu\psi_2\bar{\psi}_1\gamma_\lambda\psi_1]\}, \tag{2}$$

The first and second terms corresponding to figs. (a) and (b) respectively. The spinor part of this expression becomes, apart from numerical factors,

$$\mathrm{Tr}\,[S_F(x_3-x_2)\gamma_\mu S_F(x_2-x_1)\gamma_\lambda S_F(x_1-x_3)\gamma_\nu]$$
$$+\,\mathrm{Tr}\,[S_F(x_3-x_1)\gamma_\lambda S_F(x_1-x_2)\gamma_\mu S_F(x_2-x_3)\gamma_\nu]. \qquad (3)$$

This vanishes as is easily shown, the two terms being of equal magnitude but opposite signs. [In the second term make the replacement $\gamma_\alpha \to -\gamma_\alpha$ *throughout* (cf. eq. (A 34)). This implies $S_F(x) \to S_F(-x)$. Finally use eq. (A 35).]

The argument which led to eq. (1) can obviously be generalized: a Feynman graph containing a closed polygon of fermion lines with an odd number of vertices gives no contribution to the S-matrix in electrodynamics. This is Furry's theorem. It is seen to be a consequence of the invariance of quantum electrodynamics under charge conjugation.

14.4 In this case one obtains expressions quite analogous, mutatis mutandis, to eqs. (2) and (3) in the solution of exercise 14.3. In particular, in eq. (3) the effect is to replace each of the three gamma-matrices γ_λ, γ_μ, γ_ν by γ_5. One can then easily show that each of the traces in eq. (3), *taken by itself*, vanishes.

15.2 In the non-relativistic limit, $\omega_{\mathbf{k}} \ll M$, the scattering is elastic: $\omega_{\mathbf{k}'} = \omega_{\mathbf{k}}$, (cf. eq. (15.28)). Eq. (15.43) becomes

$$\sigma(\theta)\,d\Omega = \tfrac{1}{2}r_0^2 d\Omega(1+\cos^2\theta)$$

and

$$\sigma_{\text{Total}} = \int \sigma(\theta)\,d\Omega = \frac{8\pi}{3}r_0^2.$$

This formula was first obtained by J. J. Thomson from the classical theory of electrons and is known as Thomson scattering.

16.2 This process known as Delbrück scattering is given, in first Born approximation, by the triangle graphs of fig. 38, except that at one of the vertices, say the one labelled 1, the external field acts instead of the radiation field. By Furry's theorem (cf. exercise 14.3), the sum of the contributions of the two graphs (a) and (b), fig. (38), again vanishes.

However, this process has a non-zero cross-section when calculated in second Born approximation, the Feynman graph for which is shown in fig. 39. The cross-section for this process is very small. It may be estimated as follows.

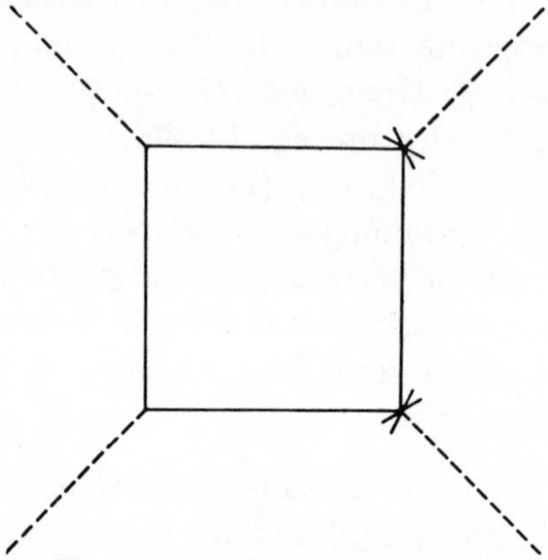

Fig. 39. Delbrück scattering.

Firstly consider the scattering of light by light (i.e. diagram 39 with free photons at all four vertices). Being a fourth-order process, we expect the cross-section to be of the order of

$$\left(\frac{e^2}{4\pi}\right)^4 \left(\frac{1}{M}\right)^2 \approx 4 \times 10^{-30} \text{ cm}^2 \tag{1}$$

($1/M$ = Compton wave length of electron).

The effect of having the Coulomb field of a nucleus of charge Ze acting at two of the vertices is to introduce an extra factor of the order of

$$\left(\frac{Z^2 e^2}{4\pi}\right)^2 = \left(\frac{Z^2}{137}\right)^2 \approx \tfrac{1}{2} \times 10^4$$

for a heavy nucleus ($Z \approx 100$), giving for the cross-section for Delbrück scattering

$$\sigma \approx 2 \times 10^{-26} \text{ cm}^2. \tag{2}$$

Although the cross-section (1) for the scattering of light by light is too small to be observable, Delbrück scattering is, for heavy nuclei, just about detectable*).

*) Wilson, R. R. *Phys. Rev.* **90**, 720, 1953.

The two phenomena which have been discussed, the scattering of light by light or by the field of an atom, are direct consequences of the non-linear nature of quantum electrodynamics, i.e. of the possible formation of virtual electron-positron pairs which may be scattered by the electromagnetic field before annihilating each other with emission of a photon. Classically such a process is of course not possible.

16.3 This follows at once from the energy and momentum conservation laws which would imply

$$p_1 + p_2 = k \tag{1}$$

(p_1, p_2 the energy-momentum four-vectors of the fermions, k that of the emitted photon). On account of the free particle conditions $p_1^2 + M^2 = p_2^2 + M^2 = k^2 = 0$ eq. (1) cannot be satisfied.

16.4 The process

$$e^+ + e^- \to \gamma + \gamma$$

is closely related to Compton scattering (cf. chapter 15)

$$e^- + \gamma \to e^- + \gamma$$

so that most of the results can be taken over from Compton scattering, provided a general Lorentz frame is used for the calculation. This is also advantageous as we want the centre-of-momentum and laboratory cross-sections which are then derived from the same general result.

(i) *Matrix element*: The matrix element

$$M_{ji} = (\Phi_j, S_B^{(2)} \Phi_i), \tag{1}$$

with

$$\left.\begin{array}{ll} \Phi_i = c_r^\dagger(\mathbf{p}_1) d_s^\dagger(\mathbf{p}_2)\Phi_0, & \Phi_j = a_m^\dagger(\mathbf{k}_1) a_n^\dagger(\mathbf{k}_2)\Phi_0 \\ (r,\ s = 1,\ 2) & (m,\ n = 1,\ 2) \end{array}\right\} \tag{2}$$

and $S_B^{(2)}$ given by eq. (14.2b) is

$$M_{ji} = (2\pi)^4 \delta^{(4)}(p_1 + p_2 - k_1 - k_2) \left(\frac{-e^2}{V^2}\right) \left(\frac{M^2}{4E_1 E_2 \omega_1 \omega_2}\right)^{\frac{1}{2}} A, \tag{3}$$

where

$$E_i = \sqrt{(M^2 + \mathbf{p}_i^2)}, \quad \omega_i = \sqrt{(\mathbf{k}_i^2)}, \quad i = 1,\ 2, \tag{4}$$

and

$$A = \bar{u}^{(s+2)}(\mathbf{p}_2)Ou^{(r)}(\mathbf{p}_1) \tag{5}$$

with

$$O = \left\{ \not{e}^{(n)}(\mathbf{k}_2)\frac{1}{\not{p}_1 - \not{k}_1 - iM}\not{e}^{(m)}(\mathbf{k}_1) + \not{e}^{(m)}(\mathbf{k}_1)\frac{1}{\not{p}_1 - \not{k}_2 - iM}\not{e}^{(n)}(\mathbf{k}_2)\right\}. \tag{6}$$

(Cf. eqs. (15.18—19)).

(ii) *Cross-section*: The differential cross-section for one photon to be scattered into the element of solid angle $d\Omega_1$ is

$$d\sigma = \frac{V^2}{v}\int \frac{V^2 d^3k_1 d^3k_2}{(2\pi)^6}(2\pi)^4\delta^{(4)}(p_1 + p_2 - k_1 - k_2)$$
$$\times \left(\frac{-e^2}{V^2}\right)^2 \left(\frac{M^2}{4E_1 E_2 \omega_1 \omega_2}\right)\{\tfrac{1}{4}\sum \ldots \sum_{m,n,r,s=1}^{2} |A|^2\}, \tag{7}$$

where photon polarizations and fermion spins have already been summed and averaged over. v is the relative velocity of the electron-positron pair. Eq. (7) becomes

$$d\sigma = \frac{1}{v} r_0^2 \frac{M^4}{E_1 E_2} d\Omega_1 \int \left(\frac{\omega_1}{\omega_2}\right) d\omega_1 \delta(\omega_1 + \omega_2 - E_1 - E_2)\{\tfrac{1}{4}\sum \ldots \sum |A|^2\}. \tag{8}$$

In this energy integral ω_2 is *not* a constant but is a function of ω_1 which is given, for each direction of emission of the photon labelled 1, by

$$\omega_2 = \sqrt{(\mathbf{p}_1 + \mathbf{p}_2 - \mathbf{k}_1)^2}. \tag{9}$$

Hence eq. (8) becomes

$$d\sigma = \frac{1}{v} r_0^2 \frac{M^4}{E_1 E_2} d\Omega_1 \left(\frac{\omega_1}{\omega_2}\right) \frac{\partial \omega_1}{\partial(\omega_1 + \omega_2)} \{\tfrac{1}{4}\sum \ldots \sum |A|^2\}, \tag{10}$$

where $\partial\omega_1/\partial(\omega_1 + \omega_2)$ is evaluated for constant $\mathbf{p}_1$, $\mathbf{p}_2$ and fixed direction $(\mathbf{k}_1/\omega_1)$. (Cf. eq. (15.26)).

(iii) *Polarization sums*: Evaluation of the spin and polarization sum in eq. (10) gives

$$\{\tfrac{1}{4}\sum \ldots \sum |A|^2\} = -\tfrac{1}{4}\sum_{m,n=1,2}\sum \mathrm{Tr}\,\{\tilde{O}\Lambda^-(\mathbf{p}_2)O\Lambda^+(\mathbf{p}_1)\}. \tag{11}$$

Comparison of this expression with eq. (15.36) shows that these expressions are identical, apart from a factor (-1), if we make the substitutions

$$\left.\begin{array}{ll} p \to p_1 & k \to -k_1 \\ p' \to -p_2 & k' \to k_2 \end{array}\right\} \tag{12}$$

in eq. (15.36), which correspond to the fact that the two fermions are now present initially, the two photons finally. Hence, from eq. (15.32), if we redefine

$$M^2\xi_1 = -p_1k_1 = -p_2k_2, \quad M^2\xi_2 = -p_1k_2 = -p_2k_1, \tag{13}$$

then from eqs. (15.36), (15.40) and (11—12) above

$$\{\tfrac{1}{4}\Sigma\ldots\Sigma|A|^2\} = \frac{1}{2M^2}\left[\left(\frac{\xi_1}{\xi_2}+\frac{\xi_2}{\xi_1}\right)+2\left(\frac{1}{\xi_1}+\frac{1}{\xi_2}\right)-\left(\frac{1}{\xi_1}+\frac{1}{\xi_2}\right)^2\right]. \tag{14}$$

Eqs. (10) and (14) give the general expression for the differential annihilation cross-section for one photon to be emitted into $d\Omega_1$.

(iv) *Centre-of-momentum system*: In this case

$$\left.\begin{array}{ll} \mathbf{p}_1 = -\mathbf{p}_2 = \mathbf{p}, & \\ E_1 = E_2 = E, & \omega_1 = \omega_2 = \omega, \end{array}\right\}$$

and

$$v = 2|\mathbf{p}|/E.$$

In eq. (10)

$$\frac{\partial\omega_1}{\partial(\omega_1+\omega_2)} = \frac{\partial\omega}{\partial(2\omega)} = \tfrac{1}{2}$$

and eq. (10), together with eq. (14), becomes

$$d\sigma = \tfrac{1}{4}r_0^2\frac{M^2}{Ep}d\Omega_1\left\{\frac{E^2+p^2+p^2\sin^2\theta}{E^2-p^2\cos^2\theta} - \frac{2p^4\sin^4\theta}{(E^2-p^2\cos^2\theta)^2}\right\}, \tag{15}$$

where $p = |\mathbf{p}|$ is the magnitude of the three-vector $\mathbf{p}$ and θ is the angle between the direction of the incident positron (or electron) and either photon.

(v) *Laboratory system*: In this case

$$\left.\begin{aligned} p_1 &= (000,\ iM) \\ p_2 &= (\mathbf{m}p,\ iE) \qquad E = \sqrt{(M^2 + p^2)} \\ k_s &= (\mathbf{n}_s\omega_s,\ i\omega_s), \qquad s = 1,\ 2, \end{aligned}\right\}$$

($\mathbf{m}$ and $\mathbf{n}_s$ unit vectors, $p = |\mathbf{p}_2|$) and

$$v = p/E. \tag{16}$$

In evaluating eq. (10)

$$\mathbf{n}_2\omega_2 = \mathbf{m}p - \mathbf{n}_1\omega_1 \tag{17}$$

whence

$$\omega_1 + \omega_2 = \omega_1 + \{p^2 + \omega_1^2 - 2p\omega_1 \cos\theta_1\}^{\frac{1}{2}}, \tag{18}$$

with $\cos\theta_1 = \mathbf{m}\mathbf{n}_1$. Hence by differentiation with respect to $(\omega_1 + \omega_2)$,

$$1 = \left[\frac{\partial\omega_1}{\partial(\omega_1 + \omega_2)}\right]_{\theta_1} \left\{1 + \frac{\omega_1 - p\cos\theta_1}{\omega_2}\right\}$$

and, from eq. (17),

$$\frac{\partial\omega_1}{\partial(\omega_1 + \omega_2)} = \frac{1}{1 - \cos\Theta}, \tag{19}$$

where $\cos\Theta = \mathbf{n}_1\mathbf{n}_2$.

In evaluating the polarization sum (14),

$$\xi_1 = \frac{\omega_1}{M}, \qquad \xi_2 = \frac{\omega_2}{M}$$

$$\frac{1}{\xi_1} + \frac{1}{\xi_2} = M\left(\frac{1}{\omega_1} + \frac{1}{\omega_2}\right) = (1 - \cos\Theta), \tag{20}$$

which follows from the conservation of energy and momentum, and

$$\frac{\xi_1}{\xi_2} + \frac{\xi_2}{\xi_1} = -2 + \left(1 + \frac{E}{M}\right)(1 - \cos\Theta). \tag{21}$$

Combining eqs. (10), (14), (16) and (19—21)

$$d\sigma = \tfrac{1}{2}r_0^2 \frac{M}{p}\, d\Omega_1 \left(\frac{\omega_1}{\omega_2}\right)\left[1 + \frac{E}{M} - \frac{1 + \cos^2\Theta}{1 - \cos\Theta}\right]. \tag{22}$$

(In this equation ω_1, ω_2 and Θ are of course fixed for a given direction of emission $\mathbf{n}_1$ of the photon, from the conservation of energy and momentum equations.)

Finally, we want to give a general expression for the relative velocity v which occurs in eq. (7). Given two particles of mass M_1 and M_2, having energy-momentum vectors $p_s = (\mathbf{p}_s, iE_s)$, $s = 1, 2$, in a particular frame of reference, we *define* the relative velocity v to be

$$v = \frac{1}{E_1 E_2} \{(p_1 p_2)^2 - M_1^2 M_2^2\}^{\frac{1}{2}}. \tag{23}$$

In a coordinate system in which the two particles have parallel momenta, i.e. $p_s = (\mathbf{n}P_s, iE_s)$ [where P_s is a number not a vector], eq. (23) reduces to the usual expression for the relative velocity

$$v = \left| \frac{P_1}{E_1} - \frac{P_2}{E_2} \right| . \tag{24}$$

Eq. (7) can now be rewritten

$$d\sigma = \left(\frac{e^2}{4\pi}\right)^2 \frac{M^2}{\sqrt{[(p_1 p_2)^2 - M^4]}} \int \frac{d^3k_1\, d^3k_2}{\omega_1\ \omega_2} \delta^{(4)}(p_1 + p_2 - k_1 - k_2) \times \{\tfrac{1}{4}\Sigma \ldots \Sigma |A|^2\}. \tag{25}$$

Since generally for any four-vector x_μ, (d^3x/x_0) is invariant under a Lorentz transformation, the cross-section (25) is itself seen to be an invariant with this definition of relative velocity.

These considerations are of course generally true, not only for the case of two-quantum annihilation of an electron-positron pair treated here. In particular, they are also applicable to photons.

16.5 (i) *Matrix element*: The matrix element, derived from eq. (14.2c), is

$$M_{ji} = (c_r^\dagger(\mathbf{p}_1') c_s^\dagger(\mathbf{p}_2') \Phi_0,\ \ S_C^{(2)} c_m^\dagger(\mathbf{p}_1) c_n^\dagger(\mathbf{p}_2) \Phi_0)$$
$$= (2\pi)^4 \delta^{(4)}(p_1 + p_2 - p_1' - p_2') \left(\frac{-ie^2}{V^2}\right) \left(\frac{M^4}{E_1 E_2 E_1' E_2'}\right)^{\frac{1}{2}} A \tag{1}$$

where $p_1 = (\mathbf{p}_1,\ iE_1)$, etc., and

$$A = \frac{(\bar{u}^{(s)}(\mathbf{p}_2')\gamma_\nu u^{(n)}(\mathbf{p}_2))(\bar{u}^{(r)}(\mathbf{p}_1')\gamma_\nu u^{(m)}(\mathbf{p}_1))}{(p_1' - p_1)^2 - i\varepsilon}$$
$$- \frac{(\bar{u}^{(r)}(\mathbf{p}_1')\gamma_\nu u^{(n)}(\mathbf{p}_2))(\bar{u}^{(s)}(\mathbf{p}_2')\gamma_\nu u^{(m)}(\mathbf{p}_1))}{(p_2' - p_1)^2 - i\varepsilon}. \tag{2}$$

The $i\varepsilon$ may be dropped at this stage as the denominators are never zero. The second term of eq. (2) represents exchange scattering (cf. fig. 16).

(ii) *Cross-section*: Eqs. (1) and (2) give for the differential cross-section

$$d\sigma = \frac{4}{v}\left(\frac{e^2}{4\pi}\right)^2 \frac{M^4}{E_1E_2}\int \frac{d^3p_1'd^3p_2'}{E_1'E_2'}\delta^{(4)}(p_1+p_2-p_1'-p_2')\{\tfrac{1}{4}\sum_{\substack{m,n\\r,s}=1,2}\cdots\sum|A|^2\}. \tag{3}$$

(iii) *Spin summation*

$$\{\tfrac{1}{4}\sum\sum\sum\sum_{m,n,r,s=1,2}|A|^2\} = \frac{a}{[(p_1'-p_1)^2]^2} + \frac{b}{[(p_2'-p_1)^2]^2} + \frac{c}{(p_1'-p_1)^2(p_2'-p_1)^2}, \tag{4}$$

where

$$\left.\begin{aligned} a &= \tfrac{1}{4}\,\mathrm{Tr}\,\{\gamma_\mu \Lambda^+(\mathbf{p}_2)\gamma_\nu \Lambda^+(\mathbf{p}_2')\}\,\mathrm{Tr}\,\{\gamma_\mu \Lambda^+(\mathbf{p}_1)\gamma_\nu \Lambda^+(\mathbf{p}_1')\},\\ b &= \tfrac{1}{4}\,\mathrm{Tr}\,\{\gamma_\mu \Lambda^+(\mathbf{p}_2)\gamma_\nu \Lambda^+(\mathbf{p}_1')\}\,\mathrm{Tr}\,\{\gamma_\mu \Lambda^+(\mathbf{p}_1)\gamma_\nu \Lambda^+(\mathbf{p}_2')\},\\ c &= -\tfrac{1}{2}\,\mathrm{Tr}\,\{\gamma_\mu \Lambda^+(\mathbf{p}_2)\gamma_\nu \Lambda^+(\mathbf{p}_1')\gamma_\mu \Lambda^+(\mathbf{p}_1)\gamma_\nu \Lambda^+(\mathbf{p}_2')\}.\end{aligned}\right\} \tag{5}$$

With

$$\left.\begin{aligned} p_1p_2 &= p_1'p_2' = -M^2\xi\\ p_1p_1' &= p_2p_2' = -M^2\eta\\ p_1p_2' &= p_1'p_2 = -M^2\zeta\end{aligned}\right\} \tag{6}$$

$$\left.\begin{aligned} a &= \tfrac{1}{2}(\xi^2+\zeta^2-2\eta+2)\\ b &= \tfrac{1}{2}(\xi^2+\eta^2-2\zeta+2)\\ c &= (\xi^2-\xi-\eta-\zeta+1).\end{aligned}\right\} \tag{7}$$

Note that b is obtained from a, eqs. (5), by interchanging p_1' and p_2', i.e. η and ζ. Hence the second of eqs. (7) at once follows from the first. Eqs. (3), (4) and (7) give the result for the differential cross-section referred to a general coordinate system.

(iv) *Centre-of-momentum system*: We specialize

$$\left.\begin{aligned} p_1 &= (p\mathbf{n},\ iE) & p_1' &= (p\mathbf{n}',\ iE) \\ p_2 &= (-p\mathbf{n},\ iE) & p_2' &= (-p\mathbf{n}',\ iE) \end{aligned}\right\} \tag{8}$$

with $\mathbf{n}$ and $\mathbf{n}'$ unit vectors and $E = \sqrt{(M^2 + p^2)}$. In this coordinate system

$$(p_1' - p_1)^2 = 4p^2 \sin^2 \frac{\theta}{2}, \quad (p_2' - p_1)^2 = 4p^2 \cos^2 \frac{\theta}{2}, \tag{9}$$

where $\cos\theta = \mathbf{nn}'$, i.e. θ is the scattering angle of one of the electrons. (The angular distribution is of course symmetric with respect to the replacements $\theta \to -\theta$ or $\theta \to \pm(\pi - \theta)$.) Hence eq. (4) reduces to

$$\{\tfrac{1}{4}\sum \ldots |A|^2\} = \frac{1}{(2p)^4}\left\{\frac{a}{\sin^4 \frac{\theta}{2}} + \frac{b}{\cos^4 \frac{\theta}{2}} + \frac{c}{\sin^2 \frac{\theta}{2} \cos^2 \frac{\theta}{2}}\right\}. \tag{10}$$

Using

$$v = 2p/E, \tag{11}$$

the differential cross-section (3) reduces in this case to

$$d\sigma = r_0^2\, d\Omega_1 \left(\frac{M}{E}\right)^2 M^4 \{\tfrac{1}{4}\sum \ldots \sum |A|^2\}. \tag{12}$$

Evaluating a, b and c from eqs. (6—7), one obtains from eqs. (10) and (12)

$$d\sigma = \tfrac{1}{4} r_0^2\, d\Omega_1 \left(\frac{M^2}{p^4 E^2}\right)\left\{\frac{4(E^2 + p^2)^2}{\sin^4\theta} - \frac{(8E^4 - 4E^2M^2 - M^4)}{\sin^2\theta} + p^4\right\}. \tag{13}$$

16.6 The centre-of-mass cross-section is best obtained directly from eqs. (10) and (12) of the solution to exercise 16.5, since from eqs. (6—7), $a = b = -c = 1$. Hence

$$d\sigma = \frac{r_0^2}{v^4}\, d\Omega_1 \left\{\frac{1}{\sin^4 \frac{\theta}{2}} + \frac{1}{\cos^4 \frac{\theta}{2}} - \frac{1}{\sin^2 \frac{\theta}{2} \cos^2 \frac{\theta}{2}}\right\}, \tag{1}$$

where v is the relative velocity of the two electrons, given by eq. (11) of the previous exercise.

If $d\Omega_1'$ is the element of solid angle and Θ the scattering angle in the laboratory system, then

$$\Theta = \tfrac{1}{2}\theta \tag{2}$$

whence the cross-section in the laboratory system becomes

$$d\sigma = \frac{r_0^2}{v^4}\, d\Omega_1'\, 4\cos\Theta \left\{ \frac{1}{\sin^4\Theta} + \frac{1}{\cos^4\Theta} - \frac{1}{\sin^2\Theta\cos^2\Theta} \right\}. \tag{3}$$

The first term in this equation is just the Rutherford scattering formula. The last two terms represent exchange effects due to the identity of the two particles in this particular case.

18.1 Using a Majorana representation in which $\gamma_4^T = -\gamma_4$, one easily shows that

$$\begin{aligned} \mathscr{H}' &= -\tfrac{1}{2}\delta M[\bar{\psi}(x),\ \psi(x)] \\ &= -\delta M\bar{\psi}(x)\psi(x) + \tfrac{1}{2}\delta M[\bar{\psi}(x),\ \psi(x)]_+, \end{aligned}$$

and the last term vanishes by eq. (8.42) and $\mathrm{Tr}\, S(0) = 0$.

20.2 From

$$S_F(p) = \frac{1}{\not{p} - iM}, \qquad S_F^{-1}(p) = (\not{p} - iM),$$

one obtains by differentiating

$$S_F(p) S_F^{-1}(p) = 1$$

with respect to p_λ

$$\frac{\partial S_F(p)}{\partial p_\lambda} = -S_F(p)\gamma_\lambda S_F(p). \tag{1}$$

Differentiating eq. (18.8) with respect to p_λ and using eq. (1), it follows, by comparison with eq. (20.3), that

$$\frac{\partial \Sigma(W,\ p)}{\partial p_\lambda} = -\Lambda_\lambda(V_1,\ p,\ p). \tag{2}$$

Eq. (2) relates the fermion self-energy graph W, fig. 23(a), to the vertex part V_1, fig. 23(c), by inserting a vertex at which a zero-energy photon is emitted into the internal fermion line of the former graph W. Eq. (2) is a particular case of Ward's identity which generally relates fermion self-energy modifications to vertex parts in this manner*).

20.3 From Ward's identity (cf. exercise 20.2) and eq. (18.15) and eqs. (20.7) and (20.10):

$$(B + L)\gamma_\nu = -\frac{\partial}{\partial p_\nu}[S_c(W, p)(\not{p} - iM)] - \Lambda_{\nu c}(V_1, p, p). \quad (1)$$

If $p^2 + M^2 = 0$, so that

$$(\not{p} - iM)u(\mathbf{p}) = \bar{u}(\mathbf{p})(\not{p} - iM) = 0,$$

then

$$\bar{u}(\mathbf{p})[(B + L)\gamma_\nu]u(\mathbf{p}) = 0, \qquad \nu = 1, \ldots 4,$$

[cf. eqs. (18.14—18) and (20.4—10)], whence eq. (20.14) follows.

Again, by using the general form of Ward's identity one can prove the relation (20.14) generally in any finite order of perturbation theory, not only to second order.

*) Ward, J. C. *Phys. Rev.* **78**, 182, 1950. A fuller discussion of Ward's identity will be found in the books by Jauch and Rohrlich and by Schweber, Bethe and de Hoffmann (see bibliography).

APPENDIX

The Dirac Equation *

In the Dirac equation

$$\left(\gamma_\mu \frac{\partial}{\partial x_\mu} + M\right) \psi = 0 \tag{A 1}$$

the γ_μ $(\mu = 1, \ldots 4)$ satisfy

$$\gamma_\mu \gamma_\nu + \gamma_\nu \gamma_\mu = 2\delta_{\mu\nu}, \qquad (\mu, \nu = 1, \ldots 4). \tag{A 2}$$

We define

$$\gamma_5 = \gamma_1 \gamma_2 \gamma_3 \gamma_4 \tag{A 3}$$

then

$$\gamma_5^2 = 1, \quad \gamma_5 \gamma_\mu + \gamma_\mu \gamma_5 = 0, \tag{A 4}$$

and we also define

$$\alpha_k = i\gamma_4 \gamma_k, \qquad \beta = \gamma_4 \tag{A 5}$$

and

$$\sigma_{\mu\nu} = \frac{-i}{2} (\gamma_\mu \gamma_\nu - \gamma_\nu \gamma_\mu). \tag{A 6}$$

In particular

$$\sigma_k \equiv \sigma_{lm} = -i\gamma_l \gamma_m = i\gamma_4 \gamma_5 \gamma_k, \tag{A 6a}$$

if k, l, m are in cyclic order.

Below we shall derive all properties of the Dirac equation which we need without using a particular representation. *We shall, however, always restrict ourselves to representations in which the γ-matrices are Hermitian.* The following representation is frequently used in the literature:

$$\gamma_k = \begin{pmatrix} 0 & -i\sigma_k \\ i\sigma_k & 0 \end{pmatrix}, \quad \gamma_4 = \begin{pmatrix} 1 & 0 \\ 0 & -1 \end{pmatrix}, \quad \gamma_5 = \begin{pmatrix} 0 & -1 \\ -1 & 0 \end{pmatrix}, \tag{A 7}$$

*) The reader is assumed familiar with the elementary theory of the Dirac equation as developed, for example, in *QM*, chapter X.

where 0 and 1 are the 2×2 null and unit matrices and the σ_k the Pauli matrices

$$\sigma_1 = \begin{pmatrix} 0 & 1 \\ 1 & 0 \end{pmatrix}, \quad \sigma_2 = \begin{pmatrix} 0 & -i \\ i & 0 \end{pmatrix}, \quad \sigma_3 = \begin{pmatrix} 1 & 0 \\ 0 & -1 \end{pmatrix}. \tag{A 8}$$

Then the 4×4 spin matrix (A 6a) is simply

$$\sigma_k = \begin{pmatrix} \sigma_k & 0 \\ 0 & \sigma_k \end{pmatrix}. \tag{A 6b}$$

We shall use the notations

$$\bar{\psi} \equiv \psi^\dagger \gamma_4 \tag{A 9}$$

where † denotes the adjoint (i.e. the Hermitian conjugate) and for any vector A_μ

$$\not{A} = \gamma_\mu A_\mu. \tag{A 10}$$

This symbol is usually referred to as '*A slash*'.

From the spinors ψ, $\bar{\psi}$ and the γ-matrices, the following five covariants can be formed:

$$\left.\begin{array}{ll} \text{scalar:} & \bar{\psi}\psi \\ \text{vector:} & s_\mu = i\bar{\psi}\gamma_\mu\psi \\ \text{tensor (six-vector):} & \bar{\psi}\sigma_{\mu\nu}\psi \\ \text{pseudo-vector:} & i\bar{\psi}\gamma_5\gamma_\mu\psi \\ \text{pseudo-scalar:} & i\bar{\psi}\gamma_5\psi \end{array}\right\} \tag{A 11}$$

For a given vector $\mathbf{p}$ and

$$E_{\mathbf{p}} = +(M^2 + \mathbf{p}^2)^{\frac{1}{2}} \tag{A 12}$$

the Dirac equation (A 1) possesses 4 independent solutions which may be taken as

$$\psi^{(r)}(\mathbf{p}) = u^{(r)}(\mathbf{p}) e^{i\varepsilon_r px}, \qquad (r = 1, \ldots 4), \tag{A 13}$$

where $p = (\mathbf{p}, iE_{\mathbf{p}})$ and

$$\varepsilon_r = \begin{cases} +1, & \text{if } r = 1, 2 \\ -1, & \text{if } r = 3, 4. \end{cases} \tag{A 14}$$

The constant four-spinors $u^{(r)}(\mathbf{p})$ must satisfy the equations

$$(\varepsilon_r \not{p} - iM) u^{(r)}(\mathbf{p}) = 0, \qquad (r = 1, \ldots 4). \tag{A 15}$$

The first two solutions ($r = 1, 2$) have energy and momentum eigenvalues $E_{\mathbf{p}}$ and $\mathbf{p}$, the last two ($r = 3, 4$) have the eigenvalues $-E_{\mathbf{p}}$ and $-\mathbf{p}$. The two sets are known as positive and negative energy solutions respectively. The remaining twofold degeneracy results from the possible spin orientations. In the theory of the Dirac equation, only the longitudinal components of spin (i.e. parallel to $\pm\mathbf{p}$) are constants of the motion. It will hence be convenient to choose the states (A 13) to be eigenstates of the longitudinal spin component. We shall take

$$\sigma_{\mathbf{p}} u^{(r)}(\mathbf{p}) = \varepsilon_r \eta_r u^{(r)}(\mathbf{p}), \qquad (r = 1, \ldots 4), \tag{A 16}$$

where

$$\sigma_{\mathbf{p}} \equiv \frac{\boldsymbol{\sigma}\mathbf{p}}{|\mathbf{p}|}$$

and

$$\eta_r = \pm 1 \quad \text{for} \quad \begin{cases} r = 1 \text{ or } 3 \\ r = 2 \text{ or } 4. \end{cases} \tag{A 17}$$

Eqs. (A 13—17) completely determine the complete set of plane wave solutions except for normalization. This we now choose as

$$(u^{(r)}(\mathbf{p}), u^{(r)}(\mathbf{p})) \equiv u^{(r)\dagger}(\mathbf{p}) u^{(r)}(\mathbf{p}) = \frac{E_{\mathbf{p}}}{M}, \qquad (r = 1, \ldots 4), \tag{A 18}$$

which is a relativistically invariant normalization to $E_{\mathbf{p}}/M$ particles per unit volume.

In the Majorana representation used in chapter 8 [cf. eq. (8.9)]

$$u^{(r+2)}(\mathbf{p}) = u^{(r)*}(\mathbf{p}), \quad (r = 1, 2), \tag{A 19}$$

(the star denotes *complex* conjugation, i.e. the spinors (A 19) are, as expected, *column* vectors, not row vectors), but this relation does not hold generally.

From eqs. (A 13—18), the following orthonormality relations are easily derived:

$$\bar{u}^{(r)}(\mathbf{p}) u^{(s)}(\mathbf{p}) = \varepsilon_r \delta_{rs}, \qquad (r, s = 1, \ldots 4), \tag{A 20}$$

and

$$(\psi^{(r)}(\mathbf{p}), \psi^{(s)}(\mathbf{p}')) = \frac{E_{\mathbf{p}}}{M} \delta_{rs} \delta(\mathbf{p}, \mathbf{p}'). \tag{A 21}$$

On account of eqs. (A 15) we define projection operators $\Lambda^{\pm}(\mathbf{p})$ by

$$\Lambda^{\pm}(\mathbf{p}) = \frac{\not{p} \pm iM}{\pm 2iM}. \qquad \text{(A 22)}$$

These have all the properties of projection operators:

$$\left.\begin{aligned} \Lambda^{+}(\mathbf{p})+\Lambda^{-}(\mathbf{p}) &= 1 \\ \{\Lambda^{\pm}(\mathbf{p})\}^2 = \Lambda^{\pm}(\mathbf{p}), \qquad \Lambda^{\pm}(\mathbf{p})\Lambda^{\mp}(\mathbf{p}) &= 0. \end{aligned}\right\} \qquad \text{(A 23)}$$

Applied to the $u^{(r)}(\mathbf{p})$, they give

$$\Lambda^{-}(\mathbf{p})u^{(r)}(\mathbf{p}) = 0, \quad \Lambda^{+}(\mathbf{p})u^{(r)}(\mathbf{p}) = u^{(r)}(\mathbf{p}), \quad (r = 1, 2), \qquad \text{(A 24a)}$$

$$\Lambda^{+}(\mathbf{p})u^{(r)}(\mathbf{p}) = 0, \quad \Lambda^{-}(\mathbf{p})u^{(r)}(\mathbf{p}) = u^{(r)}(\mathbf{p}), \quad (r = 3, 4). \qquad \text{(A 24b)}$$

It is similarly possible to introduce spin projection operators (but we shall not require these)

$$\Sigma^{\pm}(\mathbf{p}) = \tfrac{1}{2}(1 \pm \sigma_{\mathbf{p}})$$

with the properties

$$\left.\begin{aligned} \Sigma^{+}(\mathbf{p})+\Sigma^{-}(\mathbf{p}) &= 1 \\ \{\Sigma^{\pm}(\mathbf{p})\}^2 = \Sigma^{\pm}(\mathbf{p}), \quad \Sigma^{\pm}(\mathbf{p})\Sigma^{\mp}(\mathbf{p}) &= 0. \end{aligned}\right\}$$

These commute with the energy projection operators (A 22):

$$[\Sigma^{\pm}(\mathbf{p}), \Lambda^{\pm}(\mathbf{p})] = [\Sigma^{\pm}(\mathbf{p}), \Lambda^{\mp}(\mathbf{p})] = 0,$$

which again only states that the energy and the longitudinal spin component can be diagonalized simultaneously.

The energy projection operators (A 22) enable us to replace summations over only positive or only negative energy states by a sum over all four spin states, e.g.

$$\sum_{r=1}^{2} u^{(r)}(\mathbf{p})f_r(\mathbf{p}) = \sum_{r=1}^{4} \Lambda^{+}(\mathbf{p})u^{(r)}(\mathbf{p})f_r(\mathbf{p}), \qquad \text{(A 25)}$$

etc. This will enable us to use the following completeness relation in spin space:

$$\sum_{r=1}^{4} u_{\alpha}^{(r)}(\mathbf{p})\bar{u}_{\beta}^{(r)}(\mathbf{p})\varepsilon_r = \delta_{\alpha\beta}. \qquad \text{(A 26)}$$

Eq. (A 26) is an operator equation relating 4×4 matrices whose rows and columns are labelled by α and β. Eq. (A 26) follows by showing that it is correct when applied to any basis vector $u^{(s)}(\mathbf{p})$. Then, using eq. (A 20),

$$\sum_{r=1}^{4} u_\alpha^{(r)}(\mathbf{p})\varepsilon_r \sum_{\beta=1}^{4} \bar{u}_\beta^{(r)}(\mathbf{p}) u_\beta^{(s)}(\mathbf{p}) = \sum_{r=1}^{4} u_\alpha^{(r)}(\mathbf{p})\varepsilon_r^2 \delta_{rs} = u_\alpha^{(s)}(\mathbf{p}).$$

One can now verify directly that the projection operators $\Lambda^{\pm}(\mathbf{p})$ can be written in the form

$$\left.\begin{aligned} \Lambda_{\alpha\beta}^{+}(\mathbf{p}) &= \sum_{r=1}^{2} u_\alpha^{(r)}(\mathbf{p})\bar{u}_\beta^{(r)}(\mathbf{p}) \\ \Lambda_{\alpha\beta}^{-}(\mathbf{p}) &= -\sum_{r=3}^{4} u_\alpha^{(r)}(\mathbf{p})\bar{u}_\beta^{(r)}(\mathbf{p}). \end{aligned}\right\} \tag{A 27}$$

For example,

$$\begin{aligned} \sum_{r=3}^{4} u_\alpha^{(r)}(\mathbf{p})\bar{u}_\beta^{(r)}(\mathbf{p}) &= -\sum_{r=3}^{4} u_\alpha^{(r)}(\mathbf{p})\bar{u}_\beta^{(r)}(\mathbf{p})\varepsilon_r \\ &= -\sum_{\sigma=1}^{4} \Lambda_{\alpha\sigma}^{-}(\mathbf{p}) \sum_{r=1}^{4} u_\sigma^{(r)}(\mathbf{p})\bar{u}_\beta^{(r)}(\mathbf{p})\varepsilon_r = -\Lambda_{\alpha\beta}^{-}(\mathbf{p}). \end{aligned}$$

In calculating transition probabilities one has to evaluate such expressions as

$$X = \tfrac{1}{2}\sum_{r=1}^{2}\sum_{s=1}^{2} |M_{sr}|^2 \tag{A 28}$$

where M_{sr} is the matrix element of some operator O:

$$M_{sr} = \big(\bar{u}^{(s)}(\mathbf{p}')Ou^{(r)}(\mathbf{p})\big). \tag{A 29}$$

This would correspond to the transition probability from an initial state in which an unpolarized beam of electrons of momentum $\mathbf{p}$ is scattered into a final state of momentum $\mathbf{p}'$, whose polarization is not detected. Hence we average over the initial polarizations $(\frac{1}{2}\sum_{r=1}^{2})$ and sum over the final polarizations $(\sum_{s=1}^{2})$ of the two spin states of an electron. Similar expressions can of course be written down for positrons and for several fermions. If we define the operator

$$\tilde{O} = \gamma_4 O^\dagger \gamma_4 \tag{A 30}$$

then

$$X = \tfrac{1}{2}\sum_{r=1}^{2}\sum_{s=1}^{2}(\bar{u}^{(r)}(\mathbf{p})\tilde{O}u^{(s)}(\mathbf{p}'))(\bar{u}^{(s)}(\mathbf{p}')Ou^{(r)}(\mathbf{p}))$$
$$= \tfrac{1}{2}\sum_{r=1}^{2}(\bar{u}^{(r)}(\mathbf{p})\tilde{O}\Lambda^{+}(\mathbf{p}')Ou^{(r)}(\mathbf{p}))$$

by eq. (A 27), and

$$X = \tfrac{1}{2}\sum_{r=1}^{4}(\bar{u}^{(r)}(\mathbf{p})\tilde{O}\Lambda^{+}(\mathbf{p}')O\Lambda^{+}(\mathbf{p})u^{(r)}(\mathbf{p}))\varepsilon_r$$

by eqs. (A 14) and (A 25). Finally

$$X = \tfrac{1}{2}\,\mathrm{Tr}\,\{\tilde{O}\Lambda^{+}(\mathbf{p}')O\Lambda^{+}(\mathbf{p})\}, \tag{A 31}$$

since for any operator Q, using eq. (A 26),

$$\sum_{r=1}^{4}(\bar{u}^{(r)}(\mathbf{p})Qu^{(r)}(\mathbf{p}))\varepsilon_r = \sum_{r=1}^{4}\sum_{\alpha,\beta=1}^{4}\bar{u}_{\alpha}^{(r)}(\mathbf{p})Q_{\alpha\beta}u_{\beta}^{(r)}(\mathbf{p})\varepsilon_r$$
$$= \sum_{\alpha,\beta=1}^{4}Q_{\alpha\beta}\delta_{\beta\alpha} = \sum_{\alpha=1}^{4}Q_{\alpha\alpha} = \mathrm{Tr}\,Q.$$

The following rules, which are useful in evaluating traces of γ-matrices, are easily established from the anticommutation rules (A 2):

(i) For any two operators U and V

$$\mathrm{Tr}\,(UV) = \mathrm{Tr}\,(VU). \tag{A 32}$$

(ii)
$$\mathrm{Tr}\,\gamma_{\lambda}\gamma_{\mu} = 4\delta_{\lambda\mu}. \tag{A 33}$$

(iii) If $(\gamma_{\lambda}\gamma_{\mu}\ldots\gamma_{\tau})$ contains an odd number of factors, then

$$\mathrm{Tr}\,(\gamma_{\lambda}\gamma_{\mu}\ldots\gamma_{\tau}) = 0. \tag{A 34}$$

(iv) For the γ-matrices,

$$\mathrm{Tr}\,(\gamma_{\lambda}\gamma_{\mu}\gamma_{\nu}\ldots\gamma_{\rho}\gamma_{\sigma}\gamma_{\tau}) = \mathrm{Tr}\,(\gamma_{\tau}\gamma_{\sigma}\gamma_{\rho}\ldots\gamma_{\nu}\gamma_{\mu}\gamma_{\lambda}). \tag{A 35}$$

(v) If a is a complex number and A_{λ}, B_{λ}, C_{λ}, D_{λ} are four-vectors, then

$$\mathrm{Tr}\,a = 4a, \tag{A 36}$$

$$\left.\begin{aligned}\mathrm{Tr}\,(\not{A}\not{B}) &= 4(AB),\\ \mathrm{Tr}\,(\not{A}\not{B}\not{C}\not{D}) &= 4\{(AB)(CD)-(AC)(BD)+(AD)(BC)\}.\end{aligned}\right\} \tag{A 37}$$

(vi) With the summation convention (over λ) implied:

$$\left.\begin{aligned} \gamma_\lambda a \gamma_\lambda &= 4a, \\ \gamma_\lambda \not{A} \gamma_\lambda &= -2\not{A}, \\ \gamma_\lambda \not{A}\not{B} \gamma_\lambda &= 4(AB), \\ \gamma_\lambda \not{A}\not{B}\not{C} \gamma_\lambda &= -2\not{C}\not{B}\not{A}. \end{aligned}\right\} \tag{A 38}$$

Apart from spin summations, we also wish to consider summations over different polarization states of a photon, absorbed or emitted in a process. If the photon has four-momentum k_μ and is specified by the polarization vector $\varepsilon_\mu^{(m)} \equiv \varepsilon_\mu^{(m)}(\mathbf{k})$, $m = 1, 2$, (we use the four-vectors (9.17) to specify the polarization), the matrix element M_m of the process will be linear in $\varepsilon_\mu^{(m)}$:

$$M_m = L_\mu \varepsilon_\mu^{(m)}, \qquad m = 1, 2, \tag{A 39}$$

and the polarized cross-section (i.e. *no* summation over m) will be of the form (since $\varepsilon_\mu^{(m)*} = \varepsilon_\mu^{(m)}$ for $m = 1, 2$)

$$X_m = M_m^\dagger M_m = L_\mu^\dagger L_\nu \varepsilon_\mu^{(m)} \varepsilon_\nu^{(m)}, \qquad m = 1, 2. \tag{A 40}$$

In the case of an emitted photon whose polarization is not observed, one must form the sum over the final polarization states

$$\sum_{m=1}^{2} X_m = \sum_{m=1}^{2} L_\mu^\dagger L_\nu \varepsilon_\mu^{(m)} \varepsilon_\nu^{(m)}. \tag{A 41}$$

If the photon is absorbed, the incident photon beam being unpolarized, we must take half this sum corresponding to averaging over the two polarizations.

The evaluation of eq. (A 41) can be greatly simplified by using the covariant description of photons involving four polarization states. Feynman*) has shown that the matrix element (A 39) vanishes if the polarization vector $\varepsilon_\mu^{(m)}(\mathbf{k})$ is replaced by the four-momentum k_μ of the photon, i.e.

$$L_\mu k_\mu = 0. \tag{A 42}$$

The cross-section (A 40) is quadratic in the matrix element. Hence replacing *either* factor $\varepsilon_\mu^{(m)}(\mathbf{k})$ by k_μ, this expression must vanish, even if the other factor $\varepsilon_\mu^{(m)}(\mathbf{k})$ is replaced by an arbitrary four-vector v_μ. This gives two conditions:

*) Feynman, R. P. *Phys. Rev.* **76**, 769, 1949; section 8.

$$\left.\begin{aligned} L_\mu^\dagger L_\nu k_\mu v_\nu &= 0, \\ L_\mu^\dagger L_\nu v'_\mu k_\nu &= 0. \end{aligned}\right\} \qquad \text{(A 43)}$$

Taking $v_\mu = \varepsilon_\mu^{(3)}$, $v'_\mu = \varepsilon_\mu^{(4)}$ and, of course,

$$k_\mu = k_0(\varepsilon_\mu^{(3)} + \varepsilon_\mu^{(4)}), \qquad \text{(A 44)}$$

eqs. (A 43) give, subtracting the second from the first,

$$L_\mu^\dagger L_\nu(\varepsilon_\mu^{(3)}\varepsilon_\nu^{(3)} - \varepsilon_\mu^{(4)}\varepsilon_\nu^{(4)}) = 0, \qquad \text{(A 45)}$$

and, adding this equation to eq. (A 41),

$$\sum_{m=1}^{2} X_m = L_\mu^\dagger L_\nu[(\sum_{m=1}^{3} \varepsilon_\mu^{(m)}\varepsilon_\nu^{(m)}) - \varepsilon_\mu^{(4)}\varepsilon_\nu^{(4)}]. \qquad \text{(A 46)}$$

By eqs. (9.17), the expression in square parentheses in eq. (A 46) is equal to the Kronecker delta $\delta_{\mu\nu}$. Hence eq. (A 46) finally becomes

$$\sum_{m=1}^{2} X_m = \sum_{m=1}^{4} L_m^\dagger L_m. \qquad \text{(A 47)}$$

The matrix element M_m depends on $\varepsilon_\mu^{(m)}$ through a factor $\not{e}^{(m)} = \gamma_\mu \varepsilon_\mu^{(m)}$. Hence L_μ depends on μ through a factor γ_μ. Thus eq. (A 47) shows that in eq. (A 41) we may replace $\not{e}^{(m)}$ by γ_m, the summation over m being at the same time extended to run from 1 to 4.

From the derivation of eq. (A 47), it is at once apparent how to generalize this result to cases involving more than one photon.

Bibliography

Akhiezer, A. I. and Berestetsky, V. B. *Quantum Electrodynamics* (translated from the Russian by the Consultants Bureau, Inc.), *U. S. Atomic Energy Comm. Report* No. AEC-tr-2876 (Pts. I and II). (Available from the Office of Technical Services, Department of Commerce, Washington 25, D.C., U.S.A.)

Bethe, H. A. and de Hoffmann, F. "Mesons", in *Mesons and Fields*, Vol. II, Evanston, Ill.; Row, Peterson, 1955. See also under Schweber.

Bogoliubov, N. N. and Shirkov, D. V., *Introduction to the Theory of Quantized Fields*, New York, Interscience, 1959.

Dyson, F. J. *Advanced Quantum Mechanics*. (Lectures given at Cornell University, Fall, 1951. Available from the Physics Dept., Cornell University.)

Hamilton, J. *The Theory of Elementary Particles*, Oxford; Clarendon, 1959.

Heitler, W. *The Quantum Theory of Radiation*, 3rd ed., Oxford; Clarendon, 1954.

Jauch, J. M. and Rohrlich, F. *The Theory of Photons and Electrons*, Cambridge, Mass.; Addison-Wesley, 1955.

Källén, G. "Quantenelektrodynamik", in *Handbuch der Physik*, Vol. V, Part I, Springer, 1958.

Schweber, S. S., Bethe, H. A. and de Hoffman, F. "Fields", in *Mesons and Fields*, Vol. I, Evanston, Ill.; Row, Peterson, 1955.

Thirring, W. *Einführung in die Quantenelektrodynamik*, Vienna; Deuticke, 1955 and the English translation *Principles of Quantum Electrodynamics*, New York and London; Academic Press, 1958.

Umezawa, H. *Quantum Field Theory*, Amsterdam; North-Holland, 1956.

Wentzel, G. *Quantum Theory of Fields*, New York; Interscience, 1949.

Wick, G. C. "Invariance Principles of Nuclear Physics", in *Annual Review of Nuclear Science*, vol. 8, 1958.

Index*

*) References in Roman figures are to pages, in bold figures to chapters and in italics to the exercises and the hints for their solutions.